The
Power Supply
Handbook

John Fielding, ZS5JF

Radio Society of
Great Britain

American Radio
Relay League

THE POWER SUPPLY HANDBOOK

Published jointly by The Radio Society of Great Britain, Cranborne Road, Potters Bar, Herts, EN6 3JE, UK
and The American Radio Relay League Inc, 225 Main Street, Newington, CT, 06111-1494 USA.

First published 2006

ISBN 1-905086-21-0
EAN 9781-9050-8621-4

Publisher's note
The opinions expressed in this book are those of the authors and not necessarily those of the RSGB or
ARRL. While the information presented is believed to be correct, the authors, the publishers and their
agents cannot accept responsibility for the consequences arising for any inaccuracies or omissions.

Typography and design: Mike Dennison, G3XDV, Emdee Publishing
Cover design: Dorotea Vizer, M3VZR
Production: Mark Allgar, M1MPA

Printed in Great Britain by Page Bros of Norwich

The program listings, as printed in the Appendix to this book can be found at
www.rsgb.org/books/extra/powersupplies.htm

Contents

Foreword

During the writing of this book I have endeavoured to represent the contents in the simplest terms. For an engineer intimately involved on a day to day basis with power supplies and their design and manufacture, this is not always a simple task. Where the basics have been lightly treated this is because I assume the reader has some level of understanding of basic electronics, at least equal to the Amateur Radio Examination or similar. Where the subject matter requires a greater understanding I have spent more time explaining the intricacies of the topic.

The designs presented are mostly those I have personally worked on over a period of about 30 years, either for the companies I have been employed by, or for my own requirements dealing with my ham radio hobby. Some designs presented have not constructed by me and these are included 'as is'; they have been drawn from various data sheets, application notes and design notes for various integrated circuits.

I hope that this book will encourage ham radio enthusiasts and technical college students to experiment with power supplies and to learn about this fascinating topic. With today's sophisticated amateur transceivers there is little the average ham can do to construct an equivalent item. But power supplies will always be required around the shack of the amateur, either for powering a piece of purchased commercial equipment or for general use on the bench for powering circuits being experimented with. To point to an item which you have constructed with your own hands and demonstrate it to visiting friends is a small way of showing that ham radio does not have to be a 'cheque-book' hobby solely the domain of 'black box operators'.

I cannot conclude this part without acknowledging certain people who have enabled me to bring this book to the public:

Firstly I would like to thank my long suffering wife, Penny, for the countless cups of coffee and sandwiches whilst I have been battling with either a technical problem or the text of this book and for the encouragement to press on when I became despondent that I would ever finish 'The Book'.

Secondly I wish to acknowledge the assistance of Stuart McPherson, ZR5SD, Director of Electronics, Natal Technikon (now called Durban Institute of Technology), for proof reading the drafts, suggesting ways to improve the presentation and for inputs with some of the technical aspects.

Thirdly I should recognise the efforts made by one of my previous work colleagues, Ted Massam, who assisted with some of the schematics which are included here.

Fourthly I should like to express my appreciation to Dave Oxburrow of Lehmans Transformers, Durban, South Africa, for reviewing the chapter dealing with mains transformers and for correcting any errors which had crept in.

Finally, to all semiconductor and other component manufacturers who have allowed me to reprint portions of their data sheets and application notes for use here.

John Fielding, ZS5JF
Monteseel, Kwa-Zulu Natal
Republic of South Africa

What is a Power Supply?

Wisdom: *"There is no easy walk to freedom, we must go through extreme difficulties before we reach the mountaintops of our desire"* (Nelson Mandela)

A sk the various ham-radio operators you know to define what a power supply is and you will most likely get a response such as "that black / grey box plugged into the mains that powers my equipment".

Although this largely is true there are many types of power supply in common use today. Most people think of a power supply as a rather uninteresting box tucked away somewhere either at the back of the operating table or hidden away under the bench.

When one considers that the power supply is the 'source of all life' in an amateur shack, it is rather surprising to find that nearly all ham radio operators have only a hazy idea of what lurks under the covers of that rather mundane exterior. Today with the overwhelming transition to low voltage amateur transceivers, mostly designed to operate from a 12V vehicle supply, it is peculiar to find that few people use lead-acid batteries to power their station equipment. Many reasons are given: "I don't want a messy, stinking battery in the shack", or "The wife won't tolerate a battery on the floor because it might leak and ruin the carpet". These are just some excuses I have heard over the years.

However, a lead-acid battery suitably enclosed, ventilated and mounted on the outside of the shack with a dedicated charging system can be a surprisingly safe and reliable source of power. A real bonus is that in the event of the mains failing, (a not uncommon feature of the rural part of the country I reside in), you can continue to operate when the rest of the neighbourhood is plunged into darkness. And you can easily rig up emergency lighting to switch on whilst the mains is out!

I shall cover this aspect in more detail in a later chapter as the choice of the battery and charging circuit is vital to achieve reliable operation and long life from the battery.

Other forms of power supplies are used for high power linear amplifiers. Although 'solid-state' has permanently changed the face of amateur radio equipment over the last twenty years, in the high power linear amplifier stakes the thermionic vacuum tube (valve) has remained the mainstay of amateur designs and many commercially produced amplifiers still use this cost effective technology. Very few commercial designs exist for amplifiers above 200 to 400 watts that use transistors. Those that do require a hefty power supply to feed the amplifier.

Consider a 400W output linear amplifier that runs on 12V. Even assuming an efficiency of 100%, which we all know is impossible, the amplifier would require a power supply providing a current of about 33A. Factor in the efficiency ratio of around 40%, which is typical, for a true linear amplifier and you arrive at the staggering current of 83A! To allow a margin of safety for slight over-driving and tuning up into a random wire antenna with an ATU and you would need to specify a power supply with an output current of at least 100A. And what are you going to use to connect the power supply to the amplifier? Cables would need to be akin to those used with arc-welders to have any chance of carrying that sort of current with low voltage drop. Clearly anyone considering using 12V devices for this kind of power level needs to consider alternative choices.

Our lead-acid battery/charger combination might be able to supply one of these monster amplifiers for short periods until the battery voltage sank too low, but it is still not an encouraging proposition. Hence the vacuum tube with high anode potential and relatively low current still rules the roost in this area of amateur radio. The anode voltages required can be quite scary! Typically a 1kW-output amplifier would require a minimum of between 2500 and 3500 volts to operate satisfactorily. The current required would be around 0.75 Amp. The design and construction of this type of amplifier power supply is difficult, but not beyond the means of a determined constructor. I will cover these types of power supplies in a later chapter.

Smaller is better - right?

Today we seem to be besotted with the need to make everything 'palm-size'. The market push for personal devices, such as cell-phones, palm-top computers, walkie-talkies and many other portable appliances puts a real strain on the technology. Even if one could design a super-miniature piece of equipment, what are you going to use as the power source? We know that portable devices use a type of battery - usually a re-chargeable type - to power them. This battery is the power supply, or at least the prime source of power. Very often one finds that battery technology is still some way behind the rest of the electronics world. Even if one can find a suitable volume battery pack that can deliver the correct amount of energy to power the equipment either the weight, cost or availability will be a negative factor.

A common factor is that the battery occupies around 30 to 50% of the available volume and/or weight target. Small lightweight battery packs may be a point of convenience but they often have insufficient capacity to allow more than a few hours running, particularly in a hand-held transceiver. Having to carry around a spare charged battery is often not an option, and can be a hazard if it is accidentally shorted. Military radio equipment although not as advanced as commercial equipment is following this path and 'Mission Time' is an emotive subject, often specified under the best case conditions to make the equipment seem better than the competition. An oft repeated specification for hand held or man pack radio transceivers is the need for at least 12 hours battery life. Even with extensive methods of 'power saving circuitry' incorporated in the equipment the rare examples, which claim to achieve this sort of battery life; all operate the transmitter on the low power setting! A foot soldier is usually strongly against having to carry spare batteries in a combat scenario, albeit it could be a means of saving his life in an emergency, and would rather opt for extra ammunition or food/water as extra payload.

Ham radio equipment has not escaped this blind headlong dash to make everything smaller. Twenty-five years ago the average ham radio HF transceiver was bigger than a briefcase and put out around 100W. It weighed in at around 15kg (30lb) and had its own power supply built in which simply plugged into a normal wall socket. There was nothing extra needed to make it work, except the microphone and antenna. These models almost all used valves (tubes) in the output stage with mainly solid state for the rest of the transceiver circuitry. Therefore the power supply included a mixture of high and low voltage supplies. Some manufacturers went a step further and added an optional 12V DC-DC converter that allowed you to operate the transceiver mobile. But cars of those days had much more space under the dashboard to accommodate a bulky item such as a radio transceiver.

Today the latest 'state-of-the-art' HF transceiver is still only 100W output but is about the size of two VHS video cassette tapes stacked one on top of the other and weighs practically nothing. Why? Simple, the modern transceiver doesn't contain the mains operated power supply! If you want to operate from anywhere except a vehicle, you now need to purchase a matching power supply from the manufacturer - or build one - to provide the 12V the equipment is usually designed to operate from.

The mains transformer in the old fashioned transceiver accounted for more than 60% of the total weight as it was typically a heavy lump of iron. The modern HF transceiver power supply size and shape has to match the tiny radio from a cosmetic point of view. Bulky, heavy and costly mains transformers cannot be got down to the sort of volume required to fit a matching size mechanics.

Today the high current power supply uses a totally different technique to its older brother. Switch-mode power supplies have taken over in almost all areas of modern appliances, including ham radio equipment. Because the voltage is derived from the mains with direct rectification, there is no need for a heavy iron transformer. Your humble desktop computer uses a type of switch-mode supply delivering power levels anything up to 250 watts. Switch-mode supplies are lightweight, compact, cost-effective and very efficient compared to a conventional power supply.

Off-line switch-mode supplies

The AC mains input is rectified and delivers a voltage of around 380V DC to a switching circuit. This high voltage requires a transformer to provide safety isolation between the mains and the output, which is a mandatory legal requirement in most countries today. Because of the several different mains voltages in use throughout the world, switch-mode supplies often have either a universal input stage which can accept any voltage from about 100V to around 250V AC or they have a simple voltage selector switch to select either 115V or 230V AC input.

Because the switching is done at a very high frequency - typically 100kHz or higher the transformer can be made very small and light in weight compared to a conventional mains transformer that operates at 50 or 60Hz. This allows a very

low volume and weight to be achieved. To put it another way, the watts per kilogram (or pound) of a switch-mode power supply is about 30 to 50 times that of a conventional mains transformer based power supply of the same output power. These types of switch-mode supplies are known as 'off-line switchers' as they directly rectify the mains. We will return to switch-mode power supplies later in this book to look at the intricacies and subtleties of these beasts.

Although at first most constructors feel intimidated by the additional complexity of switch-mode supplies compared to linear regulated supplies, this soon disappears having built a couple of 'switchers' successfully.

Linear regulated power supplies

I have said very little so far about the old stalwart of home constructors - the so-called 'linear regulated power supply'.

Since the inception of commercially viable semiconductors in the 1950s, and then when integrated circuits (ICs) first became available in the 1960s and 1970s, the semiconductor industry concentrated on developing more and more complex ICs. This was largely driven by the American defence industry and later the 'Race to Space'. One of the first breakthroughs was the Operational Amplifier - or Op-Amp for short - this proved to be a vital building block for later generation ICs designed for voltage regulation. Early types of Op-Amps, such as the 741, are still around even today, over 40 years later, and one cannot forget to mention the most famous of all voltage regulators, the hallowed μ723. Personally I think these old-fashioned ICs belong in museums! Today there are far better, and cheaper chips, for these sorts of tasks. Of course if you bought a bucket full of these at a flea market or mobile swap meeting for next to nothing, who am I to tell you not to use them. Just be aware that the '723' and a few other early regulator ICs have a few idiosyncrasies that can give unpleasant results!

In the early days of solid state linear regulated supplies, before ICs became available, everything was done 'discretely' using lots of individual transistors, and engineers who could design stable supplies were in great demand. Today with the massive availability of IC fixed voltage and adjustable voltage regulators everyone can be an expert designer with a few simple design rules! 'Expert Systems' (as one manufacturer calls them) and the main building blocks are designed into the fixed voltage IC regulator.

Today for someone needing a fixed voltage, low current power supply, providing say 1A, a simple expedient is to use one of the many '3-terminal' IC regulators available for a very low cost. Add a suitable mains transformer, a few diodes for the rectification and a smoothing capacitor and very little else and you have a stable voltage source with niceties such as built-in current limiting all included.

On to the first course

So let's get down to basics. Stoke up the coffee or tea pot, whichever is your preference, turn off the 'idiots lantern' (television), sit back in a comfy chair, have a pen, paper and your calculator handy and let's explore our first topic.

Regulated versus Unregulated?

> **Vision:** *"Life does not require us to be the biggest or the best. It asks only that we try"* (Benjamin Franklin)

As strange as it may seem, some amateur built power supplies need not be regulated. If the equipment connected to it draws only a little current and the current drawn doesn't vary much then a regulated supply is in fact a waste. Many broadcast domestic radios or cassette recorders can operate quite satisfactorily using a 'battery-eliminator' which plugs into a normal wall socket. These often contain nothing more than a small mains transformer, rectifier diode(s) and a small electrolytic capacitor. A Morse-keyer operating on 9V could be run satisfactorily using one of these 'battery-eliminators'. The voltage isn't very stable but for the keyer it isn't that important as it most probably contains its own internal 5V regulator for the digital ICs. As long as the mains voltage remains within allowable limits no one would know any different. It is certainly cheaper than using dry-cell batteries.

However, the public mains supply in certain parts of the world is far from stable. At my home in South Africa we now have a public supply voltage of 230V AC with a tolerance of 6%, similar to the UK. But as the picture below shows this is pretty optimistic! The trace shown in **Fig 2.1** is a record of the mains voltage during early evening when all the local homes have the electric cookers

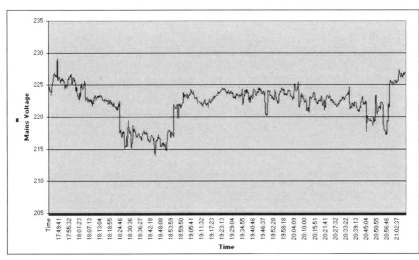

Figure 2.1: Mains voltage versus time. Note: The logging was done automatically with an Isotech DVM with a serial cable connected to a PC. The results were taken every 10s and Microsoft Excel was used to process the results and plot the graph

Officially in South Africa we now have a 230V nominal supply voltage and a tolerance of 6%, the same as the UK, but where I live it rarely gets above 225V for most of the time. As most of my amateur equipment is home brewed and uses 230V primary mains transformers from when I lived in the UK, I struggle to achieve full output from my high power valve linear amplifiers as I don't have the correct taps to set the primary to a lower voltage! Until fairly recently the national supply voltage was only 220V and then the supply used to hover around the 200V mark for most of the time.

(stoves) and water heaters (geysers) switched on. Notice the large dips and sudden peaks as the various loads cycle on and off and the slow rise and fall in the overall voltage which is typical of a rural mains supply. My house is one of the last ones at the end of a long supply route located in the wilds.

So if you have a mains supply similar to mine then a regulated supply for low voltage applications at any rate is virtually imperative. Another reason for choosing to stabilise the output voltage is that as the load current increases the voltage drop in mains transformer windings, rectifier diodes and general chassis wiring tends to increase due to I^2R losses.

High voltage power supplies used with vacuum tube equipment aren't usually regulated and the HT voltage 'follows' the mains voltage and shows dips and surges as the mains voltage changes. Fortunately vacuum tubes are pretty tolerant to this and it only really necessary to stabilise the HT voltage in the case of a VFO using a vacuum tube or the screen grid supply for a transmitting tetrode such as a 4CX250. In a later chapter I will discuss HT supplies in a lot more detail.

So how do we specify a power supply if we are looking to purchase one or comparing one make with another? Let's go onto Chapter 3 and look at specifications in detail. Only when we compare 'apples with apples' will we get a clear picture of one supply versus another and whether your last constructed supply is up to scratch.

3

Basic Power Supply Parameters

T o start with, let us run through the vital parameters of a typical power supply specification. Some of these are pretty obvious; but then again most people have only a hazy understanding. If you are confident you know this bit and think you can't learn anything from this section, then by all means skip it. But I suspect you will sneak back to it from time to time to confirm your understanding!

How is a power supply specified? Let's start with the simple parameters.

Output voltage

This is the voltage the power supply is designed to deliver to the connected load or into an open circuit. As with most things it has a tolerance attached to it. A typical power supply for 12V transceivers would have an output voltage of 13.8V. Why 13.8V you might ask?

As the equipment is primarily designed to operate in a motor vehicle with a nominal 12V battery, the limits of the battery are from around 10.8V (discharged condition) to around 14.4V (fully charged) when driven by the engine charging alternator. 13.8V has by default come to be accepted as a happy medium between these two conditions. In earlier days 13.2V was considered to be the standard but the 13.8V figure has recently become universal. One of the reasons for this is that so-called 12V RF transistors work so much better at the higher voltage. They have more gain and are capable of greater output power at the 13.8V level. The gain and output power drops dramatically as the voltage falls to 12V or below.

Where I live, the South African Bureau of Standards (SABS) lays down the limits for vehicular battery voltage for two-way radio equipment. These limits are used when type approval testing is performed. For a 12V vehicular system, the lower limit is 10.8V and the upper limit is 15.6V, which is common to many other countries. (24V vehicles use double the 12V limits, ie 21.6V and 31.2V). For aircraft radio installations the limits are defined in various international documents, and for military aircraft radio systems an added requirement is for the radio to be able to transmit & receive, albeit at a reduced specification, when the aircraft supply voltage is as low as 20V or in some cases 18V, this is known as the "Crash-Test voltage". It simulates what happens to an aircraft battery, when all charging circuits are non functional, when an aircraft crash lands. Fortunately, we don't have to bother with these stringent limits.

So, what is an acceptable output voltage? I would hazard a guess that most power supply manufacturers would aim for as close to 13.8V as possible. A further factor lies in the volts-drop in the connecting leads between the power supply and the transceiver. If you could not tolerate *any* voltage drop, you would need cables about 12mm in diameter for both the positive and negative leads. Not a very convenient option! By allowing the output voltage to be towards the upper limit, any slight voltage drop in the connecting leads is somewhat factored out of the equation. (In a later chapter I will show how remote voltage sensing can compensate for the volts drop in the connecting leads).

Output voltage tolerance

For the equipment to function correctly it has an allowable range of voltage which does not cause any malfunction. Typically for a 12V mobile HF transceiver of the 100W type that draws a substantial current, the voltage drop in the connecting leads should be as low as practical. Therefore, a voltage tolerance of, say, 0.5V below the 13.8V nominal would be acceptable. As most 12V equipment is capable of operating satisfactorily in a normal 12V vehicle environment - or so the manufacturers claim - the drop of half a volt or so shouldn't cause too much alarm.

Output voltage regulation

Output voltage regulation is the amount the output voltage deviates from the nominal when the current drawn is varied. Typically, it is measured at 10% of maximum and 100% of maximum. The amount the voltage varies when the current is changed is expressed as either a percentage of the nominal voltage or directly as the upper and lower limits.

A mythical 13.8V supply was measured and found to have a no-load voltage of 13.75V. When the output was loaded to 10% of the specified maximum the voltage fell to 13.5V. When the current was increased to 100%, the voltage fell further to 13.25V. *Note:* This measurement is made directly at the output terminals of the power supply and not at the end of the leads that connect to the load.

The output voltage tolerance is therefore:

$$\frac{\text{Measured output voltage}}{\text{Specified output voltage}} = \frac{13.75\text{V}}{13.80\text{V}}$$

This yields an output voltage which is 99.63% of the specified one, or an error of about 0.3%, which is very good.

The output regulation is:

Output voltage at 10% load - Output voltage at 100% load

13.50V - 13.25V = 0.25V

This gives a regulation of 0.25V in 13.5V or an error of about 1.9%, which is acceptable for the intended purpose.

Input regulation

Input regulation establishes how the power supply reacts to changes in the input supply voltage. Typically, the mains voltage does vary over a period of time, sometimes more than we think. The electricity authority in each country lays down what the nominal voltage is and what are considered to be the worst case upper and lower limits. Outside of these limits, the authority may be obliged to disconnect or 'cut' the supply to prevent damage to attached equipment (abnormally low mains voltage is very damaging to large induction motors and causes them to over-heat as they try to maintain operating speed by drawing excessive current). A typical specification for a country might read something like this:

Nominal voltage	230V AC
Frequency	50Hz ±2Hz
Lower limit	200V
Upper limit	250V

In the UK the nominal mains voltage is 230V and the tolerance is 6%. This gives an upper limit of about 244V and a lower limit of 216V. This does not take into account any additional voltage drops in the subscriber's cable between the power transformer and the consumer's premises. Industry uses a worse case scenario when designing power supplies to cater for cable volt drops, potential 'brown-outs' (see box) and sudden dips caused by switching surges. A typical maximum voltage would be 260V and a lower limit of 200V. These figures would cover virtually all eventualities for a 220 or 230V supply system. For our American readers who still use the 115V AC supply these figures would be about 100V to 130V.

So, what happens when we perform an input regulation test? The power supply is normally loaded to its maximum rated current and the input voltage is varied using a variable voltage transformer (Variac™). The output voltage variation is measured against the nominal input voltage, 230V in the case of the UK.

Our mythical power supply gave these results at 100% load:

230V input	V = 13.25V	
244V input	V = 13.35V	= +0.1V
216V input	V = 13.10V	= -0.15V

From the results it can be seen that the overall variation was worst on the lower input voltage, which is usually the case with this sort of power supply. Taking this expressed as a percentage it is -1.1%. The upper voltage gave a slight increase in the output voltage. This expressed, as a percentage is +0.7%.

> Brown-out is a term used by the electricity authorities. It describes what happens when a sudden large load, typically a large induction motor drawing a heavy starting current, causes the supply voltage to drop below the minimum voltage for a second or two and then recover to normal.

The overall input regulation is therefore the addition of the upper and lower voltage regulation, which is 1.8% overall. This is quite creditable and should supply the needs of our HF transceiver adequately.

It can be ascertained from the measurement that the mains transformer is maybe a little on the light side for this power supply as the output voltage sagged quite a bit more on the lower input voltage limit than the upper voltage limit. Possibly, this is due the manufacturer cutting a few costs and using a transformer or other components that are only just up the job.

By performing this test at several load ratings, say 30% of full load, 70% of full load, we could ascertain if our suspicions about the transformer are correct. Of course the transformer is just one component which can cause this. Others are the diode rectifiers, smoothing capacitors and general gauge of wiring used within the power supply. But we are getting ahead of ourselves. I will cover these in greater detail later.

Output ripple and noise

This is a measure of how much the output voltage varies about the nominal DC value due to ripple and other sources of noise. In a mains powered conventional power supply the ripple is nearly always the result of the reservoir capacitors being unable to hold the input voltage to the regulating circuitry high enough to stop it falling into the trough.

Solid-state regulators have a specified minimum input/output voltage to ensure they operate correctly. A typical value is around 3 to 5V. Failing to ensure the input voltage is always 3V above the output voltage causes the regulator to 'drop-out' and follow the trough of the rectified voltage ripple.

This manifest itself as a ripple on the output at 100Hz for a 50Hz mains system or 120Hz for a 60Hz mains system. Other sources of noise are those that enter the power supply from the mains, switching spikes, glitches etc that the regulator circuitry is unable to regulate or filter out.

Ripple and noise is normally measured at full load current, as this is the worst case for these types of supplies. Remember we are talking about conventional linear regulators for the moment. When we come to discuss switching power supplies, we have another set of parameters to consider.

Ripple is normally specified in 'mV peak to peak' and some manufacturers cloud the issue by quoting it as a percentage value of the nominal output voltage. The measurement is made with an oscilloscope connected to the output terminals and set to AC coupling, to ignore the DC component. Usually the bandwidth of the measurement is specified, typically from a very low frequency to around 20MHz. In a conventional power supply, there will be little ripple above about 500Hz and these will be due to harmonics of the rectification process. Any power supply worth having in the shack will have adequate output filtering to prevent damaging spikes reaching the attached transceiver.

What is considered a good number for ripple and noise? In my opinion any power supply of this rating which exceeds about 50mV to 100mV p-p should be investigated carefully to find the cause of the problem. Granted the HF transceiver *should* have input filtering on the DC lines, especially if it is intended for vehicular operation, but you can never be sure without testing its immunity to input ripple and spikes - a costly exercise. Professional and military radio equipment manufacturers as a matter of course test the *susceptibility* of the equipment to stringent levels to ensure it functions satisfactorily when subjected to conducted ripple and spikes. Most specifications for 24V vehicle equipment specify spikes up to + and - 100V for a maximum of 100µs which are caused by ancillary equipment in the vehicle. Amateur equipment rarely matches up to this stringent testing, but again they cost much less than the other types of equipment!

However, the vehicular battery supply is an evil source, one semiconductor manufacturer calls it "The Supply from Hell", and it has many nasty transient voltages present due to the other electrical systems sharing the common 12V battery. A seemingly good way of extracting 12V from a motor vehicle is to use a plug in adapter to the cigarette lighter outlet. However, I have noticed that fewer motor manufacturers are fitting these, perhaps because of the anti smoking lobby! I will cover this topic in more detail in later chapters.

Transient load regulation

Whilst talking about transients we also need to measure how the power supply reacts to rapidly changing loads. The output regulation tests are performed with a static load, which is varied slowly between two fixed extremes. Transient load testing more accurately establishes how the power supply is able to handle loads that are closer to the real world.

In an amateur HF transceiver operating on SSB or CW, the current drawn during transmit is very 'peaky' with a relatively low current being drawn during 'key-up', in the CW case, or not speaking into the microphone in the case of SSB. In an ideal power supply, the output voltage would remain absolutely constant during these conditions. However, because of the design of the voltage regulation circuits the output voltage lags a bit behind the demanded current.

You can imagine the various parts of the regulator circuitry being a bit like a ship's crew. A potential divider - the 'lookout' - monitors the output voltage and reports variations to the control circuitry - 'the bridge'. The output current is controlled by a pass transistor, which passes more or less current to keep the output voltage constant. The output pass transistor is the 'engine room' and the 'captain' on the bridge controls the main voltage sensing and comparison circuitry, the decision-maker.

When the load is suddenly increased and more current is drawn, the lookout reports to the bridge that something has gone awry and the output voltage has taken a sharp drop. It needs more 'Oomph' from the engine room to correct the situation. The captain orders "more steam" to the engine room and it complies. This all takes a finite time. During this time the output voltage sags below the required level until the engine room turns up the current. This sudden dip in output voltage is called a "load induced transient".

The opposite happens when the load is suddenly reduced from near maximum to a much lower level. The lookout reports that the output voltage is now too high and the captain orders the engine room to "throttle back" to reduce the output current. Again a transient occurs, but this time the output voltage suddenly jumps up to a higher level when the load is reduced. Of the two this is the potentially more damaging, if the over-shoot of the output voltage exceeds the safe working voltage of the attached equipment.

Consequently we need to establish how well the power supply is able to limit the transient excursions to safe limits, or the attached equipment may be irreparably damaged because of a sudden over-voltage condition.

This is the basis of transient load testing and is something that lots of amateur built power supplies (and some so-called professional supplies!) fall down badly on. If the load were relatively constant there would be no need to subject the power supply to this testing. But SSB and CW are about as bad as you can get for a power supply to handle and should be done as a matter of course for any amateur constructed power supply.

Transient load response testing

Transient load testing requires at the minimum a load that can be rapidly switched between two current levels. It is fairly easy to arrange with a couple of high power resistors for the load and a big power transistor to switch in the second resistor. One resistor is sized to draw about 10% of the maximum and the second to draw 90%. The transistor switches the second resistor into and out of circuit to vary the load. The output voltage is monitored with an oscilloscope in the same way as the ripple test with AC coupling selected on the 'scope.

Professional power supply designers can purchase equipment that does this testing. It consists of a variable 'current-sink' which can be controlled electronically and a variable frequency function generator to drive the current sink. The function generator can be programmed to generate a square wave, triangle wave or a sine wave; the repetition rate can be set and the 'on-time' of the maximum load as well as the minimum and maximum current drawn. This allows the design engineer to thoroughly explore the way the power supply reacts to many different types of load transients.

This sort of equipment doesn't come cheaply, but a home constructor can make a simple transient test jig with a few junk box components. I will give details of a design I use in a separate chapter covering test equipment.

What is a good transient response? What we are looking for is a low value of peak to peak induced AC voltage as the load is increased and decreased. Looking at the 'scope trace can tell you a lot about the way the power supply regulation circuitry can handle violent changes in the output load.

I will cover this topic again in more detail in the chapter on Linear Regulators and again in the chapter about Switch-mode supplies. Linear regulators generally are more able to cope with large transient loads than switch-mode supplies and we can stipulate what is a good and bad figure.

For a step-change of load from 10% to 100%, with a linear regulator, the figure to aim for is around 1% maximum change. A switch-mode supply is often much worse, 2 to 5% is typical. But it is not the absolute magnitude of the voltage transient that is so important as the way the output voltage recovers in a controlled manner. A poor design would see the transient lasting for a fairly long time before it returned to acceptable levels. The sudden increase in the load will cause the voltage to drop and then as the load is returned to the lower level the voltage will rise above the nominal before returning to the nominal. The 'scope trace may show the voltage oscillate above and below the nominal before the oscillations die away and the output is once again pure DC. This is known as an 'under-damped response'.

Damping - why it is so important?

Imagine a motor car with faulty shock absorbers. When a wheel hits a pothole or a bump in the road, the wheel suddenly moves violently. The springs try to limit the amount the wheel rises or falls, but it is the shock absorbers (dampers) that control the rate of change, absorbing the excess energy. With faulty shock absorbers, the wheel carries on bouncing for a long time, until expanding and contracting the spring uses up all the transient energy.

With a motor vehicle with good shock absorbers, the wheel makes maybe one or two up and down movements before it returns to a stable condition. With the faulty shock absorbers, the system is out of control for a long time. With the good shock absorbers, the system is quickly brought back to a stable condition.

The good shock absorber case results in a 'critically damped' response, ie the system returns quickly to a stable state in a controlled way in the minimum time. The faulty shock absorber system is 'under-damped' and takes a long time to return to equilibrium. Maybe a second and third pothole or bump occurs before the wheel has had time to stop bouncing from the first one. This sets up an uncontrolled oscillation that can quickly reach dangerous magnitudes, causing the driver to lose control of the vehicle.

Transient load regulation, or rather the lack of it, is often the cause of inexplicable 'blow-ups' in the attached amateur transceiver whilst transmitting SSB or CW because the transient voltage gets bigger and bigger due to repetitive shock loads. The 'captain' and the 'engine room' are suddenly opening the throttle and just as suddenly closing it to try to bring the voltage under control. Sooner or later the sensitive RF transistor has exceeded its safe working voltage and the result is a loud bang!

Which brings me to a vital question you have to honestly answer. Would you connect up your expensive transceiver to a power supply without doing this test?

There are several other causes of sudden failures with linear regulated power supplies that I will cover in later chapters.

Without getting embroiled in deep mathematical formulae, Bode plots and stability criteria, (which after all is not the intent of this type of book) let me just say this. The control circuitry in any regulated power supply is in essence a 'servo-loop' and can be analysed mathematically with standard formulae or by using modern computer software before the power supply is constructed to see if any potentially unstable regions exist. If one or more are found the design can be 'fine-tuned' to reduce these unstable regions to an acceptable level. Any reputable manufacturer should have done this analysis before committing a design to manufacture, and backed it up with rigorous testing in the development phases with a transient load test set-up. I will delve a little deeper into this topic when I discuss linear regulated and switch-mode power supplies in greater detail in later chapters.

Electronics engineers have wondered for many years what the secret is to semiconductor devices. I can reveal the secret. It is smoke! You will find that once the magic smoke has been released from the transistor or IC it no longer works. And so far engineers and scientists have not been able to replace the smoke to make the device work again.

Current limiting and short circuit protection

Any power supply worth its salt should be able to cope with accidental shorts on the output. Many amateur constructed supplies fair poorly in this regard, sometimes simply because the constructor is too scared to do the test! This can have disastrous results when something inevitably goes wrong. It could be you accidentally drop a screwdriver across the output terminals or worse still, something 'gives up the ghost' in the attached equipment it is powering.

Remember the 'magic smoke' I talked about earlier. You can be sure that lots of that smoke will emerge if the power supply cannot survive a dead short across the output.

Current limiting comes in two flavours for regulated power supplies. The first is a circuit which does not allow the current to exceed a certain value, this is known as 'Constant Current' limiting. The output voltage gradually decreases from the nominal as the load is increased once the maximum current is exceeded.

Limiting the output current sets the maximum current that can be drawn. As the load gets closer to a short circuit the output voltage sinks lower and lower until it is zero with a dead short across the output of the supply. This places an undue strain on the power transistors, which have to pass all the output current and also now will have all the rectified DC applied across them in this situation. This results in a very high dissipation in the pass transistors under this fault condition.

The second type is what is known as 'fold-back' limiting. Here the current limiting circuitry progressively reduces the output current to a low level as the load increases past the nominal maximum rating. When the load has become a dead short, the current will have reduced to almost zero.

At around the onset point of limiting the two types behave in a similar manner, but the fold back type does a lot to reduce the strain on the output transistors. Running at high current causes a lot of heat to be generated, not just in the pass transistors but also the transformer, rectifiers and other components. Under a dead short condition the whole of the voltage from the transformer rectifier combination is developed across the output 'pass transistors'. These may very well expire under these conditions, failing short circuit. The safe junction temperature of modern silicon transistors is about +150 to +200°C. Exceed this by a small amount and the silicon fuses and becomes a short circuit, result - more magic smoke!

Now imagine what happens when an external short causes the output transistors to fail. When the short is removed instead of the supply returning to the 13.8V that we designed it for, it will jump up to whatever the transformer and rectifier supplies, often as much as 30V under no load condition. More magic-smoke, but this time from your expensive transceiver (BTDT = been there, done that! The reason for a long period of misery and a big dent in the bank account).

To give some indication of the strain the pass transistors can be subjected to; I measured a commercial power supply I have which is made by one of the leading Japanese suppliers of amateur equipment. This supply is a nominal 13.8V at 12 A. It uses a transformer that gives 22V AC on the secondary under no load conditions. Under full load conditions the secondary voltage sags to around 15V AC. So using the standard formula (V_{dc} = 1.414 x V_{ac}) we can ascertain that the rectified DC across the smoothing capacitor will be 31V off load and 21V at full load.

Assume that the current limit is set to exactly 12A, which in practice is too low for a 12A supply and should be closer to 15A. However, the 12A will suffice for our explanation.

Under a dead short condition the supply, if it did not have fold back current limiting, would limit the current to, say, 12A. Taking the measurements I made on this supply, we see that at 12A the input to the regulator pass transistors is 21V, and all this voltage is across the transistors. Therefore, this would dissipate 21V x 12A which is around 250 watts in the pass transistors. This may be too much for the heatsink to dissipate quickly enough and the transistor junction temperature would then rise rapidly and could be exceeded. More magic smoke!

With the fold back current limiting working correctly the supply should reduce or fold back the current to around 5A maximum. Now with the diminished load the smoothing capacitor voltage would rise to approach the 31V measured off load. Let us say it gets to 25V. The dissipation in the pass transistors will be the product of the difference between the input and output voltage mulitplied by the output current. The output voltage is zero because we have a solid short across the output terminals. So the dissipation is 25V x 5A which equals 125W. Still not a happy situation, but the pass transistors can probably cope with this for a short time, if the heat sink is big enough.

The ideal situation would be for the fold back limiting to reduce the current in the pass transistors to close to zero, but about 2A would suffice. This would give a dissipation of about 50 to 60W, which the transistors and the heatsink should be able to cope with indefinitely.

Incidentally, this highlights one of the main failings of the conventional linear regulator. At up to 50% of the rated current there is nearly as much power dissipated in the pass transistors as is being delivered to the load! Only from 50% to 100% output is the situation reversed. To put it simply the linear regulator is very inefficient; at best, 60 to 70% at full output in a well-designed supply. Inefficiency means that a lot of heat is being generated hence the big heatsinks common with linear power supplies.

In my 13.8V nominal 12A 'guinea pig' supply, the pass transistor dissipation is shown in **Table 3.1**.

The results don't look too bad at first sight, but this is a cleverly designed power supply. This is simply because the transformer has been carefully designed to make the secondary voltage collapse to a lower than normal level, which takes most of the strain off the pass transistors, a cunning trick by the manufacturer. This is a case of sizing the transformer to be just big enough for the job.

Output Current (A)	Output Power (W)	Dissipation in output transistor (W)	Efficiency (%)
1	13.8	16.2	46
2.5	27.6	38	42
5	69	56	55
10	138	74	65
15	207	63	76

Table 3.1: Dissipation in 'guinea pig' power supply

In fact, the overall efficiency is worse than that shown because I haven't included the extra power needed to drive the control circuitry and driver transistors, which amounts to about another 3A. In the chapter dealing with linear regulators, I will give more accurate measurements, but for now these will serve to highlight the problem.

Don't over-engineer!

The above example should be a warning to intending amateur constructors. Many home brewed power supplies use a transformer which is totally 'over the top', often because a transformer was found at a flea market or swap meet which looked suitable. Fred at the local radio club built a similar power supply a few years back and his transformer seemed about the same size and weight.

But looking at a transformer tells you nothing about how it reacts to heavy current loads. A transformer that is designed for use in a car battery charger may look identical but it is designed with a completely different set of criteria. In a car battery charger the secondary voltage is deliberately designed to collapse as the load is increased, by building the transformer with a flux limited core. This is a case of very poor output voltage regulation deliberately being used to achieve a particular end. Don't use a transformer intended for a battery charger for a linear regulated supply at anything more than 60% of its rating, as it will give disappointing results!

Measure the output voltage regulation using a variety of heavy-duty load resistors to draw as much current as you need before deciding to incorporate the 'bargain transformer' in your supply. I will cover the selection of a transformer in a later chapter and what current the transformer secondary needs to supply. Surprisingly enough, it is often quite a bit more than the maximum DC output current!

By using a transformer which is over-designed you also stand to waste a lot of hard earned cash, especially if you have to get the transformer made by a company. These faults are often due to ignorance, something I hope this book will resolve. To see for yourself what the use of an oversize transformer does to the pass transistor dissipation, assume the rectified secondary voltage is a solid 20V DC and does not drop no matter what the load. Run the calculations yourself and see what dissipation is required. In such a case, you would scarcely need any regulating circuitry!

Testing current limit and short circuit limit

I have deliberately differentiated between the two parameters, as they are not necessarily the same in a power supply.

To test for current limiting you need a load that can be varied from a high resistance to a resistance approaching zero ohms. It may well be that you can find a suitable variable high wattage resistor, but most of us are not that fortunate. You can build a suitable variable current-sink for a relatively small outlay in parts and your effort. I will include a suitable design in a later chapter detailing test equipment.

Along with the current sink, you will need an ammeter, which can measure a current somewhat higher than required, and a voltmeter. Most AVOs or digital multi-meters only allow you to measure up to 10A, so you will have to resort to some alternative method that I will deal with later.

One final warning about testing current limiting. *Don't use incandescent lamps to test power supplies.* These have a very large 'in-rush current' when cold, and can draw excessive current when first connected. The initial current 'spike' can drive the power supply current sensing into a lock-up situation, which may take too long for it to recover. This can cause an otherwise OK power supply to go into a 'melt-down' mode!

Over voltage protection

Finally, we turn to the last of the main parameters we shall use to specify a power supply.

It should be clear by now that the conventional linear regulator type of supply has one potentially disastrous failure mode. This is when the pass transistors fail in a shorted condition. If this happens to a supply attached to your transceiver the likelihood is that not only will the power supply transistors need replacing, but probably costly items within the transceiver because they would have been subjected to an over voltage condition.

What is needed is some circuit in the power supply to detect the output voltage exceeding a safe value and to shut off the supply should this occur. Assuming that nothing has failed in the power supply, this can be done quite simply with a 'Supervisory IC', many of which are available.

However, take the worst case scenario where one or more of the pass transistors have shorted. Telling the current limit or supervisory circuit to shut down the supply is useless because no matter what the control circuitry attempts to do, the dead pass transistor is no longer listening. It has failed with a dead short from input to output placing the full-rectified voltage onto the output - braindead! This is a very serious condition and needs rapid and drastic action!

This situation is often countered with a piece of circuitry called a 'Crowbar'. This monitors the output voltage and if it exceeds a safe value - in the case of our 13.8V supply, we would choose a voltage of about 15V as the activation point - it switches on a large thyristor (SCR) which is connected across the main input smoothing capacitor. When the thyristor is fired it latches on until the mains switch is turned off or the fuse blows. An example is shown in **Fig 3.1**.

In series with the transformer secondary winding is a suitably rated fuse, at least there is one in my power supplies! When the thyristor is triggered the smoothing capacitor is shorted to ground reducing the voltage to zero - pronto! This short - or crowbar - across the input causes the fuse to blow and this protects the power supply and the attached equipment from over voltage surges.

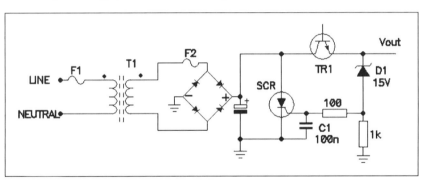

Fig 3.1: Basic crowbar circuit

You may ask why I place the fuse in the secondary circuit and not in series with the output of the smoothing capacitor? With the fuse placed after the smoothing capacitor the voltage is DC. A fuse when it starts to rupture can draw an arc across it and a DC arc tends to carry on. Placing the fuse in a part of the circuit where the voltage is AC means that every half cycle the voltage drops to zero. This means that the arc is extinguished more easily.

The crowbar is simple and reliable and can save expensive damage to attached equipment should the power supply pass transistors fail short circuit.

However, testing is not so simple. We do not want to induce a failure in the power supply to see if the crowbar trips at the correct voltage. But with a little ingenuity, an amateur can get around the problem. There are two ways to test the crowbar circuit. Depending on whether the power supply is one you constructed, or one you purchased and may be subject to warranty conditions, will help you to decide which method to use.

For the home constructed power supply, you should be familiar with the circuitry, the internal layout and the location of the major components. Identify the crowbar detector input and disconnect the power supply output voltage from it. Substitute a bench power supply with a suitable voltage range. Fire up the power supply and connect a load of about 10% across the output. Adjust the bench power supply voltage slowly upwards from 13.8V to the point where the crowbar activates. Read off the bench power supply voltage, this is the trip point. Replace the fuse with a new one of the same rating; connect everything back the way it should be. Test complete!

For a purchased power supply, in which opening it up to do this test may void the warranty, or a power-supply you are not familiar with, we have to use a slightly different technique. We require an external variable voltage power supply and a silicon diode, such as a 1N5400 as shown in **Fig 3.2**.

Connect the power supply under test to a load of about 10% of its full rating, in our case about a 1A load, so a 15Ω 25W resistor would suffice. Connect the bench power supply with the 1N5400 diode connected in series with the positive lead. Connect the negative of the bench supply in parallel with the one under test. Set the output of the bench supply to about 13V to start with and switch both supplies on. Adjust the output voltage of the bench supply upwards slowly until the output voltage of the supply under test starts to rise, as indicated either by the front panel voltmeter or a separate voltmeter connected across the output terminals. Continue increasing the bench power supply voltage until the trip point is reached. Watch the voltmeter closely to see the exact voltage at

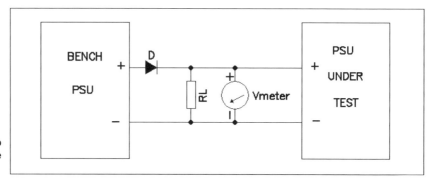

Fig 3.2: Test set up for over voltage testing

which the supply trips. When done, disconnect the external power supply and diode and replace the fuse. Test complete!

Well, enough of this for now. I suspect you want to get your teeth into something a bit juicier, so let's move onto the next topic - Linear Power Supplies.

Basic Linear Regulator Circuits

Endurance: *"Only by weaving our way through the forest often bumping into obstacles, can we ever get on the right track to achievement"* (Henry Ford)

In the preceding chapters we have talked about linear regulators in very general terms. Now we can start to explore them in greater detail. There are two basic types of linear regulator circuits and from these are derived many different variations. The two most common ones are known as the 'Shunt Regulator' and the 'Series Regulator'.

Shunt regulator

The Shunt Regulator is somewhat similar to a simple Zener diode stabiliser, but utilising a transistor to obtain more output current. The major advantage of the shunt regulator is that it is inherently short-circuit proof and can sink as well as source current. However, there the advantages stop as they have several disadvantages, the main one being a very low efficiency at low load. A typical version of the basic shunt regulator is shown in **Fig 4.1**.

The PNP power transistor, TR1, is biased with a Zener diode, D1, and resistor, R2, providing the base current to the transistor. The emitter has a low value resistor, R1, from the unstabilised supply line. The output is taken from the emitter with the collector connected to the common negative line. Because all the output current has to flow via R1 the magnitude of current the shunt stabiliser can supply is limited by the value of the resistor and the power rating. When the load is disconnected the transistor turns on harder to hold the output voltage constant and all the current flows through TR1, causing a high dissipation in the transistor.

The shunt stabiliser is effectively a 'current-boosted-Zener' and operates in a very similar way. Because of this, the transistor and heatsink have to be sized to handle all the power dissipation when the load is disconnected. However, one advantage of using this version which uses

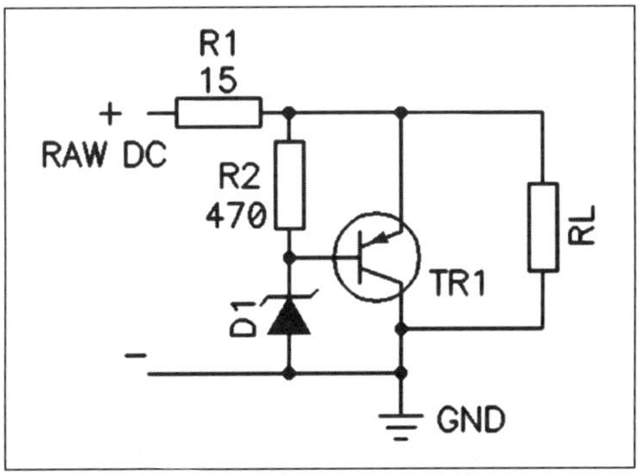

Fig 4.1: Basic Shunt Stabiliser

> The shunt regulator is an excellent choice for stabilising the screen grid of a large tetrode valve because it can absorb the negative screen current which valves such as the 4CX250 often generate at low drive levels. If the screen were fed with a series regulator the screen voltage can quietly creep upwards and the voltage can becomes too much for the fragile screen decoupling capacitor which is built into the air flow socket and it fails catastrophically. These air flow sockets are expensive and normally irreparable once the decoupling capacitor has failed due to over voltage.

a PNP transistor, is that the collector is at ground potential and can be bolted directly to the heatsink without any insulating mica washer. A similar version can also be constructed with a NPN transistor by turning the whole circuit 'upside down', but this would then require an insulating mica washer to prevent the collector shorting out.

A further advantage of the shunt stabiliser is that it inherently has built in over-voltage protection. If the input voltage rises the transistor simply turns on harder to shunt the excess current to ground.

Another version of the Shunt Stabiliser is shown in **Fig 4.2**. This provides two different output voltages, a 5V supply from the Zener, so the current that can be drawn is somewhat limited, and the main output that can supply a higher voltage and current.

Basic series stabiliser

The Series Stabiliser use the same number of components as the Shunt Stabiliser but does not suffer the poor efficiency at low output currents. The majority of linear regulator power supplies use a form of this circuit. The basic circuit shown in **Fig 4.3**.

This particular circuit is designed to supply a +5V digital rail drawing about 100mA from a nominal 12V supply. The NPN transistor is connected in series between the input voltage and the output voltage, hence its name. The base of the 2N3053 has a 5.6V Zener diode connected between it and ground. This establishes a stable voltage, the reference voltage.

The NPN transistor is configured as an emitter follower and the emitter tries to maintain the same voltage across the emitter to ground as the base voltage.

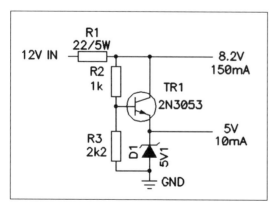

Fig 4.2: Dual output shunt stabiliser

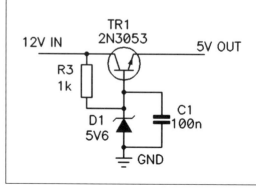

Fig 4.3: Basic series regulator

However, because it is a bipolar junction transistor (BJT) there is an inherent voltage difference of about 0.6V between the base and emitter. Therefore the emitter develops a voltage of 5.6V - 0.6V = 5V. The 100n capacitor between the base and ground is to filter out the inherent wide-band noise that Zener diodes generate.

One important thing to note is that the leakage current between the collector and emitter, that all transistors exhibit to some extent and gets worse at high junction temperatures, means that it always needs a minimum load resistor. Typically for the circuit in Fig 4.3 we would need a minimum load of about 1% (1mA) which can be catered for by a 4.7kΩ resistor wired permanently across the output. Without this resistor the output would tend to float up to the input voltage under very light loads.

When the load current is very low the output voltage is approximately 5V, but as the load current is increased the output voltage gradually drops below the 5V as the collector-emitter voltage drop in a BJT increases with current. The maximum collector-emitter current possible to a first order, and hence the output current, is dependant on the current gain of the transistor and the value of the resistor feeding the base. In the circuit shown, the base resistor is 1kΩ and hence the maximum base current is (12V - 5.6V) / 1kΩ = 6.4mA. However, the Zener requires a minimum current to provide regulation and this will be about 1mA in practice. Examining the data for the 2N3053 we can see that the current gain (h_{fe}) lies in the region of 50 to 250. This sets the maximum output current at around 250mA when the h_{fe} equals 50.

It is prudent to use the lower of the two figures given for h_{fe} when calculating the output current as the inherent trend with bipolar junction transistors is for the current gain to fall as the collector current goes up. If we had chosen the upper limit of the h_{fe} the maximum output current would have been about 2A which is an unrealistic figure for a 2N3053 which has a maximum safe collector current of 1A.

One other thing to note about this simple circuit is that it operates in 'open-loop' mode, there is no direct connection between the output and the input. So it is not intelligent enough to know that the output voltage does not conform to the required 5V. (The Shunt Stabiliser on the other hand has a closed-loop circuit and so changes in load current and input voltage variations are catered for).

Applying a heavy load causes the output voltage to drop, because the 1kΩ resistor is unable to provide enough current to the base to bring the voltage back to the correct level. The 2N3053 is rated at 1A maximum collector current with a collector dissipation of 800mW. We can calculate the maximum safe collector current knowing these facts.

Assume the input voltage is fixed at 12V for this calculation. Also assume the output voltage remains steady at exactly 5V.

There will be a constant voltage across the collector-emitter junction of:

$$12V - 5V = 7V$$

For a maximum dissipation of 800mW the current will be:

$$P_{diss} / V_{ce}$$

Therefore:

$$0.8 / 7V = 114 \text{ mA}.$$

So it is obvious that the simple circuit can only really supply about 100mA before the dissipation in the transistor becomes a major factor.

What happens when we apply a load that is greatly in excess of the 100mA? When this happens the output voltage drops below the 5V due to the increased collector-emitter voltage drop and the current climbs to a dangerous level. Under short-circuit condition the output voltage has fallen to zero volts and all of the 12V input voltage is now across the transistor collector emitter junction. The dissipation in the transistor would be:

$$P_{diss} = I_{max} \times V_{ce}$$

$$I_{max} = 250mA \ \& \ V_{ce} = 12V, \text{ therefore } P_{diss} = 3W$$

As the maximum safe dissipation of the 2N3053 is only 800mW, the transistor will be seriously over-dissipated and certain to fail with 'magic smoke'. From this we can see that the basic circuit is definitely not short circuit proof!

The basic circuit has several disadvantages:

- Limited output current.
- Not short circuit proof.
- Output voltage not very stable with changing load.

One way of obtaining more current without over-dissipating the transistor is to lower the input voltage from 12V to about 8V. The transistor needs at least 3V across the collector-emitter junction for it to function correctly. By lowering the collector voltage to 8V we can now draw a little more current without exceeding the 800mW rating. This would now allow a current of 266mA to be drawn before the 800mW dissipation is reached. However, it should be remembered that this is only a low power regulator and cannot tolerate a short-circuit across the output, use it at your own risk! A quick and dirty way of making this simple circuit more tolerant of shorts on the output is to include a low value resistor in series with the collector supply. This degrades the regulation somewhat but makes it able to tolerate short over current periods. This is often used in simple equipment where the inclusion of something more elaborate would not be economically viable.

Increasing output current

To obtain more output current requires putting more 'current gain' into the circuit, and as this needs to pass more current we would need to augment the output stage with a more suitable transistor. Amongst the myriad of possible transistors to choose from we need to keep practicalities and cost in mind. Availability is also a major factor, it is all very well choosing a 'super-transistor' which would do the job superbly, but if you have to mortgage the house or wait for several months to obtain one then it is not very suitable!

I will take the more conservative route and select an old stalwart, the 2N3055, as it is cheap, readily available and made by many semiconductor manufacturers. It has one other advantage; it is very robust and can tolerate a lot of abuse when properly heatsinked. The revised circuit is shown in **Fig 4.4**.

You will notice that the 5.6V Zener (D1) now has an extra diode (D2) connected in series with it. This diode provides the additional 0.6V required as we now have two base-emitter voltage drops between the input and output. If D2 were not added the output voltage would only be about 4.4V. (We could replace

D1 with a 6.2V Zener and omit D2, but although a 6.2V Zener is a recognised standard component it tends to be somewhat harder to find).

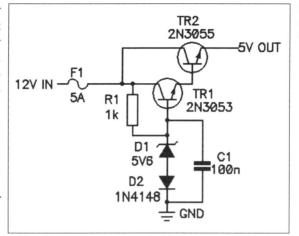

Fig 4.4: Boosting output current with an extra transistor

Here we can see that the output of TR1 directly feeds the base of TR2. They are connected in a Darlington configuration. Of course we could have chosen one of the many Darlington transistors made but for now we will stick with our original approach.

The base current of TR2 is 'boosted' by TR1 to a much higher level. The current gain of a typical 2N3055 lies between 20 and 70. We will again take the conservative approach and select the lower of the h_{fe} ratings. This measurement gives us an overall current gain of the product of the two transistors, 50 for the 2N3053 and 20 for the 2N3055. This is a total gain of 1000. So assuming the same base current into TR1 of 6mA from our original circuit this yields a maximum current of 6mA x 1000 = 6A.

The maximum collector current rating of the 2N3055 is 15A, so our calculated 6A seems to be well within the safe working area. The maximum safe dissipation of a 2N3055 is 115W when the collector temperature is held at 25°C. With adequate heatsinking we should be able to get close to this, say, 50°C at which point we can safely 'guesstimate' that the dissipation would be around half the 25°C figure or about 60W. For more accurate figures we would need to examine the thermal resistance figures for the 2N3055 and the proposed heatsink. However, 60W is good enough for now. Armed with these basic figures we can roughly calculate the safe maximum current based on the collector dissipation.

Assuming we want an output voltage of 13.8V and our transformer, rectifier and capacitor combination gives around 20V, we can plug in these numbers into our calculator and see the result.

- V_{in} = 20V
- V_{out} = 13.8V
- P_{diss} = 60W

The voltage across the 2N3055 will be:

20V - 13.8V = 6.2V (exceeds the 3V criteria)

$P_{diss} = V_{ce}$ x I_{ce}

Therefore $I_{ce} = P_{diss} / V_{ce}$ = 60 / 6.2 = 9.6A (exceeds the 6A criteria)

As this is below the 15A maximum rating we can initially assume that the 2N3055 will be able to safely handle this current when correctly heatsinked. These are very rough basic calculations but serve to tell us that the basic design concept is fairly sound. The one area of concern is the ability of the TO-3 package to get the required amount of heat away into the heatsink and the required heat sink, these I will tackle a little later.

Potential problems with the TO-3 package

The TO-3 package for transistors was originally designed by a semiconductor applications engineer named Richard (Dick) Moss and was patented by him when he worked for RCA.

Talking to Dick some years ago he told me that he now wasn't particularly impressed with his design since it was a very early development idea and better thermal packages have been developed in the later years.

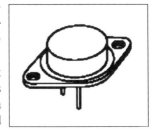

Fig 4.5:TO-3 packaged transistor

The one big problem, which he now realises was a bad idea, is that with the TO-3 package the clamping pressure is applied at the extreme ends of the package. This causes the centre of the package - where the silicon die is attached to the copper heat spreader - to lift off the heatsink as the fixing screws are tightened down. The bottom of the TO-3 package is made of a soft copper alloy, which deforms with little effort.

In a motor car cylinder head the studs or bolts which serve to clamp the head to the cylinder block are distributed around the cylinders to spread the pressure out as evenly as possible. Bolting at only the two extreme ends of a head would cause the head to lift in the centre and cause a leakage of the combustion gas.

By clamping the TO-3 package at the extreme edges causes the thermal resistance to be very sensitive to how much clamping pressure is applied. Very often the slight lifting of the centre of the package off the heatsink causes a large reduction in possible dissipation and hence a large rise in junction temperature. Applying a thick blob of heatsink compound aggravates the problem. In actual fact the TO-3 package, like a lot of other semiconductor packages, is deliberately slightly bowed during manufacture to reduce this problem, the ends where the screws fit are made microscopically higher than the centre. Provided the screws are tightened to the recommended figures the package will pull flat onto a smooth heatsink surface. However, if the transistor is removed and replaced a few times the soft copper heat spreader plate loses it's bowed shape and the centre lifts.

Perhaps it would be enlightening to the reader at this juncture to explain how transistors are tested during qualification to let you see how important this aspect is.

The manufacturers of the transistor, when testing the dissipation rating, do not clamp the transistor down in the same way you and I do when we install it on a heatsink. Instead they use a fixture that presses down around the whole of the case. This exerts a constant pressure, which better prevents the centre from lifting. In fact several heatsink manufacturers make similar clamping adapters for the TO-3 package, which yield much better results than the two screws at the edges of the heat spreader.

Fig 4.6: Current sharing resistors in emitters

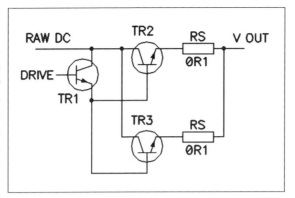

Because of this inherent problem with the TO-3 package it is safer to use two parallel transistors to carry the load current and hence reduce the dissipation in each device. The 2N3055 is perfectly capable of carrying the 15A the data sheet specification gives when correctly heatsinked. However the 115W-dissipation figure is a bit of a misnomer. This is measured with an 'infinite heatsink'. The manufacturers use a water-cooled copper block to hold the heat spreader flange at 25°C for this measurement. This is a very artificial way of doing things and one which rarely can be replicated in real life. However, it is a standard method used throughout the semiconductor industry and one that is unlikely to change in the future.

I have only seen this done in one piece of equipment. It is a 10kW audio amplifier, which resides in the environmental lab at my previous employers works that is used to drive a 'shaker table' used for vibration testing. Rows and rows of TO-3 devices bolted to a massive copper heat spreader which in turn is cooled with water flowing through a refrigerated heat exchanger. Not the sort of thing an amateur is likely to resort to!

In view of these factors and because 2N3055s are relatively cheap it is better to play safe and use two devices for a supply of this type. A rough rule of thumb I have always used is one 2N3055 for every 5A required. This also improves the overall reliability as the output devices are much less stressed and when one considers the possible consequences of short circuits it brings added peace of mind.

However, a new problem now arises. Although the two transistors are the same types, even from the same batch lot, they will have slightly different current gains.

Remember the gain spread for the 2N3055 can be anywhere between 20 and 70. What this means is that the transistor that has the higher current gain will try and 'hog' all the current and very little will pass through the lower gain device. If we don't do something to share the current more or less equally the higher gain device will dissipate far more power than the other and will probably fail.

By inserting a low value resistor in the emitter of each device and then connecting these resistors together the slight differences in V_{ce} are factored out and the two transistors will then have identical V_{ce} figures. This ensures each transistor does its fair share of work.

One downside to adding the sharing resistors is that there are more loss making elements in circuit, but the resistors can be quite small. A value of 100mΩ is usually sufficient for a transistor such as the 2N3055 and this will only drop 0.5V when 5A is flowing in each transistor. This is illustrated in **Fig 4.6**.

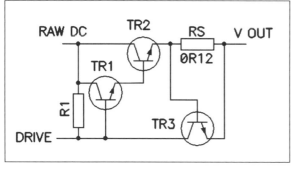

Fig 4.7: Current sensing circuitry

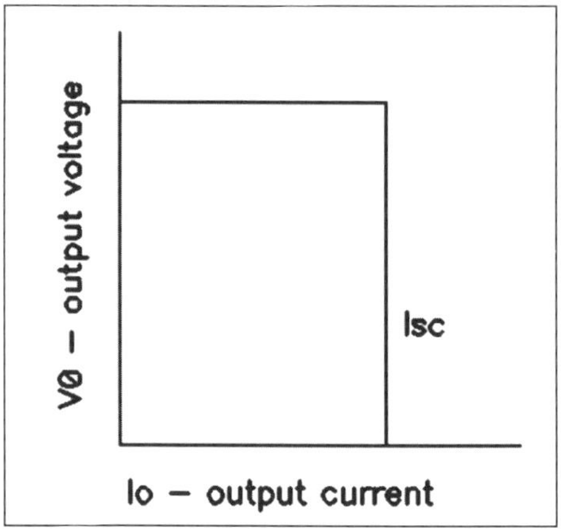

Fig 4.8:Current limiting response

Current sensing circuitry

Turning now to **Fig 4.7**, in which I have added a few extra components, we can examine how the current sensing portion works.

TR3 is a low power transistor with its base and emitter connected across a low value 'current sense resistor', Rs, which is in series with the output. All the output current flows through this resistor and when the current exceeds a pre-set value it causes a voltage to be developed sufficient to turn on TR3. This in turn causes the base drive to TR1 to be reduced by pulling the base voltage down towards ground. By selecting the correct value for this current sense resistor we can set the current limit to whatever we need. The basic formula for this is:

$R_{sense} = 0.6V / I_{max}$

Let us choose a current limit of 5A.

Then $R_{sense} = 0.6V / 5A = 0.12\Omega$ which is a standard E12 value.

The dissipation in this resistor at 5A will be:

$I^2R = (5 \times 5) \times 0.12 = 3W$, a 5W wire-wound resistor would be suitable.

This type of current limiting is called 'Constant-Current' (**Fig 4.8**) as the available current cannot exceed a fixed maximum. However, it is not the most

Fig 4.9: Fold-back current limiting circuit

Fig 4.10: Current limiting response

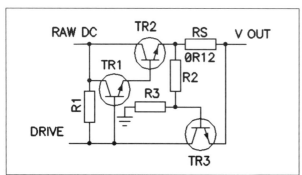

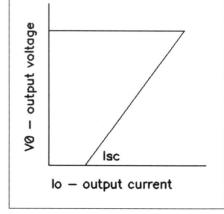

optimum type as under a short circuit the transistor still passes the maximum current and all the input voltage is across it, causing a high dissipation.

A much better method is to use what is called 'Fold-Back' current limiting. This is illustrated in **Figs 4.9 and 4.10**. Here the current limit sensing voltage is derived from a potential divider that causes the current to decrease once a certain maximum is passed. This form of current limiting is used in a great number of IC voltage regulators to limit the package dissipation.

Voltage feedback circuitry

Having sorted out the current sensing and limiting circuits we can now incorporate the final item which is the voltage feedback circuitry. This is detailed in **Fig 4.11**.

A potential divider, comprising resistors R3 and VR1 connected across the output, senses the output voltage. The mid-point of these goes to the inverting input of the 741 op-amp. The non-inverting input of the op-amp has a voltage reference connected to it, provided by R1 and D1. The voltage divider provides an output which when the ''servo-loop' is balanced will be the same as the voltage reference. The value of this voltage reference could be almost any value, but it has been chosen to be 5.1V in this circuit.

Why choose such an odd value? Zener diodes exhibit temperature tolerances with varying temperatures. It just so happens that around 5V, with standard Zener diodes, the temperature tolerance falls to around zero. 5V is not a standard value, but 5.1V is.

So by choosing a 5.1V Zener diode we get very little change in the reference voltage with a wide range of temperatures. This means that once we have selected the potential divider resistors to suit our required output voltage we can be confident that changing temperatures won't cause the output voltage to wander about.

To provide a small variation in the output voltage to allow us to trim the voltage to an exact value the potential divider has been split into two resistors, one fixed and one a preset resistor, VR1. By adjusting the preset resistor we can trim or 'tweak' the output voltage to our exact requirement.

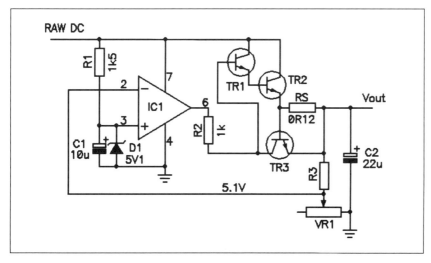

Fig 4.11: Basic regulator circuit

How the voltage feedback works

Imagine we have set the output voltage to our required 13.8V with a very small load connected. Now we increase the load. As we do so, the output voltage sags slightly and the divided down sample of the output voltage, which connects to the inverting input of the op-amp, also falls by the same percentage. The output of the op-amp tries to maintain a constant output voltage by 'servo-ing' the loop with negative feedback. This causes the output voltage of the op-amp to rise slightly to maintain status-quo. The output of the op-amp is not 13.8V but is two base emitter junction drops above the required 13.8V, or around 1.2V more than the output voltage, plus the voltage drop across the current sense resistor. Now you can see why we needs about 5V extra as the input voltage to ensure we have enough 'headroom' to make the control circuitry work.

It is important that the output voltage is sensed *after* the current sense resistor or else the output voltage would steadily drop as the load current increased. Which brings us to another trick we can do with output voltage sensing.

Remote sensing

In most cases we want the output voltage that is applied to the attached equipment to be constant. Isn't that what a regulated power supply is supposed to do? Well yes, but what about the voltage drops in the leads that connect the equipment to the power supply. They also have some voltage drop that increases as the load current increases. The power supply doesn't know about this extra voltage drop and is oblivious to any volt drop in the leads; it simply maintains the correct voltage at its output terminals. But by sensing the voltage at the equipment and not the power supply, we can factor out this volt drop.

By connecting a separate pair of thinner leads that go to the equipment input terminals we can sense the voltage there, and not at the power supply output terminals. But a basic problem now arises.

What happens when the equipment is disconnected from the power supply? If we did this, but left the sense leads still connected to the input of the equipment, the power supply would think the output voltage was far too low and turn up the voltage in an attempt to rectify the problem. This would allow an abnormally high voltage to be developed, akin to an output transistor going short circuit. What we need is another sensing scheme that also takes into account what the power supply is trying to do.

Fig 4.12: Remote sensing

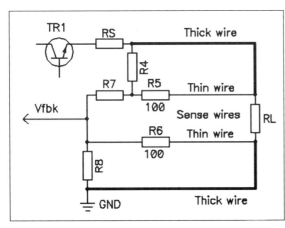

We can get around this problem by having two sensing routes. One directly across the equipment and a second which monitors the power supply output voltage - local sensing. This could be just two sets of leads, one heavy pair for the main current and one thinner pair for the voltage sensing at the equipment end. But the thinner pair would try and carry some of the output current and because they are thin and have a higher voltage drop would cause a false reading.

By splitting the sensing and inserting low value resistors in series with the remote sensing leads we can stop this. The rather strange assembly of voltage sensing resistors in **Fig 4.12** performs this task. R7 and R8 perform the normal voltage divider function, but in the case of either of the sense leads being accidentally disconnected, R4 serves to hold the output voltage to a safe level.

Metering voltage and current

Many power supplies have just a blank front panel with maybe an on/off switch and an indicator to tell us the supply is switched on. Most laboratory bench supplies have separate meters for voltage and current. It would be nice if we could see from time to time what the power supply was actually doing; a great confidence builder!

Voltage metering

This is fairly simple and only needs a suitable milli-ammeter with a scale to suit the voltage range of the power supply and a resistor to give the correct full-scale reading. This resistor is called a 'multiplier' as it multiplies the full-scale deflection of the milli-ammeter to whatever we require.

But hold on, didn't you just say a milli-ammeter? But we need a voltmeter. Yes, I said milli-ammeter but a milli-ammeter can also indicate voltage. Taking a typical 1mA full-scale deflection meter we can ascertain what voltage is required to give full-scale deflection (FSD).

Using my 'ever close at hand' *RS Components* catalogue, a typical 1mA meter has a resistance of 75Ω. Using Ohms Law we can ascertain that for a current of 1mA flowing in this resistance we get a voltage of 75mV FSD.

We would want a FSD of 15V for our nominal 13.8V PSU to give a good indication. This requires a resistor in series of 14.925kΩ, which unfortunately is not a standard value. We could use a 15kΩ and suffer a little inaccuracy. However by adding several resistors in series we can get there.

Using a 12kΩ resistor leaves a deficit of 2.925kΩ which can be made up from a 2.7kΩ and a 500Ω preset pot. Or alternatively we can use a 12kΩ and a 5kΩ pre-set, which will give a coarser setting but still 'do-able'. Which way you choose will probably depend on what you have at hand in your junk box. Calibration is done by adjusting the preset whilst comparing the meter indication with your DVM.

Current metering

The meter used for current measurement needs to indicate the required full-scale deflection. Suppose you needed it to read 5A. It would be nice to use the same meter movement as the volt-meter so one meter could perform both tasks with a switch to change over, after all meters are expensive!

Let us use the 1mA movement and design the required meter shunt. We need to shunt the majority of the 5A through the parallel resistor, in our case 4.999A. The meter shunt needs to develop 75mV across it when 4.999A flows. Using Ohms Law gives a resistance of 0.01499Ω or 15mΩ is close enough, which is a standard value if you can find a supplier who will sell you just one of these! You could make one using Ni-Chrome wire or copper wire wound on a suitable former, messy but possible if your DVM can measure to such accuracy. Personally I don't have the patience for such things.

But why waste money when there is an alternative means? We already have a low value resistor used for the current sensing and by using a couple of resistors we can use this to give our required FSD of 5A. To recap, the current sensing resistor develops approximately 0.6V when the power supply goes into current limit. By reducing this in the same way as we did for the voltage multiplier we can achieve the same end.

We need to drop a voltage of 600mV - 75mV = 525mV at a current of 1mA. This needs a resistor of 525Ω, again a non-standard value, which also needs to be adjustable to calibrate the meter against a known accurate meter. By using a 470Ω resistor and a 100Ω preset pot we can get the required reading.

I have included **Fig 4.13**, which is a schematic for a bench power supply that uses the LM317 IC regulator. This little jewel supplies around 1.5A and is variable over about 3V to 15V. It is one I designed a while back as a project for amateur radio examination students and since then many have been built. It is ideal for powering experimental circuits in the shack. The main reason for including it is to demonstrate how easy it is to use a cheap 1mA meter to display either current or voltage. The scale is re-calibrated to show 0 to 15 using *Letraset*, which gives 15V full scale, 1.5A or 300mA by mentally multiplying the 15 by 20.

The current limiting is performed by TR1 with the current sensing being in the negative or return lead. There are two ranges for the current limit, 300mA and 1.5A. When SW2 is open the current flows only in R7 and the base of TR1 is biased on when 300mA or more flows, pulling the adjust pin of the LM317 pin towards ground. When SW2 is closed the current limit is increased to around 1.5A as R8 and R9 are added in parallel with R7.

Note that neither the positive or negative output terminal is connected to ground. Hence, the power supply can be used as a positive or negative supply by grounding the appropriate terminal.

Fig 4.13: Simple bench supply using LM317 IC regulator

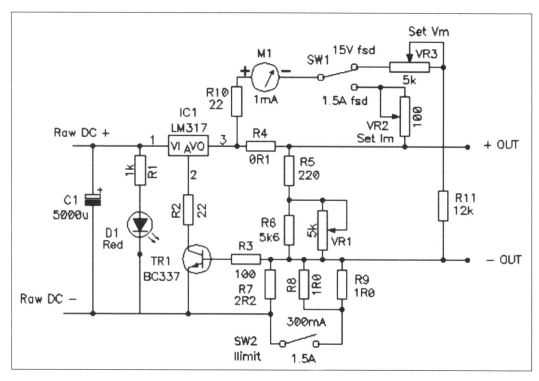

Note: The LM317 needs mounting on a suitable heatsink with an insulating washer as the tab of the LM317 is not at ground potential like some other IC regulators.

All you need to add is a suitable transformer and bridge rectifier. A 20VA transformer with a 12 to 15V secondary would be about right (*RS* part number 207-144 or 207-526 would suit UK mains voltage).

Adding over-voltage protection

Finally let us add a safety feature which will protect our expensive equipment should anything go wrong in the power supply causing the output voltage to become too high. A very good simple circuit uses a Zener and a high current SCR to blow the fuse in the input circuit.

I have sketched out the basic circuit in **Fig 4.14**, which with the values shown will work for a 13.8V supply. If you need a different voltage trip point then it is easy to change by substituting a different voltage Zener. The main pass transistor is TR1. Don't forget the fuse between the transformer secondary and the bridge rectifier or it won't work the way it is supposed to! The 100Ω resistor and the 100nF capacitor prevent spurious triggering.

Integrated circuit voltage regulators

Some of you may be disappointed that I have said very little so far about IC voltage regulators. This has been deliberate, as I believe that using these without appreciating what is inside them teaches us very little about how they work. (Most of my students seem to want to run before they can walk, which causes them to trip up). Most IC regulators contain a lot of transistors connected together in one convenient package, sometimes with a power stage and almost always with the very stable voltage reference Zener, to provide the basic elements for voltage regulation. In most cases very few external components need to be added to make one of these work and most contain some form of current limiting.

Traditionally there have been many IC regulators brought onto the market, from the simple LM78xx series which are fixed voltage with an output current capability of about 1A to more exotic types. One of the ones I mentioned in my opening comments was the µ723. This has been around a long time and although superseded by many of the later devices is still very much in use by amateurs today. It does however suffer from one serious shortcoming. It is very prone to bursting into self-oscillation. This causes the output voltage to be

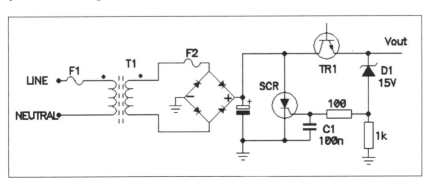

Fig 4.14: Simple crowbar circuit using a Zener and SCR

modulated, usually at a very high frequency of around 20kHz or more when shocked with stray RF signals. This is because it is not an 'internally frequency compensated' type as all the later types are today. It requires the careful selection of a compensation capacitor to be fitted between two of its pins to provide stability. Depending on whether it is used in its bare form to provide a maximum current of 150mA or in a current boosted power supply with additional pass transistors determines the value the value of the feedback capacitor. Getting the value wrong can have some interesting results!

A few cautionary words about IC regulators

Many of the IC regulators will oscillate or 'take-off' at supersonic frequencies if the input and/or output decoupling is poor or if the grounding is suspect. Devices such as the LM78xx series have a tendency to oscillate at around 50MHz if care is not taken in these aspects. Virtually all the examples I have come across require at least a 100nF (0.1µF) capacitor from input and output to ground for stability, in some cases they need a much bigger value capacitor if the input is a long way from the raw DC supply. In such a case a capacitor - about 47µF or larger - needs to placed close up to the input terminal and grounded solidly to the common or ground pin. Using these ICs is somewhat akin to VHF construction techniques, after all a cure for a 50MHz oscillation requires VHF grounding and decoupling methods to be effective!

I was recently asked to sort out a 2m FM transceiver, which was causing splatter on one of the local repeaters. Reports received stated that when it was transmitting on one repeater channel it could be heard on the adjacent repeater input channels and was opening up the other local repeater. I first of all suspected the synthesiser as the equipment used an old-fashioned design synthesiser. However, testing it with a very good spectrum analyser showed nothing above -90dBc, and I plotted the transmitter phase noise response to show the owner that all was OK. Giving him the rig back soon brought renewed complaints.

I then suspected that something was awry in the repeater receiver and advised the club to check out the receiver. This turned up nothing untoward. So it was back to the transceiver. I borrowed it for a few more days and ran extensive tests from home using my 2m transceiver as a monitor as well as my spectrum analyser. Still nothing was found. Finally I admitted defeat and took the 2m transceiver back to the owner to do one more set of tests. As soon as it was coupled up in his shack the problem re-occurred.

Then the penny dropped. All this time I had been using other power supplies to test the 2m transceiver as his home-brew power supply (bought second-hand from a local constructor) also powered his HF station and he did not want to part with it. Hooking up the 2m transceiver to another power supply gave a clean signal.

I then looked inside the station power supply and guess what I found? A µ723 regulator driving a pair of 2N3055s in a home brew circuit! And I could see that it didn't have *any* compensation capacitor fitted, a sure way of making it unstable.

I then remembered my unhappy attempts many years previously to make a µ723-regulator work satisfactorily. The 723 would 'take-off' with the 2m RF present and go into wild oscillation which a 'scope showed was about 25kHz, exactly the same as the frequency difference of the adjacent channel repeater!

The 25kHz ripple was about 6V p-p and was modulating the synthesiser because the IC regulator in the transceiver that supplied the 8V to the synthesiser was 'dropping out' during the troughs and causing massive adjacent channel 'sprogs' which swamped the nearby repeater. You can be sure the original builder didn't check it for hum and ripple or else he would have spotted the problem then and there.

I still don't like the 723 for this reason, but I know of quite a few amateurs who think they are marvellous!

However, apart from this sorry tale there are many perfectly good IC regulators on the market. I will cover some of these later with some of my pet circuits which I fall back on when I need something in a hurry and don't have the time to design something from scratch or I simply don't feel inclined to design something new.

A note on IC regulators

If you have used one of these three-legged wonders you may sometimes notice that the manufacturer's application note shows a diode connected across the device. This is connected in such a way that it is reverse biased. The reason it is included is in case the supply is feeding a load with a large value capacitor across it. You shouldn't in actual fact do this as the large value capacitor slows down the transient response capabilities of the regulator and can be harmful, but a lot of attached equipment will have one.

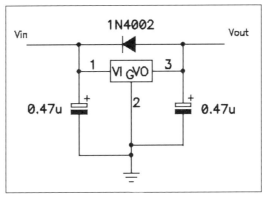

Fig 4.15: Protection diode and decoupling capacitors

When the input voltage is removed, the output capacitor tries to discharge through the IC. This is potentially damaging to the internal structure and can cause it to fail. Many of the more modern ICs have this diode included within the package, so check with the manufacturers data sheet to see if it necessary to fit one externally.

I once had a rather heated disagreement with one of our techno-boffins at work when I showed him my proposed circuit for a new power supply as part of the obligatory 'Design-Rule Check'. He criticised my circuit because I had not shown a 1N4002 across a particular IC regulator. Finally, having shown him the manufacturers data sheet showing the diode was provided internally, he apologised. But I still fitted one anyway to keep him happy!

Voltage regulators for automotive applications

Many automotive applications use fixed voltage regulators. Because of the harsh electrical environment prevailing in automotive electrical systems it is as well to look at some of the problems encountered.

Some people assume the lead-acid battery acts like a large "capacitor" and serves to smooth out the transients and other signals appearing across the main 12V-supply line. Whereas a lead-acid battery acts like a large storage element for DC it is not very effective when the signals are AC or pulsating DC. A lead-acid battery at high frequencies acts like a low value resistor to the charging current from an alternator. Today the vast majority of vehicles use an alternator to charge the battery and supply the bulk of the required current demand. The battery is therefore used to supply current demand over and above the alternator's capabilities (and when the engine is stopped).

An alternator is normally geared up from the engine crankshaft as much as 5:1. So if the engine is turning at 6,000rpm the alternator shaft could be spinning as fast as 30,000rpm. Because most alternators are 6-pole designs the frequency of the alternator pulsating DC output voltage can be as high as 10kHz. Bridge rectifiers act as frequency doublers hence the pulsating DC is twice the alternator output frequency. Lead-acid batteries are almost an open circuit at such high frequencies. If you connect an oscilloscope across a typical vehicle battery and then start the engine the waveform displayed on the 'scope is the result of the pulsating DC flowing through the internal resistance of the lead-acid battery as the alternator brings the battery voltage back to the set point. In some cases this can attain a peak-peak value of 10V when the alternator first starts recharging the battery. This pulsating DC is what causes the characteristic 'alternator whine' on some car radios or audio equipment. This is because the radio does not have sufficient filtering in the supply to reduce this to acceptable levels.

The most severe supply line disruptions occur during starting, where the battery has to supply all the current to drive the starter and other systems until the engine fires and runs.

Let us look at the use of fixed voltage regulators in more detail. Suppose we needed a stable 8V supply to supply some item in a vehicle. If the current drain were not too high then a simple solution would be one of the IC voltage regulators. These range from 100mA output up to approximately 5A and require very little in the way of components to work well. However, the 'drop-out' voltage is what concerns us. Most fixed IC regulators have a drop-out voltage of approx. 2.5 to 3.5V. Hence, if the input voltage falls below about 10.5V the regulator will drop out and the regulated supply will begin to fall in voltage.

During engine cranking on a cold day, the battery voltage can drop below 8V. In severe cases it is not unknown for it to descend to as low as 5.5V when the starter is initially engaged. The reason for this is the amount of current the starter draws under different operating conditions. When the engine is warm, and hence the oil is also warm the resistance to turning is much less than when the engine is very cold. When an engine is cold the parts are fairly tight and hence have a fair amount of friction and the oil is like treacle. Hence, the starter motor struggles to turn over the engine for starting. If the battery temperature is also low, below +10°C, the capacity will be reduced (a lead-acid battery at 0°C has a capacity of approx. 65% its capacity at +30°C). These factors all contribute to severe dips in the terminal voltage when a heavy load is applied, such as the starter motor.

A typical measurement for a starter motor contains three different operating parameters. The first is known as the running current drain, when no load is applied. In other words it is what is measured with the motor removed from the vehicle and run on the bench. Typical current drain for this might be as little as

60A for a small vehicle and somewhere around 200A for a large diesel starter motor. This is known as the 'free-running-current'.

The second measurement is made on a dummy engine with a brake applied to simulate the load the starter will encounter in service. As is to be expected the current drawn is somewhat higher than the free-running mode. Figures of typically 300 to 500A are common for small engines.

The final measurement is known as the 'locked-rotor' condition. In this test the starter motor is fastened to a jig and the output shaft clamped so it cannot turn. This test is performed very quickly because the motor will draw a very large current under this condition. If the test were carried on for more than a few seconds the motor would burn out.

The locked-rotor condition is what happens when the starter is first engaged and before it has started rotating the engine. Under this mode the current drain can be many thousands of Amps for a short period. On diesel engines the value of the current is about 6,000A.

The importance of knowing these facts is to be able to appreciate what happens to the battery voltage when the starter is first engaged. Even with a fully charged battery in excellent condition, and with good wiring, the battery voltage will momentarily dip to as little as 6V for a few tens of milli seconds. After the starter motor has started turning the engine over the current drain drops to perhaps 25% of the initial current and then slowly falls as the engine rotational speed reaches the normal cranking speed. (The modern starter motor is a series wound machine and the current at high rpm is much less than at low rpm because of the Back-EMF generated by the rotor or armature when spinning fast). With a high compression engine, such as a diesel, the cranking current is not constant; it varies as the crankshaft speed varies when the cylinder on the compression stroke has the piston rising to top dead centre causes a greater load to be applied.

If the voltage regulator is supplying a computer that requires a stable 5V supply to operate, then the 5V supply can drop out and possible data corruption could occur. If the computer is the main engine management computer for a spark ignition engine then severe damage can also occur to the starter because the ignition pulses may occur in the wrong place in time and the engine could kickback when cranking if the computer crashes. For these reasons the industry designed 'Low Drop Out' regulators especially for automotive applications.

Low drop out regulators

These are normally fixed voltage regulators for 3.3V and 5V computer ICs. Typical drop out voltages are as little as 25mV for the low current devices and as much as 200mV for a 1A device. Therefore, as long as the battery voltage remains above 5.2V it will remain satisfactory for a 5V computer IC.

We still need to cater for the high input ripple due to the alternator charging the battery after a prolonged period of cranking. Some modern alternators can supply as much as 140A for short periods when charging a discharged battery. The internal resistance of the battery although very low is not zero and so the charging current induces a ripple voltage due to the ESR of the battery. It is common practice to place a large electrolytic capacitor across the incoming 12V-line to serve as a reservoir capacitor. This is often used in conjunction with a low forward voltage diode to isolate the battery supply when the starter draws

Fig 4.16: Input filtering for an automotive 5V computer supply

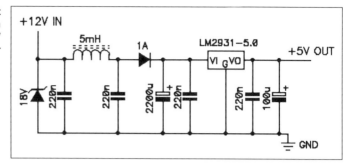

a heavy current. This capacitor needs to be able to supply the entire computer running current during the initial starter engagement and hence it needs to be quite a large value. We will see a similar situation when we cover the Off Line Switch Mode supplies in a later chapter.

This capacitor needs to be backed up with a large value inductor in series with the supply and some smaller value capacitors to serve as high frequency filtering to reduce the alternator whine on the supply. If the alternator peak to peak ripple lowers the input voltage to the regulator below the drop out voltage it can still cause the computer to crash. All of these factors need to taken into consideration when designing automotive electronics, especially the types that if a malfunction occurs can cause accidents, such as ABS or Stability Management systems being fitted to modern vehicles.

Fig 4.16 shows the minimum circuitry for a 12V vehicle application using a low drop out regulator, in this case a National Semiconductors LM2931-5.0 delivering 5V at 100mA. The tranzorb across the input serves to clamp any spikes to approx. +18V and -1V. This needs to be a beefy device and a type rated at 1.5kW is normally selected. The series diode should be a Schottky type with a PIV of at least 30V. The forward voltage of this diode (and the inductor volts drop) adds to the regulator drop out voltage so any voltage lost across the series diode or inductor degrades the ultimate drop out performance. This diode also backs up the tranzorb for reverse polarity protection. The 220n capacitors are types with good high frequency performance such as ceramic or polyester foil.

The two 220n capacitors fitted across the regulator input and output are necessary for high frequency stability in the regulator IC. Without these the regulator can oscillate at a frequency of several megahertz.

The LM2931 also requires a large electrolytic capacitor in parallel with the output to preserve low frequency stability; National Semiconductors recommend a value of 100µF with a low ESR. A parallel diode is not required across the IC because the series diode prevents back feeding into the 12V-battery supply.

Using three-terminal regulators

Many of the commonly available regulators are made with fixed output voltages and some are made with variable output voltage. The common fixed output regulators are available in 5V, 8V, 12V, 15V and 24V with output current ranging from 100mA to as much as 5A. Often the higher current regulators are a bit expensive and so it is nice to be able to use the cheaper varieties with an external pass transistor to boost the current.

However, what about the case where we need an output voltage different to the standard versions and we don't have an adjustable version to hand. We can alter the output voltage upwards quite simply. Suppose we needed a

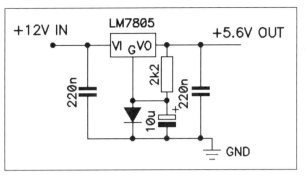

Fig 4.17: Using a silicon diode to raise the output voltage by 0.6V

5.6V supply to deliver 1A. By inserting a silicon diode in the common leg of the regulator, as in **Fig 4.17**, we increase the output by the diode forward voltage. This is known as 'jacking-up' the output.

The diode only needs to be a low power type such as 1N4148 or 1N914 because the current flowing is very small. The diode needs to be well decoupled and fed with a small bias current from the output to maintain a constant forward voltage. The output voltage variation with large temperature variations will be worse than the regulator on its own, typically about -2mV/°C but this is not normally a problem if the ambient temperature is fairly constant. If the output needs to be increased to say 6.2V then a second silicon diode can be used, this however degrades the output voltage more with temperature. If a high voltage is required, say 75V, then a Zener can be used in place of the silicon diode. The output voltage will be the normal regulator voltage plus the Zener value. Using 2 x 30V Zener diodes of 500mW in series will give 60V and a 15V regulator will achieve the required 75V (**Fig 4.18**).

The disadvantage of the high voltage supply is the limited input voltage range. The 15V version of the LM78xx series is only rated to 35V; hence the maximum input-output voltage is limited to 20V. Therefore in this application the maximum safe input voltage is only 95V. There are better regulators for this type of application and these can safely withstand higher input-output differentials. One such device is the Texas Instruments TL-783, which is a high voltage version of the LM-317 and can be adjusted between 1.25 to 125V with a maximum current of 700mA and a maximum input-output differential of 125V.

Another method is to use a variable resistor to alter the output voltage (**Fig 4.19**). This method allows a finer setting of the output voltage but has inferior output voltage variation with temperature.

(left)   Fig   4.18: Obtaining a high output voltage

(right)   Fig   4.19: Varying the output voltage with a variable resistor

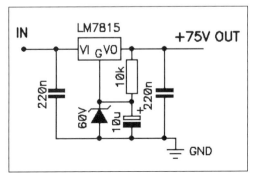

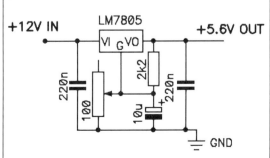

The major problem with all of these methods is that the device tab is no longer at ground potential and so an insulating thermal film needs to be placed between it and the heatsink. Normally the tab of a TO-220 package is bolted to ground as well as the centre lead being soldered to ground.

Boosting the output current

When we require more output current than the standard 1A from a LM78xx series regulator we can use an external pass transistor as shown in **Fig 4.20**.

The problem with this circuit is that the supply is not guaranteed to be short circuit proof. By adding another transistor (**Fig 4.21**) we can solve this problem. TR1 is a low power device such as a BC327 or 2N2907.

Fig 4.20: Using an external PNP transistor to increase the output current

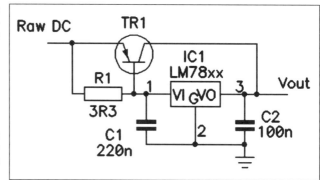

Fig 4.21: Current boosted regulator with short circuit protection

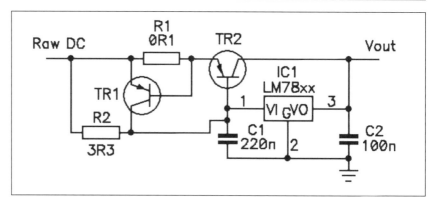

Transformer, Rectifier & Capacitor Basics

Before we continue exploring linear regulator supplies any further we had better take a closer look at the 'front-end' of our basic power supply.

So far we have assumed that the source of the rectified DC feeding our regulator has a vague reference to a transformer, rectifier and smoothing capacitor. To be able to design the 'back-end' regulator we need to know in some detail what the 'front-end' consists of, and vice versa.

Today for low voltage power supplies the almost universal set-up is a large iron-cored mains transformer and a string of diode rectifiers arranged in a bridge configuration. I intend doing nothing to change peoples attitude about this as I firmly believe it is the best option, both technically and from a cost point of view, for moderate output currents.

The one main advantage of the bridge rectifier is that only one secondary winding is needed which makes the transformer a bit cheaper than one using two secondary windings centre tapped for a bi-phase rectifier. Granted you need four diodes for a bridge versus only two diodes for a bi-phase rectifier, but two extra diodes are usually cheaper than an extra secondary winding.

As you will see a little later the bi-phase rectifier is however definitely superior for very high current supplies albeit at the extra expense of the transformer windings. A summary of the various types can be found in the Appendix.

Fig 5.1: Selection of transformers. The transformer on the left is from a WW2 VHF transmitter (T220) and is rated at 230VA. The bottom right transformer is a modern high voltage type for a 4CX250 amplifier. This transformer has an almost identical core size but is rated at 500VA. The top transformer is for a multiple output supply

Effective winding resistance

One of the factors determining the secondary current that a transformer can supply is the effective winding resistance (EWR). The formula for this is:

$$EWR = N^2 \times R_p + R_s$$

Where:

N is the turns ratio between the primary and secondary

R_p is the primary DC resistance

R_s is the secondary DC resistance

How to specify the transformer

Many amateurs seem more than a bit hazy when specifying a transformer for a new power supply. One of the biggest problems is they either over-engineer, which wastes money, or they commit the equally severe sin of under-engineering due to ignorance of the subject.

By under-engineering you run the risk of damaging the transformer by trying to extract too much current from it, which usually leads to severe over heating, premature failure and a need to replace the transformer with something more up to the job - then you discover that the new transformer won't fit into the existing box as it is much bigger than the original one! Let us take the basics step by step.

Primary voltage specification

This is pretty easy and will depend on where in the world you live, or intend to travel to if you want to take your power supply on holiday.

Taking the UK as an example. The nominal supply voltage is 230V AC with a frequency of 50Hz plus and minus 2Hz. The upper and lower limits are 244V and 216V in round numbers. Add onto this a 5% margin for exceptional circumstances and you arrive at the worst case limits of 205V to 255V or thereabouts. Should you plan to visit a country with a radically different AC mains then you should consider taps for the primary.

Let us suppose you intended to visit the USA with its nominal 115V supply then a tap for this would be appropriate. The best solution would be to ask for the transformer to be wound with two primary windings; each rated at 115V nominal. For use in the countries which have 230V mains these would be wired in series and for 115V countries they would be wired in parallel. This can often be done with a simple voltage selector switch.

Make sure the phase of the windings is clearly marked, otherwise you could connect the two winding in 'anti-phase' for 230V and get nothing out! Usually transformer manufacturers use a '0' notation to indicate the start of a winding. So a suitable transformer would be specified as:'0 to 115V + 0 to 115V'.

Unless you are really technically competent and well versed in transformer design (in which case you probably won't be reading this book anyway!) don't bother to specify the primary current rating, as the competent transformer manufacturers will do this calculation as a matter of course during the design. There are some things that are best left to the experts. Adding unnecessary technical details will in most cases cause confusion and could result in a transformer that no longer meets your requirements.

One thing I learned many years ago is not to tell the designer how to design your transformer. He is far more capable than I am and I rely on his expertise to give me the most cost-effective solution, especially important if you are purchasing a large quantity.

I was involved in a design for a lead-acid battery charger for an invalid carriage many years ago and wrote a transformer specification, which was then sent to a local manufacturer for prototyping. When the transformer came back it was found to behave in a weird way and was unsuitable for the intended circuit. On asking the transformer designer why the transformer didn't do what I expected he replied: "If you had told me it was for a battery charger I would have used a totally different set of formulae to design it than the normal regulator type". A lesson learned the hard way!

In dealing with a transformer manufacturer or designer tell him clearly what the transformer is intended for - don't leave him guessing.

Duty cycle rating

A transformer intended for amateur service does not normally need to be rated for 100% duty cycle, unless you intend doing some very serious contest operating. SSB and CW have a duty cycle of about 30% in practice and with short transmissions and extended periods on receive the effective duty cycle drops even lower to around 15 to 25% maximum. If your operation is mainly FM or RTTY then you will need to rate the transformer for close to 100%, approximately 70% would be about right as you don't normally transmit for long periods. I hope your RF amplifier transistors are adequately rated and well heatsinked!

Modern transformer manufacturing has dramatically increased the energy throughput per unit volume compared with 30 years ago. The days of 'Admiralty Rating' will probably not be seen again, where the transformer was rated for 100% duty cycle for 24 hours at maximum ambient temperatures and humidity. This is an extremely costly rating and leads to an overly bulky and heavy transformer, although it was great for reliability!

Modern winding techniques and materials allow higher core temperatures than 50 years ago. Today the latest polyurethane triple-insulated winding wires are safely rated to at least +200 C, which allows smaller cores to be used. These all help keep the size, weight and cost down. Add to this superior transformer lamination material and the transformer shrinks even more. Advances in magnetic materials have come along in leaps and bounds since the end of World War 2. Today using modern silicon alloy steels for the laminations the cost and weight of a typical transformer has been cut by up to 25% and 50% respectively.

In the old days you could safely estimate the potential power rating of a transformer by simply weighing it. Today things are not so simple. With today's materials a transformer rated at 500VA weighs approximately 7kg and a 1kVA transformer weighs approximately 15kg. This can be used as a very rough rule of thumb. If someone offers you a similarly rated transformer and it weighs a lot different then be suspicious. 'Nuff-Said!!

A local transformer manufacturer I regularly deal with estimates that on average the size of a typical mains transformer has decreased some 30% in the last

> When I asked my friendly transformer designer what he considered would be a suitable transformer for a HT supply I was building some time back for a 432MHz K2RIW amplifier, we discussed the anticipated application and I told him I wanted a transformer suitable for occasional contest use and EME. He designed a transformer with a 35% duty cycle, which was less than half the price I had originally been quoted by another manufacturer and 1/3rd smaller!
>
> His definition of 'intermittent operation' is key down at full output for 30 minutes and then 30 minutes receive. This gave a maximum core temperature of less than +100°C, which the transformer was easily able to handle with the 100mm-cooling fan within the power supply cabinet.

twenty years by using these modern materials and the cost saving is even more, when inflation is included.

Why a transformer gets hot

Heating within the transformer comes from several causes. The copper-loss in the windings normally only contributes a very small fraction. The bulk of the losses occur in the magnetic laminations with eddy current losses accounting for the greater part of the total loss. Even so a mains transformer is remarkably efficient, figures of 97% or more are fairly typical for transformers of 1kVA and above. Below 100VA efficiencies can still go as high as the low 90% region. But here the actual total power dissipated is still low in watts, so the actual heating effect is still not a problem. The bigger the transformer the more power it can safely dissipate as it has more surface area to conduct the heat away. Fan cooling a transformer, even with a small fan, reduces the temperature by a far greater amount than you would initially think.

Testing a transformer

Let us suppose you have found what looks like a suitable transformer at a local swap meet (rally) and want to confirm it will do the job. Apart from loading up the secondary with suitable load resistors or lamps, (the one time you can safely use lamps as dummy loads!), and checking things like secondary voltage under load and how hot it gets under full load current after, say, 30 minutes; there is one other important test you should do. (I am assuming the transformer is known to be in good working condition with no shorted windings, obvious signs of damage or other apparent faults).

The 'residual magnetising current' test is one of the most telling criteria. This measures how much of the primary current is being used to generate the residual flux and make up the losses in the magnetic circuit. A figure to aim for is less than 10% of the maximum primary current. Anything over this should make

> It is very good idea to give a second-hand transformer, (which may have been lying in Fred's garage for several years), a good heat run in the domestic oven at about +150 C for a couple of hours to dispel any moisture. Do this whilst the 'Domestic Executive' is out or you may get it in the neck!

you suspicious about the transformer. In an ideal transformer the current drawn by the primary with the secondary open circuit would be zero.

To perform the test is fairly simple. Measure the primary current being drawn when the secondary is loaded to its full rating and then remove the secondary load and measure the residual primary current. If the primary current does not drop to less than 10% of the original full load current there is something wrong.

Very small transformers have residual magnetising current figures of around 15 to 20% and this is part of the reason they tend to run hot. This current is simply being wasted as heat due to inefficiencies in the magnetic circuit!

Specifying the secondary winding parameters

This more than anything else this is the part most home-constructors get confused about. Assuming you are going to order a custom made transformer or choose one from a standard list you need to know what to ask for or find in the list. Many amateurs get this part wrong, often with disastrous results.

What secondary current do you need? If you said the same as the DC output current you would probably be *wrong*.

OK, then try this one. What secondary voltage do you need? If you said the output DC voltage divided by 1.414 you would also be *wrong*.

The secondary current required depends on the rectifier and smoothing circuit you intend to employ. The secondary voltage is slightly more complicated but can also be specified with a high degree of accuracy.

Let us go back to basics

The secondary needs to supply an output voltage which, after all losses are taken into account, is greater than about 5V above the required DC output voltage - *under worst case conditions*. For this we normally mean lowest mains voltage, output current at maximum, the transformer at maximum rated temperature and measured at the trough of the DC ripple voltage. Quite a lot of variables!

The amplitude of the current peak can be quite high, for example on a 3A supply I designed the measured peak secondary current was approximately 10A for about 20° of the waveform. This means that the diodes chosen should be adequate for the purpose and able to handle high peak currents as well as the calculated average current. Let us examine the rectifier story in more detail.

It is as well to appreciate that the current flowing in the secondary when feeding a rectifier and capacitor input filter is anything but sinusoidal. In fact if you use a current probe to measure the secondary current you will get a big surprise. The current will be very peaky and only flows for a short duration and not for 180° as the sinewave voltage does.

This is because when the secondary voltage plus the diode forward voltage exceeds the voltage across the capacitor the current flows into the capacitor and the load. As the capacitor looks like a very low impedance the charging current is very high. When the secondary voltage is less than the capacitor voltage no secondary current flows.

Rectifier fundamentals

We know that a silicon diode has a nominal forward voltage drop of about 0.6V at room temperature of +25°C. However, this is for a small current. When the current goes up so does the forward voltage drop. Taking a typical diode rated at 10A, the forward voltage drop is specified as 0.7V maximum at 1A and nearly 1V at 10A.

As there are two diodes effectively in series in a bridge rectifier we need to subtract twice the nominal diode forward-voltage drop from the secondary voltage when making the calculation.

One thing in our favour is that silicon diodes have a slightly lower forward voltage drop at high junction temperatures, but don't count on this helping you. The diodes will need good heatsinking in any case to get the heat away. After we have established the secondary current you can calculate the power dissipated in the rectifier diodes at full load, I think you will be surprised how much power is wasted!

Also you have to factor in the 'regulation rating' for the transformer. Regulation rating is the amount the secondary voltage changes between zero load current and the rated maximum.

The secondary voltage under open circuit conditions will always be higher than when loaded up to its maximum rated current. The rule in transformer designing is to always specify the secondary voltage at the rated current.

The reason for this is many fold. Part of the voltage drop is due to copper loss (the resistance) in the primary and secondary windings and part is due to the magnetic circuit imperfections, including eddy current losses in the magnetic circuit.

A 'good transformer' will have a regulation rating of less than 10% - for 'good transformer' you can read 'expensive'! We will probably have to settle for something less than this and somewhere between 15% to 20% is likely, especially if the core or wire gauge has been 'down-sized' to cut the cost.

Let us suppose we have a 15% regulation rating due to financial or size / volume constraints. This means that we need to specify the secondary voltage to ensure we always have at least 5V excess input / output voltage under worst case conditions.

Suppose we need a minimum of 13.8V + 5V = 18.8V DC under all worst case conditions, including the trough of the ripple voltage. This would equal 13.3V AC at the secondary, assuming we didn't take the extra losses into account. For low mains we can take as being nominal -6% for amateur purposes. So the secondary losses look like this:

- Volts drop due to bridge rectifier diodes   ≈2V
- Volts loss due to low mains at 216V input   ≈2V
- Volts drop due to regulation factor   ≈1.1V
- Total voltage 'lost'   ≈5.1V

In order to allow for all worst case conditions we would need a nominal secondary voltage of 18.4V AC. This means that when the output is lightly loaded the rectified voltage will be around 29V DC with the input at 230V, and at 255V the output voltage will be nearly 32V DC. Having decided on this let us now look at the secondary current required.

Secondary current calculations

A bridge rectifier used with a capacitor-input filter has a 'conversion efficiency' of less than 100%. In fact it is closer to 60%. The exact relationship is as follows:

$I_{dc} = 0.62 \times I_{ac}$

So we in fact need a secondary current of at least 1 / 0.62 which is around 1.6 times the final output current! Our 10A nominal output supply will require a transformer secondary able to provide at least 16A. No wonder many amateur power supplies do not give the 'designed for current'! Factor in the extra current needed to power the regulator control circuitry and pass transistor base current etc and you can calculate that you need to allow a couple of extra Amps on top of this.

We can safely say that a 2N3055 will need a base current of 1/20th of its collector current, which is another 1/2A or so. Allowing a bit of margin and choosing an 18A secondary will suffice. However, if your 10A secondary was used it could, maybe, give an adequate margin of safety with a 60% over-load for short periods, but I don't want to try that - thank you!

Different rectifier types and their affect on design

I mentioned earlier that I prefer the bridge rectifier for most power supplies. However, I need to qualify that statement. If I were designing a power supply that needed to supply more than about 20A DC, I would shift to the bi-phase option, which needs a centre tapped secondary. The reason is the 'rectification-efficiency'. Back to basics.

In a bridge rectifier feeding a capacitor-input filter (**Fig 5.2**), only 62% of the AC secondary current makes it into DC. This means we need to specify a transformer with a 1.6:1 ratio for the secondary current. In a bi-phase rectifier feeding a capacitor-input filter, the conversion factor of AC in to DC out is higher than the bridge circuit. (See Appendix 1 for details of the common rectifier configurations).

In the bi-phase rectifier feeding a capacitor-input filter (**Fig 5.3**) the ratio is 1:1. So our 10A DC supply would need a secondary with only a little more than the DC output current, to drive the extra circuitry. In fact at a pinch a 10A secondary would do nicely, as we don't often need 100% duty cycle. But the trick is to find a suitable transformer with a tapped secondary. The cost of winding a tapped secondary is higher but for the very high current applications the trade-off between the extra transformer cost and the saving on two high current diodes

Fig 5.2: Bridge rectifier capacitor input filter

Fig 5.3: Bi-phase full wave rectifier capacitor input filter

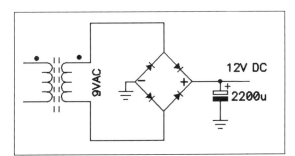

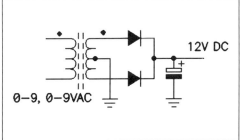

A quick calculation when picking a transformer for use with a bridge rectifier and capacitor input filter of only allowing two-thirds of the secondary rated current will be a good 'ball-park' figure. So if you find a transformer rated at, say 30A, it will only be suitable for a 20A DC output power supply if you use a bridge rectifier and capacitor input filter and you need a 100% duty cycle.

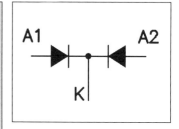

Fig 5.4: Dual diode for bi-phase rectifier duty

gets quite small. In fact you may find it cheaper to go the bi-phase route if you can get diodes at a sensible price. As in most forms of engineering design there are many variables to consider.

A good choice would be the BYV72 series made by Philips (**Fig 5.4**). This is a 100V PIV rating diode with each diode rated at 20A average current.

How transformers are rated for power

Transformers are rated for power using VA and not Watts. VA is short for Volts multiplied by Amps and is similar to the DC condition. The reason we use VA is because the current and voltage in an inductor are not in phase, in fact in a perfect transformer with zero winding resistance the voltage and current flowing in either the primary or secondary would be 90° out of phase. Because of this we cannot use Watts because the product of voltage and current constitutes a reactive source or load.

In practice, because the losses in a typical transformer are so low, efficiencies are around 97% or so, the VA and Watts can be interchanged. So if a transformer is rated at 100VA it can supply approximately the same equivalent heating power - RMS power - as 100W of DC.

For our application with an 18.4V secondary at 18A the transformer rating will be 18.4 x 18 = 331.2 VA at 100% duty cycle. We can intelligently reduce this to around 75%, or 250VA, as we don't often require 100% duty cycle. What we are choosing to do here is to specify a lower VA rating to reduce the cost and then over run it by 25% for short periods. Provided we do not overdo this it will be satisfactory and give a small increase in core temperature.

Now what about the smoothing capacitor? This is also a pit-fall for many amateur constructors.

As an example. The transformer shown on the left in **Fig 5.1** has the following secondary windings.

680V @ 0.21A
6.3V @ 5A
6.3V @ 5A
5V @ 5A

The total secondary load when all the windings are fully loaded is therefore 230.8VA and the input current when fed with 230V AC will be approx. 1.1A assuming an efficiency of 90%.

Capacitor selection

There is a common rule of thumb that power supply designers use for smoothing capacitors. This one concerns how many microfarads (μF) are required per Amp of output current when a capacitor-input filter is used. This factor is highly dependent on the parameters of the transformer secondary, the resistance of the winding and the magnetic circuit losses, and gives to a first order the winding regulation and the rectifier forward voltage drop. The standard curves used by many designers originate from a set of charts published by Schade in 1943 and have since appeared in several engineering textbooks.

Schade originally developed these charts for vacuum-tube rectifiers, which have a high forward resistance unlike semiconductor diodes that have very low forward resistance. Consequently the resistance of the rectifier valve acts like a R-C filter when driving a capacitive load. This reduces the ripple voltage, unlike a semiconductor that has negligible forward resistance. Today the curves have been 'fine-tuned' by solid-state experience. Many power-supply designers use the '1,000μF per Amp' rule as being the acceptable minimum.

A formula to determine the minimum capacitance is:

$$C = \frac{I_{in(avg)}}{8 \times f_r \times V_r}$$

Where:

- $I_{in(avg)}$ = average input current
- f_r is the ripple frequency, (2 x the mains frequency for bridge/bi-phase and 1 x for half-wave)
- V_r is the allowable ripple voltage - peak to peak in volts

For a 10A average input current for a 50Hz mains and a maximum peak-peak ripple of 1V we can calculate the capacitor needed as being 12,500μF minimum. So for our 10A supply would we need a minimum of 12,500μF? *Wrong!* What about the secondary current? We just calculated that as being 18A.

We need to factor this into our equation as well and we come up with a value of around 23,000μF. I would play safe and increase this at least 25%. Remember the equation was for the minimum value. Electrolytic capacitors have a rather loose tolerance, typically the actual capacitance can vary by as much as -20% to +50% from the marked value. Choosing a capacitor of at least 27,000μF would be certain to be adequate.

So what else do we need to specify? What about the voltage rating? We can easily calculate this knowing the secondary voltage, diode voltage drop, regulation and the mains parameters. Off load at nominal mains input we will see around 29V DC and at +6% mains this will go up to about 32V. So a 35V capacitor should cover this nicely. (V_{dc} = 1.414 x V_{ac})

What else do we need to specify? We need to ascertain the ripple-current rating. What is that? Well, remember the secondary current was 18A maximum. Where do you think the remaining 8A goes to after we have taken out our 10A as DC? It flows in the smoothing capacitor as ripple current!

Wow - 8A - that is a lot of current! It sure is and it causes the capacitor to heat up because of the series resistance of the capacitor, the Equivalent Series

Fig 5.5: Capacitor ESR

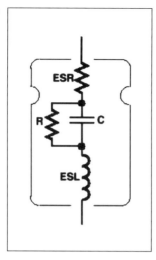

Resistance (ESR). Although the ESR of modern electrolytic capacitors is very low, it is not zero and this causes the heat (see **Fig 5.5**).

Ripple current rating is normally specified at the maximum safe working temperature. Today capacitors routinely work at +85 C case temperature for average types and "Industrial and Computer Grade" types go up to +105 C. For most amateur applications the +105 C types are not normally required and the +85 C types will usually be quite acceptable.

Note: The safe temperature is not the ambient temperature, it is measured at the case of the capacitor. If the capacitor case temperature rises 25°C above ambient this puts an upper limit on the ambient of +60°C for a +85°C rated device.

What sort of ESR can we expect?

Modern electrolytic capacitors are considerably better and smaller than those of 30 years ago when I started designing power supplies. However, like most electronic components they are sensitive to high and low temperatures. The ESR usually goes down as the temperature goes up and vice versa as the temperature goes down. The ESR of a typical electrolytic capacitor increases by about a factor of 4 when the temperature drops to -10°C from +25°C.

ESR causes heat to build up within the internal structure, in severe cases the electrolyte can reach a temperature sufficient to cause it to turn to a vapour, which builds the internal pressure within the sealed case. Most aluminium electrolytics have a safety vent incorporated within the rubber seal or a deliberately weakened portion of the can - often a punched in X or similar on the top. This is designed to rupture and release the excess pressure so preventing the thin wall aluminium can from bursting.

The hot electrolyte is extremely caustic and will quickly corrode aluminium and other metals as well as being extremely difficult to clean up after a venting period.

In a severe case it is not unknown for the rubber bung to be blown out of the case like a champagne cork at high velocity and this can cause serious damage to anything in its path and an awful mess of pulverised caustic soaked paper and aluminium foil spread everywhere which is a real task to clear up! It also has a very pungent smell which, if you have had it happen, you won't forgot for a long time.

One other odd thing about aluminium electrolytic capacitors is that the higher voltage types have lower ESR and hence can handle higher ripple current than lower voltage ones with the same capacity rating. This is due to the different aluminium foils used for different voltage ratings. The higher voltage rating capacitors use a thicker foil and hence the can size and volume goes up. Because the can now has more surface area it can dissipate the heat more effectively. Also the higher the ripple frequency the more they are able to handle ripple current. We will see this factor again when we cover switch-mode power supplies.

I once bought an old amateur home-brew valve AM transmitter at a junk sale and took it home. Plugging it into the mains just as lunch was served I left it running on standby whilst I went down to lunch. Some minutes later I heard a muffled explosion from the upstairs shack. On investigation it was found that the large 350V electrolytic had 'let go' and punched a hole clean through the top cover and embedded in the ceiling, such was the force of the explosion!

Another tale involves a naughty school friend who used to bury high voltage smoothing capacitors from junk domestic radios in the family garden. Running a long length of twin-core bell wire from one of these to the mains caused a huge crater to be blown in the rose bed. One day he blew the padlock off the garage door using the same trick.

A trick we 'senior engineers' at a previous employers played on new apprentice engineers was to put a small low voltage electrolytic across the line and neutral terminals in the 13A plug for a soldering iron and wait for the apprentice to plug in the iron. This would blow the plug to pieces with a loud bang when it was switched on.

Anyway *don't try these tricks as they are extremely dangerous*. As young engineers we did silly things out of ignorance. The reason I mention them is to highlight how dangerous electrolytics can be if improperly treated.

Effect of ESR on ripple voltage

A capacitor with a low ESR will have very little ripple voltage impressed across it. A high ESR will have a higher ripple voltage. If we assume that the ripple voltage is 2V p-p this is a RMS value of ≈700mV. If the ESR is 0.1Ω then the ripple current flowing is 0.7 / 0.1 = 7A. If the ESR is reduced, the ripple voltage will decrease, but the ripple current will also increase. Taken to extremes if the capacitor ESR were zero ohms it would have an infinite ripple current flowing. Many amateurs make the mistake of increasing the capacitor value far in excess of that required. As long as the ripple voltage minimum value remains above the drop out voltage of the regulator then the ripple voltage is relatively unimportant.

A typical 15,000µF / 35V capacitor has an ESR of 0.039Ω at 120Hz, if two are connected in parallel the effective ESR is about 0.02Ω. If the ripple voltage across the capacitor is 2V p-p this is a ripple current of 35A. The maximum ripple current rating for a capacitor of this type is approximately 5A so two in parallel can handle about 10A maximum. Hence, to ensure the ripple current remains below 10A this sets a maximum ripple voltage of 0.2V RMS.

Selecting a suitable capacitor

Taking a typical electrolytic capacitor manufacturer - Nichicon - whose products I regularly use in my designs, I can detail some of the suitable capacitor part numbers from their catalogue.

A suitable Nichicon type for most amateur applications (ie reasonable cost!) would be the LK series, which are available in voltage ratings of 16V to 450V and capacitance ratings of 47µF up to 33,000µF - although the higher voltage types don't go above 560µF. The LK series is rated at up to +85°C case temperature and designed for vertical mounting on printed circuit boards with 'Snap-In' type terminals. They are low-cost compared to other makes and types.

A clue is to first look at the required ripple current rating and the voltage rating. I would select as a first attempt a capacitor in the region of the 27,000µF required and with a voltage rating of at least 35V and see what the ripple current rating was.

The closest one in the list is 27,000µF at 25V, which is too low on the voltage rating, but it does have a ripple current rating of 6.6A at 120Hz. In the UK the 50Hz mains frequency when full-wave rectified will produce a ripple frequency of 100Hz. So we can see that the allowable ripple current of 6.6A would be a little lower, in fact the derating factor is given as 0.88 for 50Hz, 0.90 for 60Hz and 1.00 for 120Hz. From this we can interpolate that the derating would be somewhere between the 60Hz figure and the 120Hz figure and would be about 0.95. This means the capacitor can only safely handle a ripple current of 0.95 x 6.6A = 6.3A at 100Hz when the case temperature is +85°C. From this we can conclude that it will not be suitable and we need to look again. It is also a bit tall being 35mm diameter and 50mm high.

Looking further around the 27,000µF region we find that nothing else seems suitable as the range stops at 22,000µF in the 35V series which is still too low both in capacity and ripple current rating of 6.25A.

How about paralleling two or more smaller capacitors to get the required ratings? A very good idea and one commonly done as a means to cut down on the required volume required.

Taking a 15,000µF at 35V capacitor from the range we see that it can safely handle 5A of ripple current at +85°C. By paralleling two of these smaller capacitors we can achieve a ripple current rating of 10A and get an effective capacitance value of 30,000µF at 35V which is very adequate for our purposes. Each capacitor is 35mm diameter and 35mm high. By paralleling two or more capacitors we lower the current flowing in each capacitor. Spreading out the heat generating components helps to lower the case temperatures and is a good move, which yields greater reliability.

Diode selection

Finally we can select the diodes to be used. Many applications for a power supply of this type can use one of the packaged bridge rectifiers designed to be bolted to a heatsink and equipped with solder terminals or 'push-on' connectors (for example the one shown in **Fig 5.6**). These are available for various voltage ratings and currents. The manufacturers data must be carefully studied. A bridge rectifier feeding an inductive or resistive load can be utilised at the full rating. However, where the bridge is feeding a capacitive load, such as our smoothing capacitor, the rating is somewhat reduced. International Rectifier gives a rating of 25A for an inductive or resistive load and 20A for a capacitive load for the nominal 25A type.

So what current rating do we need? At least the secondary current of 18A calculated earlier. I would play safe and pick a 25A bridge. Watch the heatsink temperature though, especially if you intend to use the same heatsink as the output transistors as they will raise the temperature of the bridge diodes well above ambient. From the data sheet of a typical 25A bridge it is only rated at 25A at case temperatures below +50°C. At +80°C case temperature its current handling capability has fallen to 15A which is insufficient for our needs. At +120°C it can only safely handle 5A, so watch your heatsinking carefully.

Fig 5.6: Typical packaged bridge rectifier with push-on connectors

On second thoughts I would rather pay the little extra money and use the 35A version, it is the same physical size, rated at 28A feeding a capacitive load and only costs about 10% more.

The voltage rating also needs careful selection. The secondary voltage is already decided as being about 20V AC and the PIV required is twice the applied peak rectified voltage. This gives a figure of:

$$20 \times 2.828 = 56.6V$$

We need a diode bridge with at least a 60V rating and a good choice would be a 75V device.

What about transients? The public mains supply is a source of many spikes and other 'nasties' which can give short voltage transients of up to 50% above the nominal in the worst case. We need a diode bridge that can safely cope with all these unwanted voltages. A wise move is to derate any rectifier by at least 25% from its specification. So we need to look for a voltage rating (PIV) of at least 80V and preferably higher. Choosing a 100V PIV device will be good for reliability.

Now calculate the power dissipated in the diodes when 18A is flowing, using 1V as the diode forward voltage and don't forget there are 2 diodes each carrying the same current. Your answer should be 36W. Where does this 36W come from? The transformer secondary, which is another reason linear regulators are not particularly efficient.

One other important factor we also need to look at is the 'Surge-Current' rating of the diode. Typically a modern silicon diode can safely handle 40 times the normal rated current for a period lasting one-half cycle. US semiconductor manufacturers use a time period of 8.33ms, as this is half of one cycle for 60Hz mains.

The surge current rating is a very important aspect, because when we first switch on the capacitor is discharged and looks like a dead short across the rectifier. Also the current waveform is anything but a sinewave. The current flows in pulses similar to a square wave when the applied voltage is near the top of the sinusoid.

This means that the peak current flowing is a lot more than the average. From measurements I have made with a current probe the current can be up to 5 times the average when feeding a large capacitive load. However, diode ratings can usually cope with this sort of high current peak. The International Rectifier data for a 35A bridge shows that the bridge can safely handle a 475A current peak for a half cycle.

In-rush-current limiting

Have you noticed the 'Thwung' that sometimes occurs when you switch on your big power supply? The "Thwung" you hear is the windings, the laminations and the metal lid of the supply suddenly moving due to the magnetic jolt they receive when you switch on if the mains is at a peak of the cycle.

The result of switching on when the mains voltage is near or at the peak of a cycle is that the inrush-current into the transformer, rectifier and capacitor is very high. In fact it can often exceed the peak rating of the diodes. It also gives the mains on-off switch a very hard life. It is a good plan to incorporate some sort of inrush-current protection in big power supplies. It also takes some of the sting out of the inrush-current into the smoothing capacitor, which can damage them.

Figs 5.7 and 5.8 detail some ways of dealing with this problem. A simple solution is to use a negative temperature coefficient thermistor (NTC) in series with the secondary. This at switch-on is cold and has a high resistance, after a few seconds the current flowing causes the thermistor to heat up and the resistance falls to a very low value. However, it doesn't work well if the power supply is switched off and on again almost immediately. This is because the NTC does not have a chance to cool down before the supply is again switched on.

Some of the little bits of circuitry work by inserting a low value resistor either in the transformer primary or the secondary to limit the peak current during switch-on. After a short time the resistor is shorted out allowing full voltage to be available. This in-rush-current protection is especially important when building a high voltage supply for a linear amplifier as the in-rush-current can attain values much higher than the peak diode current and often causes lots of 'sparks and smoke'. I will return again to this topic in that section.

Fig 5.7: Surge limiting using a negative temperature coefficient thermistor (NTC) in series with the secondary

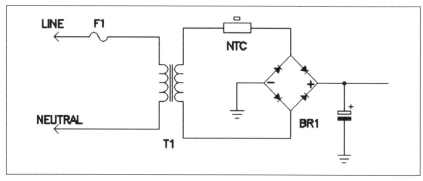

Fig 5.8: Surge limiting using a current limiting resistor. The relay RY shorts out the resistor R1 when the output voltage has risen to near full supply voltage

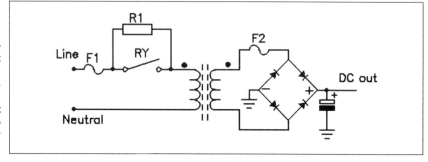

Voltage doubler high voltage power supplies

I have deliberately left this topic to now because I am not at all in favour of this type of rectifier circuit. Many commercial linear amplifiers use the voltage-doubler to develop the anode voltage and a lot of old published designs specified this type of rectifier. Because of this many hams think they are acceptable. Well, I hope to change people's view as to why they are not good news.

A typical full wave voltage-doubler circuit is shown in **Fig 5.9**. The transformer only requires a single secondary winding, the same as a bridge rectifier, except the secondary voltage is only half that of a bridge configuration. Because of this the average secondary current required is more than twice that of a bridge rectifier and the narrow pulses of peak current are extremely high. This requires heavier gauge wire and makes for a more expensive transformer. Also the secondary peak current and the ripple current flowing in the rectifiers and the smoothing capacitors can become excessive, leading to overheating in the transformer, rectifier diodes and the smoothing capacitors with ultimate failure. The high peak secondary current flowing requires considerable care with the secondary copper losses and the peak flux in the core.

The required secondary voltage and capacitor safe working voltage also need to be carefully selected or the output voltage off-load will be too high for the capacitors. The doubler develops an output DC voltage of 2.828 times the nominal secondary voltage. Off load this can rise to closer to 3.25 times the secondary voltage because of the regulation factor of the transformer.

One of the other serious failures of the full wave doubler circuit is the poor regulation under load. In the off-load condition the output voltage is twice the peak secondary voltage. However, with even a moderate load the output voltage falls to a value of twice the RMS secondary voltage, a regulation of about 30 to 40% which is quite poor, even though the transformer may have an excellent regulation figure. The regulation can be improved slightly by increasing the value of the smoothing capacitors but this is at the expense of higher peak capacitor and diode currents.

The required capacitor peak ripple current can approach a figure of four times that of a bridge circuit supplying the same output current and voltage, because the secondary is sourcing raw AC into the capacitors. Once one appreciates all these facts, the supposed cost saving by only having one secondary is a bit fallacious as the secondary of a voltage doubler transformer contains more than twice the amount of copper as a bridge type. All the other components need to be rated higher, which pushes the cost above a bridge circuit. A bridge circuit has much superior regulation with none of the hassles. All in all, it is not a very satisfactory circuit, in my opinion.

Voltage multiplier circuits are best suited to EHT applications where the output cur-

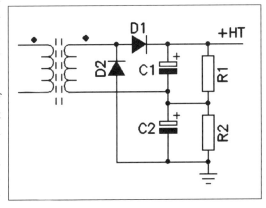

Fig 5.9: Full-wave voltage doubler circuit

Fig 5.10: A typical bridge/doubler input stage for an off-line switch-mode

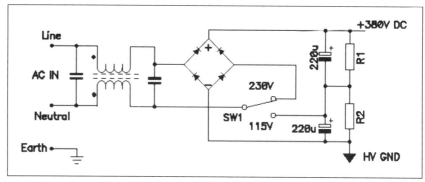

rent is fairly small, such as the high voltage needed for cathode ray tubes used in oscilloscopes. Voltage triplers or quadruplers are often used driven by a low current high voltage winding on the main transformer.

Today the voltage doubler circuit is most often found as the input circuit to an off-line switchmode supply designed for both 115V and 230V inputs. This is done by strapping out two of the diodes in the bridge and connecting the neutral terminal to the centre tap of the capacitor bank, to make the rectifier into a doubler when 115V operation is required. Here the poor regulation is of less importance, as the current is relatively low and the switchmode supply copes with the varying input voltage. A typical voltage doubler is shown in **Fig 5.10**.

Connectors

Many power supplies will require connectors. All will require a connector from the incoming mains to the internals of the box and most will require an output connector to convey the regulated voltage to the appliance.

For input connection some power supplies used a three-core mains lead permanently attached. This in my opinion is a poor choice as it always seems to get caught on some object on the bench whilst moving the PSU around. My personal preference is a type of detachable connector such as the 3-pin 'kettle cord' used on PCs and other items. These can be obtained with in-built transient suppressers, which simplify the design of the transient protection.

Many power supplies use binding terminals for the DC output. These are often the type that accept 4mm banana plugs. The current rating of the input and output connectors need to be adequate for the currents anticipated.

Mains Input

The use of a two-core mains lead is not legal in many countries, unless the equipment is 'double-insulated', but a lot of early amateur commercial equipment has this type. In most countries today it is mandatory to have a connection between the public mains earth and any exposed metalwork. This is to prevent electric shocks.

I once had a Yaesu FL-2100 HF linear amplifier that had only a two-core mains lead. When the linear was plugged into the mains but not connected to anything else I got a hefty jolt when I touched the linear metalwork and another piece of equipment. On investigation it was obvious why the metalwork was giving me a severe tickle. The metalwork was sitting at about 115V AC with respect to ground. Yaesu had fitted decoupling capacitors between the line and

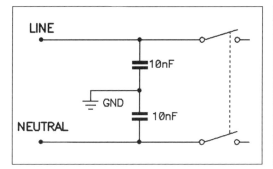

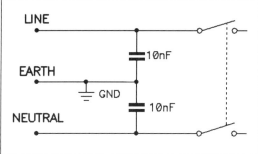

Fig 5.11: Incorrect method of decoupling the mains input

Fig 5.12: Correct method of decoupling the mains input

neutral poles to the chassis to prevent RF getting into or out of the linear. To get around this problem it was necessary to discard the original two-core mains lead and fit one using three cores, the earth lead being connected to the metalwork to comply with local regulations. This eliminated the chassis sitting at half the mains potential. **Figs 5.11 and 5.12** illustrate the right and wrong ways of earthing power supplies.

Output connector

The output voltage and current will determine the minimum specification for the connector type used. If the power supply is a high voltage type for a valve linear amplifier, the output current will be quite low but may experience high peak currents if a flashover occurs. Adequate insulation breakdown is normally the most important criteria, but the connector chosen needs also to be able to carry the required current.

For low voltage supplies the current rating is normally the most important criteria, the majority of connectors can safely handle the voltage rating. When very high currents are being carried, the contact resistance of the connector is quite important. Many connectors have a limited contact resistance specification, which is only guaranteed for a limited number of mate/demate cycles. A common number is usually about 50 times before the connector is no longer within specification. When a connector is repeatedly mated/demated the abrasion of the contacts wears away the low resistance plating to expose the base material. This increases the contact resistance. If the contact resistance is too high the high current causes the connector to heat up and the tension of the contacts may be adversely affected, causing a higher contact resistance. This generates extra heat and even more contact resistance. The problem spirals out of control and the connector may get so hot that its own insulation melts, the attached wire insulation melts or the contact material suffers permanent damage. In severe cases the contacts may arc and the base material is rapidly burned away.

6

Introducing Switch-mode Power Supplies

> **Imagination:** *"Imagination is more important than knowledge"* (Albert Einstein)

Today almost every item of domestic and other electronics seems to contain some sort of switch-mode supply. Cellular telephone handsets utilise switch-mode supplies to generate the positive and negative supply required by the RF power amplifier stages and positive voltages for the processor ICs as well as chargers for the battery. Personal computers have for many years used off-line switchers, even ham radio equipment have had them included in some way or another. The Kenwood TS-700 2m multi-mode transceiver of 1970s vintage had a crude sort of switch-mode supply to generate the 20V rail for the PA stages from the 12V input.

Many people who don't know any better think that putting a switch-mode supply inside a sensitive radio is crazy as it can generate horrific interference because of the rapidly changing switching currents. However, with care in the design and construction, adequate screening and filtering switch-mode supplies can be made surprisingly quiet. Like it or not the 'switcher' is here to stay, and when one understands the subtleties of these supplies most of the bad feelings go away.

For compact, lightweight supplies the switcher is hard to beat, and they often cost far less than a conventional linear supply of the same power rating.

How much better is a switch-mode supply?

An excellent example of the differences between the switch mode supplies and linear regulators was presented in the SGS Thomson Micro-Electronics book *Power Switching Regulators - Designer's Booklet 1st Edition*, published in 1993. The company name has since changed to ST-Microelectronics but the data given is timeless.

Switching regulators are more efficient than linear types so the transformer and heatsink can be smaller and cheaper. But how much can you gain?

We can estimate the savings by comparing equivalent linear and switching regulators. For example suppose we want a 4A / 5V supply.

Linear

For a good linear regulator the minimum dropout voltage will be at least 5V at 4A. The dropout voltage is given by:

$$Vi_{(min)} = V_o + V_{drop} + 1/2\ V_{ripple}$$

Using a 60Hz supply with a 10,000μF smoothing capacitor and assuming a minimum mains voltage of 80% of nominal we need a minimum of 13.25V DC at the input of the regulator. It is prudent to raise this a bit so we will choose 14V. Power dissipated in series element is : $P_d = (V_{in} - V_o)$ x I_o = 36W. Note that this is a 20W supply! The heatsink will need to have a thermal resistance of 0.8°C/W or better. The transformer needs to supply a power of 14V x 4A = 56W. It must therefore be dimensioned for about 62VA to take care of the assumed transformer efficiency factor of 90%.

Component	Linear	Switching
Transformer	62VA	30VA
Heatsink	0.8°C/W	11°C/W

Table 6.1: Comparison between component specifications in the power supply examples

Switching

In contrast, the L296 switching regulator IC using the same nominal input voltage of 14V will dissipate a maximum of 7W. This power is divided more or less equally between the IC and the recirculation diode. It follows that the transformer needs to be about 30VA and the heatsink needs to have a thermal resistance of about 11°C/W.

Comparison

The approximate cost savings are 50% on the transformer and around 80% on the heatsink, as shown in **Table 6.1**.

As well as the obvious cost savings one other point should be noted, and that is the lower operating temperatures within the equipment allow a smaller and cheaper box to be used without as many cooling slots.

If you now turn back to Chapter 3 where I showed you this collection of data on a Japanese 12A power supply, we can draw some inference of how much more current we could get if the supply was converted to a switching type.

In my 13.8V nominal 12A 'guinea pig' supply the pass transistors performed as in **Table 6.2**.

At the maximum output current of 15A the total power supplied by the transformer / rectifier / smoothing capacitor bank to the regulator is 207 + 63 Watts. This is a total of 270W. Assuming an efficiency of 85% we should be able to achieve ≈16.6A from the same set-up. In fact I have done this conversion and obtained over 20A output with an efficiency of over 90% at maximum current without over-stressing the transformer or rectifier diodes. Everything runs much cooler at the normal 12A-output level. However, the converter used was a little bit special, as these sorts of currents require more care to get everything working correctly. I will give some details of how I did this later in the chapter.

Table 6.2: Performance of the 'guinea pig' supply in Chapter 3

Output Current	Output Power	Dissipation in output transistor	Efficiency
1A	13.8W	16.2W	46%
2.5A	27.6W	38W	42%
5A	69W	56W	55%
10A	138W	74W	65%
15A	207W	63W	76%

Origins of the switch mode supply

The original electronic DC-DC converter is based on the design known as the Royer Converter after the Dutch inventor. This is normally a self-oscillating multi-vibrator with one or two transistors. The basis of a typical Royer Converter is shown in **Fig 6.1**. This circuit was widely used in DC-DC converters to supply the high voltage for valve equipment operating from a 12V vehicular battery supply in equipment such as the Pye Cambridge and Vanguard VHF transceivers. The operating frequency is low typically only a few kilohertz and used germanium PNP transistors because of the low saturation voltage offered by these devices.

The Royer Converter has no connection between the input and the output and hence is not regulated. Under a short circuit condition on the output the oscillator can stop running which provides some protection if correctly designed. The oscillation frequency is determined by the inductance of the transformer secondary and the 1uF capacitor resonates the network, hence it is limited to fairly low frequencies. The waveform is a quasi-square wave that is smoothed by the high inductance to a quasi sinewave at the secondary feeding the rectifier. Its efficiency is fairly low; typically about 75% at best when fully loaded.

Types of switch-mode supply

There are a myriad of varieties commonly used, however as this book of necessity has to be kept to a reasonable size I will only be covering the most popular types in detail.

The common switch-mode supplies are:

- Buck converter
- Boost converter
- Isolated Forward converter
- Isolated Fly-back converter

There are several other types, which I will touch on as they are becoming more common today.

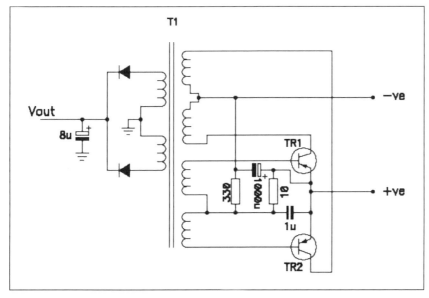

Fig 6.1: Royer converter

Type of converter	Max power rating	Max input voltage	Max output voltage
Buck Converter	up to 1kW	100V DC	100V DC
Boost Converter	up to 150W	50V DC	500V DC
Flyback Converter	up to 200W	400V DC	several kV
Forward Converter	up to 400W	400V DC	100V DC

Characteristics of switch-mode types

Although it is impossible to make hard and fast statements about the maximum power rating of a particular type, generally they can be broken down into low power and high power types. The input voltage used has a great deal of effect on the power output rating. Of the four types listed, two are only really suitable for low input voltages because of the lack of isolation between the input and output.

A voltage higher than 30V AC or 50V DC is legally considered potentially lethal, where the input voltage is higher than 50V DC an isolation barrier needs to be provided between the input and output. The Buck and Boost converters are non-isolated types whereas the Flyback and Forward converter use a transformer between the input and output to provide the safety isolation, which makes them suitable for off-line converters using rectified mains.

Typical maximum inputs and outputs of the four main types are shown in **Table 6.3**.

A use for the Boost Converter, which is now extremely common, is to use it to provide the rectified 400V DC input for an "universal input' off-line switch-mode supply. Here the Boost Converter is used in a power factor correction (PFC) circuit to bring the power factor presented to the mains supply close to a resistive load, and also eliminates harmonics of the rectification and switching being injected back into the mains supply. In the case of the supply being connected to a 115V supply the rectifier is normally configured as a bridge. The Boost Converter now takes the raw rectified 115V AC, at about 165V DC, and increases it to 400V, which is the same as when operating from a 230V AC input.

Power factor correction using electronics was originally used in aircraft 400Hz supplies provided by the engine driven alternators. Without PFC circuitry the current drawn from the alternator would be much higher than the expected average current and the other systems operating on the same supply could be adversely effected. It also reduces the wiring size as the harness now only has to cater for the average current and not the higher peak currents, this reduces the weight which is very important in aircraft.

Other uses for the Boost Converter-PFC circuit is in fluorescent lamps, which traditionally have poor power factors without a capacitor to correct for this, these are known as 'electronic-ballasts'. New legislation in most countries now makes PFC and harmonic rejection a requirement for type approval of any power supply designed to operate off the mains.

Operation of switch-mode supplies

All switch-modes operate in a similar fashion. Instead of a series transistor being used as a 'variable resistance', which is how the linear regulator works, the switch-mode supply utilises a transistor as a switch to alternately switch the input voltage through to the output in an on and off fashion. By varying the rate of the switching duty cycle an output voltage can be held at a constant value.

The simplest variety of switch-mode is known as the 'Buck Converter'. It belongs to a family known as 'Forward Converters', and gets its name from the fact that energy is transferred whilst the 'switch' is on (closed) and the energy is passed forwards (towards the load) in this condition. In contrast the 'Boost' and 'Flyback' converters transfer energy to the output when the 'switch' turns off.

Buck converter operation

The Buck converter gets its name from an old terminology used in the electrical power distribution industry. In mains distribution networks the voltages are converted using transformers and another common name for a step down transformer is a 'Buck transformer'. (A transformer intended to step-up the voltage is known as a 'Boost transformer'). In a transformer the power remains the same - neglecting any internal losses - and the voltage or current can be converted to a lower or higher value. For example, if a supply provides a maximum of 1kW at 1000V we can calculate that the current flowing in the supply is 1A. Using a step-down transformer to reduce the voltage to 250V means that we now have a current of 1000 / 250 = 4A, neglecting any losses in the transformer. If the secondary voltage were 10V then the secondary current would be 100A.

The Buck converter works in a similar way. It can only operate as a step-down converter; that is, the output voltage can only be equal to the input voltage or less than it. It does this by opening and closing a semiconductor switch that is between the input and output. When the 'switch' is closed the output voltage is the same as the input voltage (**Fig 6.2**). When the 'switch' is open the output voltage is zero (**Fig 6.3**). By having the 'switch' closed for 50% of the time (and of course open for the other 50%) the average output voltage is 50% of the input voltage.

By varying the on and off times - and hence the percentage of on to off - we can obtain any output voltage between zero and the input voltage. For example:

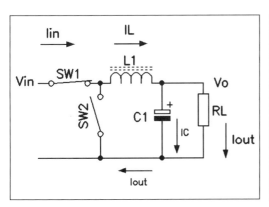
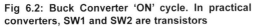

Fig 6.2: Buck Converter 'ON' cycle. In practical converters, SW1 and SW2 are transistors

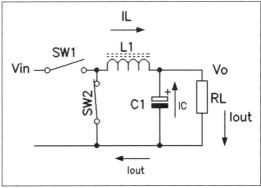

Fig 6.2: Buck Converter 'OFF' cycle. In practical converters, SW1 and SW2 are transistors

If the input voltage is 50V and the 'switch' is on for 20% of the time and off for 80% of the time, the average output voltage is 10V. This type of converter is known as a 'Pulse Width Modulated' converter as the width of the pulse - the ratio of on to off time is varied at a constant frequency. Some of the early types of switch mode converters utilised a variable frequency with a constant off time and this type of converter is now finding new applications with certain types of modern ICs intended for very efficient converters.

The output voltage in a Buck converter is defined by the duty cycle, D:

$$D = (V_{out} / V_{in})$$

The maximum value for D is 1 or 100%. The switch 'on-time' is T_{on} and the rest of the switching period is T_{off}

The time for one complete cycle is T.

$$T = T_{on} + T_{off}, \text{ and}$$

$$T = 1 / f, \text{ where f is the switching frequency in Hertz, and therefore:}$$

$$D = (T_{on} / T)$$

The pulsating raw output voltage from the switch is not suitable to drive anything, except perhaps a lamp where the rapidly changing voltage has little effect due to the inherent thermal lag in the filament, or small DC motors to obtain a speed control. What we need is something to smooth out the rapidly pulsating output voltage and which can also store energy. The storage device can then supply the load current when the switch is open, so removing the ripple voltage, in the same way as a smoothing capacitor does.

The devices we select are an inductor and capacitor connected as an L-C filter pole. However, an inductor or capacitor on its own is unable to supply the load when the switch is open as there is nothing to complete the circuit in the output network. What we need is another switch to operate in anti-phase with the main switch. This second switch will be closed when the main switch is open and open when the main switch is closed. If the second switch was left closed when the main switch was also closed we would have a direct short across the input and a big bang would occur! The basic circuit of a Buck Converter is shown in Figs 6.2 and 6.3.

Notice the current flowing in the inductor, I_L, always flows in the same direction. The current in the capacitor, I_C, however flows into the capacitor when SW1 is closed and out of the capacitor when SW1 is open. The inductor and capacitor form a low-pass filter that removes the switching frequency. But it is the energy storage capabilities of the inductor that makes the Buck converter operate.

Principle of energy storage in an inductor

When a square wave voltage is applied to an inductor of substantial value, the current that flows in the inductor is a triangular waveform (**Fig 6.4**). The ripple current flowing in the inductor produces a magnetic field that performs the energy storage.

During the portion of the cycle when SW1 is closed and SW2 is open (T_{on}) the current in the inductor increases to a peak value, I_{max}, with a triangular waveform. The average current flowing in the inductor is the DC output current, I_{OUT}. When SW1 opens and SW2 closes (T_{off}) the inductor current starts to ramp downwards to IMIN, a point below the average DC output current. The

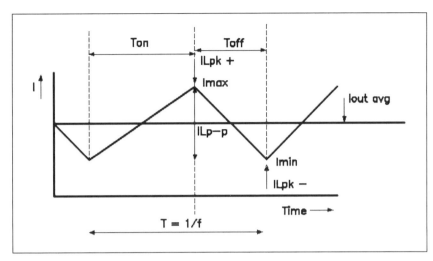

Fig 6.4: Typical inductor current waveform in a DC-DC converter

value of this ripple current is equally displaced about the average DC output current. The inductor ripple current is known as I_L. The peak inductor current, I_{LPK+}, is $I_{OUT} + I_L/2$. The current flowing in the output capacitor is the total inductor ripple current I_L. The output voltage is held relatively constant by C1 as it alternatively charges and discharges.

Problem with the basic buck topology

SW1 and SW2 can be replaced with semiconductors that have a low forward voltage drop. In early Buck Converters it was common to use NPN or PNP switching transistors for SW1, but SW2 was always a problem. Sequencing the switching of SW1 and SW2 correctly was fraught with problems as the finite time it takes to turn on or off a semiconductor needs to be taken into account. Early semiconductors designed for switch-mode supplies were very slow by today's standards. Switching frequencies of only some 20kHz were possible with these early devices.

The operation depends critically on the correct switching of SW1 and SW2. There needs to be a very well defined period in the transition when both SW1 and SW2 are off. If SW2 is turned on before SW1 has opened fully the input current is shorted to ground and a large current spike flows in SW2 during the transition period. This effect is known as 'shoot-through'. It erodes the efficiency severely and can cause the transistor that is used for SW1 or SW2 to fail. Therefore it is essential to ensure that SW2 cannot be turned on before SW1 has completely opened. (I will return to this problem a little later).

In order to get around this sticky problem, designers in the past shied away from using a transistor for SW2 and instead used a diode; this is known as a 'recirculation diode' or 'catch diode'. This diode needs to have a low forward voltage as it conducts all the circulating output current during the switch off-time. A suitable device that has the necessary low forward voltage is a Schottky diode, which has a typical forward voltage drop of around 0.5V.

If the diode had an excess forward voltage, or was slow to turn on or off, a great deal of power would be dissipated in the diode and this erodes the efficiency. Schottky diodes are almost the ideal device to use as they have switching times of a few nano-seconds due to low internal capacitance, low inductance and very low forward voltage drops. The forward voltage drop only becomes an issue when the output current is very high, typically above ≈10A.

Like the conventional rectifier diode, the forward voltage of a Schottky diode also increases somewhat as the current increases and falls as the diode junction heats up. When calculating the effect the forward voltage drop has on the overall power dissipation most designers like to use the worst case condition. For a typical Schottky diode this is about 0.5V at maximum rated current.

One point to appreciate is that with a Buck Converter operating from a high input voltage and a low output voltage is that the duty cycle will be low. The time period when the diode conducts is the inverse of the switch on time, equal to t_{off}, and hence the diode is conducting for a large percentage of the total switching cycle. This means that the diode needs to be adequately rated to cope with this condition.

To illustrate the problem let us examine a typical Buck Converter. We need a step down converter from 24V to 5V that can provide up to 10A. The output current in part also flows through the input switch, SW1, and this has a forward voltage drop as well. Assuming that we will end with an overall efficiency of 85%, (which is still far better than a linear supply) we can calculate the basic parameters.

- Power out   = 5V x 10A = 50W
- Efficiency   = 85%
- Power in   = 50/0.85 = 58.8W
- Total dissipation   = 8.8W

The power loss in the diode will be the product of the average output current times the forward voltage drop:

P_{diode} = 0.5V x 10A = 5W

The diode will need heatsinking. As we can only tolerate a total of 8.8W and the diode already accounts for 5W, the rest of the circuit components have only 3.8W to be shared between them if we are going to meet our target of 85% efficiency. The power dissipated in the switch transistor can be calculated to a first order by using the value of average input current flowing multiplied by the on-resistance of the transistor.

The average input current will be highest for the lowest input voltage. We are using a 24V input supply, which could be a vehicle battery. In this case the voltage extremes would be approximate 21V to 30V.

The highest input current will occur when V_{in} is at the minimum value, $V_{in(min)}$:

I_{in} =   Power in / $V_{in(min)}$ = 58.8W / 21V = 2.8A

Apart from the switch and the diode there are many other components which have a direct bearing on the efficiency. The inductor will have some resistance and other losses related to the core, the input capacitor & output smoothing capacitor also have an ESR that dissipates some power due to the ripple current flowing. These four major items cover around 99% of the loss making components. I will deal with some others later but for now these will adequately cover the main culprits.

Note: The average input current is usually very much lower than the output current when a large step down ratio is used, unlike a linear regulator were the input current is always slightly higher than the output current.

The on resistance of a typical mosfet switch designed for 60V operation is around 30mΩ. The on resistance is known as R_{DS-on}, which is the resistance between the Drain and Source when conducting. A mosfet of this size will have a safe dissipation of around 50W when correctly heatsinked.

Power dissipation in the mosfet, $P_{diss(sw)}$, will be I^2 x R_{DS-on}

Where I =2.8A and R_{DS-on} = 30mΩ,

$P_{diss(sw)}$ = $(2.8)^2$ x 30mΩ= 0.24W.

The mosfet will require minimal heatsinking at this dissipation level. As neither the inductor nor the capacitors are likely to dissipate very much power the overall efficiency will probably turn out to be better than the 85% figure we estimated. I have written programs to do this sort of calculation. These are included in the Appendix as complete listings for use with a general Basic program.

Note that this is only an approximation of the loss in the switching device and the total losses in the switch will be somewhat higher. In a mosfet operated at high frequency the predominant loss is the on resistance losses but other losses such as capacitive conduction losses can add another 30% to this figure. The exact power loss in the mosfet can be calculated but for now the on resistance, which is the dominant term, will be sufficient for us. Note also that we haven't yet considered the short-circuit conditions that can occur.

The resistive losses in the inductor and capacitors are treated in a similar way. Before we can ascertain what these are we need to calculate the current flowing in each of these items.

Inductor current and flux

The current flowing in the inductor is not pure DC. It consists of two components, one is the average DC output current and the second is the inductor ripple current, I_L. The waveform of the inductor ripple current is a triangular shape; this is because the inductor 'integrates' the square wave input. The magnitude of the inductor ripple current is heavily dependent on the inductor value. For an inductor of infinite value the ripple current will be zero. However, an inductor with an infinite value would have a high resistance, which isn't good from an efficiency viewpoint.

A practical consideration is to reduce the inductor value to reduce the copper losses but we also need to keep in mind the magnetic losses in the inductor core. Flux is the product of current and the number of turns on the core. This is known as Ampere-turns. Flux is measured in Teslas (T) or milli-Teslas (mT). In the old days when I was at college we used Webers and later Gauss. Some of our American friends still use Gauss in application notes but it is easy to switch between the two, 1000 Gauss is equal to 100mT.

The inductor has to store energy and whereas there are many magnetic materials we could use a consideration must be made for the magnetic losses, operating frequency, the need to keep the magnitude of the flux down to sensible values and the physical size of the inductor.

The magnetic flux in an inductor can only reach a finite value before the core begins to saturate. If the core is driven into saturation it loses its ability to store energy in the form of flux. If this should happen, the inductance value drops very rapidly and the only thing limiting the current will be the resistive component in the winding wire. Typically a safe upper limit is somewhere between 200 and 300mT for most magnetic materials (2000 to 3000 Gauss). There are however some exotic materials on the market which can sustain peak flux levels some 3 to 4 times higher than common or garden variety cores. One such type is Kool Mµ™ made by Magnetics Inc which has a Curie temperature of 500°C - although the coating on the cores reduces the operating temperature range to 200°C. Kool Mµ™ cores can sustain high flux density levels because they have a saturation level of 10,500 Gauss. As the name suggests they run cooler than powdered iron cores due to the lower core losses this material has. Another core type from the same manufacturer is the High Flux type. This has a saturation flux density of 15,000 Gauss.

In order to store energy the magnetic material *must* contain an air-gap. Flux of any great value cannot be stored in ungapped ferrite or similar material. Typical storage inductors are illustrated in **Fig 6.5**.

Permeability

The inclusion of a ferrite or other magnetic material dramatically raises the value of inductor. If a single turn of wire is wound with an air core it might have an inductance of, say, 50nH. By winding this same turn onto a magnetic core or rod with a permeability of 100, we achieve 100 times the inductance - 5µH. This unique property of magnetic materials allows us to achieve high values of inductance with few turns, and hence low resistance.

The core could be a type of ferrite, which has a high permeability and so needs few turns to obtain the required inductance value. But ferrite's saturate easily with very little flux. (Ferrite typically has a safe maximum operating flux density of 350mT at +100°C). A ferrite core would need to have an air-gap to work satisfactorily. The air-gap reduces the permeability drastically and therefore it requires more turns to reach the required inductance value. Air can store a lot of energy in the form of magnetic flux and is inherently non-saturating.

A very good low cost material to use for a storage inductor for switch mode supplies operating below about 150kHz is Powdered-Iron. This inherently is a distributed-gap type of core. The composition is similar to ferrite. The grains of the material are formed into either toroids or other shapes and bonded together

Fig 6.5: Typical storage inductors wound on toroidal cores

with an epoxy binder that is non-magnetic. When the core has been baked at a high temperature the epoxy binder hardens into a tough material. Toroids are a convenient shape to wind the wire onto and can be simply mounted onto printed circuit boards using the lead-out wires to support it.

Powdered iron is made by several manufacturers and operates satisfactorily at up to about 150kHz, with low losses. For operation at high peak flux density, higher frequencies and high ambient temperatures there are now today better materials. Kool-Mμ™ and Moly-Permalloy™ are but two of the modern materials which although more expensive than powdered iron can operate at higher flux densities and higher temperatures in smaller sizes than powdered iron cores of the same power rating.

Ferrites saturate very abruptly when the maximum peak flux density is exceeded. We say they saturate 'hard' and the inductance drops to practically zero with the current going through the roof! Powdered iron, Kool-Mμ™ and Moly-Permalloy™ have a more gradual saturation characteristic, we say they saturate 'softly'. Because of this they are very much more tolerant of minor saturation and give more latitude for errors in the inductor value.

Effect of temperature on the permeability

High temperatures affect permeability. When the core is raised to a high temperature it suddenly loses all its permeability and the inductance falls to practically zero. This critical temperature is known as the Curie Temperature - named after the french scientist Madame Curie who did extensive research into the physics of magnetic materials.

The same thing happens with ferrite and other magnetic materials used for switch-mode inductors and transformers. Running close to the Curie Temperature is extremely dangerous and is to be avoided at all costs. Typically the Curie point for most magnetic materials used for switch-mode supplies is about +200°C. Powdered iron cores typically have a maximum safe operating temperature of +130°C. Drastically overheated cores expand very rapidly and set up gross stresses in the brittle material and they have been known to explode and spray hot pieces of shrapnel in all directions.

This effect is also used in soldering irons to maintain a constant temperature. The older range of Weller irons use a magnet attached to the tip which when cool attracts a metallic switch to close the circuit and allow current to flow to the heating element. When the magnet reaches its Curie Temperature the magnet suddenly loses its magnetic properties and the switch is opened cutting off the heating current. When the tip cools down slightly the magnet becomes active again and the switch is again closed. This repeated cycling, on and off, of the heating element maintains a relatively constant tip temperature.

Inductor value versus current

All inductors wound on magnetic materials have a characteristic regarding the inductance value as the current is increased. As the DC flowing increases, the apparent inductance goes down. If an inductor is measured at a very low flux density, using an inductance bridge, the value indicated would be higher than when its full rated current is flowing. For powdered iron cores and similar materials the

An analogy to this effect is a simple compression spring. If a fixed load is placed on the top of the spring the coils will close up somewhat. When the load is increased too much the coils will touch and we say the spring has become 'coil bound' and cannot accept any more load. However, if the load is only half that required to cause the spring to be coil bound then a small alternating load can cause the spring to oscillate around the average load point. In the inductor the fixed load is the DC output current and the small variable load is the ripple current. The coil bound situation is when the inductor saturates.

shift down in inductance value is around 10 to 20% when maximum current flows. This is because the magnetic material is starting to swing up into the non-linear region of its permeability curve, increase the current by another 20% or so and the onset of saturation is approached with a sudden loss in inductance. Manufacturers of wound cores normally state the maximum current that can safely flow for a 10% reduction in inductance.

The magnitude of the current that can be safely carried by an inductor, and therefore the total power loss allowable, is partially determined by the winding resistance and partially by the peak flux density. Both factors contribute to losses in the inductor. The losses associated with copper loss (the winding ohmic loss) cause the wire to act as a heating element which transfers the heat into the core and the magnetic core losses cause the core to heat up internally. High core temperatures cause the permeability to fall and make the core easier to saturate. It is common to find that when an inductor is designed the current that it is rated for is a balance between these two loss mechanisms.

The optimum situation is for the resistive losses to be equal to the core losses, 50% of the total power loss in each. We have always to keep in mind the DC current and ripple current magnitude. A core can only safely handle a certain peak flux density, and to make life simpler for people like me the inductor manufacturers, usually calculate this back to the maximum peak current allowable.

As the inductance value and peak flux density have such a major bearing on the design of the smoothing choke we have to finely balance these two quantities. An inductor in which very little ripple current is flowing will have a high value of inductance and hence a large ohmic loss as well as being physically large and expensive. A good compromise is allow the ripple current to reach a value which is between 20 and 40% of the average DC output current, this reduce the size and cost to acceptable proportions.

The value of the inductance required for a particular application depends on the output current, allowable ripple current, maximum input voltage and switching frequency. You simply cannot 'thumb-suck' an inductor value out of thin air and expect it to work correctly! Although with powdered iron cores there is far more latitude for slight errors and liberties taken, you shouldn't make a habit of abusing this privilege. To do so will have your cores over heating badly.

The only thing one can say with any certainty is that at high currents the required inductance is lower than for lower current applications and the core volume will be greater than for a lower power application. But this presents a problem. If the supply has to be able to supply very small output currents as well as fairly high currents then it is imperative to do the calculations using the lower current value. If the application requires an output current which runs from 100% to about 50% as a minimum then the current value used in the calculations should be 50% to be on the safe side. The critical factor is the magnitude of the peak inductor current. At very light loads, with a low inductance value, the peak inductor current will be practically the same as when the output is at maximum output current. Hence the core chosen should be able to tolerate the higher peak flux levels.

Many switch-mode IC application notes specify an inductor value and work back from this to get the other parameters to finalise the design. Although for many cases this is acceptable it is *not* the correct way to do things. Because in 90% of the cases it appears to work satisfactorily, some engineers have fallen into the trap that this is the correct way to design. This approach is only satisfactory if the output current is always near or at the maximum design figure.

The inductor has a direct effect on the ripple current. The inductor ripple current ΔI_L decreases with higher inductance and increases with higher V_{in} or V_{out}.

The formula to calculate the inductor ripple current is:

$$\Delta I_L = \frac{V_{in} - V_{out}}{f \times L} \times \frac{V_{out} + V_d}{V_{in} + V_d}$$

Where: V_{in} is the input voltage
V_{out} is the output voltage
f is the switching frequency
L is the inductance
V_d is the diode forward voltage

Buck converter inductance calculation

Now I have laboured the point to death about how important it is to get the inductor value correct, I can now divulge the formula for this component.

There are many textbooks and application notes, which give different formulae for the minimum inductor value required, based on certain assumptions. All of these are workable, with some limitations, but no single formula I have tried is 100% correct for every application. The one formula I have come across, which errs on the safer side, is shown below, this gives an answer which is the minimum inductance able to support the required ripple and output current, this yields a value for the critical inductance - L_{crit}.

Critical Inductance:

$$L_{crit} = \frac{(V_{max} - V_o) \times V_o}{V_{max} \times \Delta I \times f}$$

Where: V_{max} = maximum input voltage
V_o = nominal output voltage
ΔI = inductor ripple current (pk-pk), Amps
f = switching frequency, Hertz

Note: This formula requires one to choose a value for the inductor ripple current. This determines what value of inductor is required. The ripple current is normally expressed as a percentage of the output current. A low value will require a larger inductor value and a high value means the inductor value can be reduced at the expense of some additional core loss. A typical value for this in practice is between 20% to 40% of the output current. It is as well to bear in mind that half of the ripple current value will be subtracted from the total peak current to give the output current possible with a certain value of inductor. With a 20% ripple current rating the potential output current will be reduced by 10%.

Taking an example to illustrate the use: We need a step down converter from a 12V vehicle supply to provide 5V at a constant 2A for a logic circuit. A 12V vehicle system has a working voltage range of 10V to 15V. The maximum input voltage we select is therefore 15V. The switching frequency is chosen as 100kHz. The ripple current value we shall choose to be 40%, = 0.8A.

$$\text{Therefore} \quad L_{crit} = \frac{(15 - 5) \times 5}{(15 \times 0.8 \times 100kHz)} = 42\mu H$$

Therefore the lowest value of inductor we can use is 42μH. Remembering that a manufacturer typically specifies the inductance reduction at peak current of about 10% means that we are not in fact looking for a 42μH inductor but a value of nearer to 47μH. It would be prudent to increase this by approximately 30% to be safe; a standard value of 56μH would be appropriate.

From this we can calculate the value for the total inductor peak current. The total peak inductor current I_{rms} is given by:

$I_{rms} = (\Delta IL / 2) + I_{max}$

This yields a peak current value of 2.4A which the inductor *must* be able to support without saturating. It would be prudent to design around a slightly higher value of, say, 3A minimum to cater for the short circuit current limiting condition. Having established what value of inductor to look for in a manufacturer's catalogue we can narrow down the possibilities.

However, we also need to know what magnitude of flux the proposed core can safely handle. We already know we are looking for a ready-wound core that can safely handle 3A, and it needs to have a minimum inductance of 56μH at full output.

The manufacturer will often list the maximum flux the core can handle as well as the maximum current. The most important one is the maximum flux density the core can safely handle under worst case conditions. This is quoted by the manufacturer as B_{max}. This value is usually given in milli Tesla (mT). The most stressful condition is at high line voltage and minimum output current as the ripple current will be at the highest level here.

Provided size is not a major factor always pick a core with a 25 to 50% greater current rating than the maximum calculated. This will allow a bigger margin of error under short circuit conditions - we do after all want our supply to be able to work safely under shorted output conditions. Like the series regulator, the most stressful condition for a Buck regulator is with the output shorted at maximum input voltage as all the input voltage appears across the inductor. The factor of $(V_{max} - V_o)$ in the formula gives us a clue. When V_o = zero, L needs to be increased to keep the inductor ripple current to a safe level. By choosing a core just able to work under normal conditions we run the risk of driving it into saturation when a short circuit condition is applied, this is a dangerous condition and could negate the current limiting set point. Always remember that high inductance values will support a higher output current than a lower value. It is always better to increase the inductance than reduce it.

One further point, which needs to be appreciated, is what happens when the output is shorted. If no current limiting is incorporated the control circuitry will attempt to drive the duty cycle to maximum in an attempt to raise the output voltage up to the set point. This would be extremely stressful for the switch transistor and cause certain failure. Current limiting causes the duty cycle to fall to a very low value, typically as low as 2%. But now a further problem arises. The period for which the recirculation diode conducts is the inverse of the switch on time. In this case the diode will be conducting for virtually 100% of the time and the circulating current will be at the maximum. This causes a high dissipation in the diode, which needs to be rated to handle this level of current and well heatsinked. If the current limit was set to 2A x 1.25 = 2.5A the dissipation will be 2.5A x 0.5V = 1.25W and a diode capable of safely dissipating about 2W continuously would be needed.

Input capacitor

The input capacitor is a *very* important item in a Buck Converter, in fact apart from the inductor and diode I have seen more problems with this item than anything else, because the constructor did not appreciate how critical its selection is. You *cannot* use a normal type for this application; it will explode in severe cases due to the high ripple current flowing.

When the switch turns on, the converter ingests great 'gulps of square wave energy' in the form of current pulses. The input current will in many cases be provided by a supply that is not well regulated and will cause the input voltage to abruptly dip as the current is pulled from the input supply. Any ohmic loss or inductance in connecting wires will also aggravate this effect. This input energy must be maintained throughout the complete switching cycle, with as little voltage dip as possible, for the converter to operate satisfactorily. This energy is best provided by a large reservoir capacitor placed as close as possible to the input switching device with very low inductance tracks or leads, especially the grounding. Every millimetre of track constitutes an inductance of $\approx$1nH and because of the rapid rise time of the current this causes a large voltage spike to be generated which aggravates the input voltage dip. The type of capacitor chosen is usually aluminium electrolytic in parallel with a ceramic multi layer ceramic of about 0.1μF to better cope with the high frequency switching currents. These capacitors need to be carefully selected, as they must be a type that not only has a low ESR but also low self inductance (ESL) to minimise this effect.

The input capacitor not only needs to be a type with a very low ESR and ESL but also capable of sustaining high ripple currents. The worst case is when the input voltage is twice the output voltage (D = 0.5) and in this case the input ripple current reaches a peak equal to half the output current. At input voltages far removed from this condition the input capacitor ripple current falls away to lower values.

Caution: If the input capacitor also happens to be the smoothing capacitor of a mains rectified supply then the ripple current rating needs to be carefully chosen as there are two sources of ripple current present - one derived from the mains frequency (tens of Hz) and the other from the switching frequency (tens or hundreds of kHz). These will algebraically add to cause a much higher peak current. In cases like this it is better to interpose an inductor between the

Fig 6.6:
Isolating inductor between rectifier and input capacitor

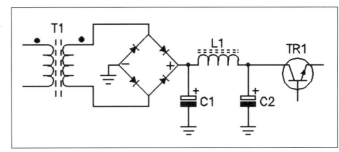

smoothing capacitor and a separate input capacitor (**Fig 6.6**). This will isolate the two sources of ripple current and each capacitor then only has its own ripple current to worry about.

Many different manufacturers make capacitors suitable for this application. The important parameter is the ripple current that the capacitor can safely sustain without over-heating. The lower the ESR the cooler the capacitor will run. The best type of capacitor to use is an Os-Con made by Sanyo, but these are expensive and limited to around 25V maximum. Often several paralleled low ESR aluminium electrolytic capacitors will make for a cheaper (although bulkier in volume) solution.

A word of warning about using tantalum capacitors

Normal tantalum capacitors are unable to sustain high ripple currents. They are also prone to sudden failure when the input supply is first connected as they have poor in rush current capabilities and often need a low value resistor of 10Ω for every amp of in rush current to be connected in series to prevent destruction due to this. This destroys any ESR capability they might have! Today we have available certain types which are rated for high in rush current made by several manufacturers but these are more expensive than aluminium electrolytics and not significantly lower in volume.

Output capacitor

The output smoothing capacitor in a Buck Converter has a much easier life. As it is fed via an inductor the waveform of the ripple current is not a square wave but a triangular one and the magnitude is generally low. The value of capacitor ripple current flowing is the same as the inductor ripple current; in fact it is the same current. If the inductor ripple current has been pushed up by reducing the inductor value, then special attention needs to be paid to this capacitor and a type the same as the input capacitor may be required to keep the output ripple voltage to acceptable levels.

Output ripple voltage is the product of the inductor ripple current multiplied by the output capacitor ESR. If the inductor ripple current is 2A peak peak and the capacitor ESR is 100mΩ then the output ripple voltage will be:

$\Delta V_0 = 2 \times 0.1 = 0.2V$ p-p

(which is generally considered to be too high for most applications).

200mV p-p represents a percentage of 4% for our +5V supply and will probably not be acceptable for a digital supply. Using the calculated peak-peak ripple current of 0.8A in our worked example we would need a capacitor with an ESR of less than 0.062Ω to limit the ripple voltage to 50mVp-p (1%) which should be adequate for the intended purpose.

Normally it is necessary to parallel several smaller value aluminium electrolytic capacitors to arrive at an acceptably low ESR. The value of the capacitor needed to supply the output current during the switch off time can be calculated from standard formula. But it is the capacitor ESR and ESL which have the dominant effect and it is these that set the output ripple voltage. Once the capacitor value has been increased sufficiently to obtain a low ESR then the capacitance value is normally many times that required to perform the energy storage.

An alternative is to use an exotic solution such as a Sanyo Os Con capacitor. These types are considerably more expensive but offer very low ESR values compared to conventional aluminium electrolytics. They have one other advantageous characteristic, they do not significantly change in ESR value over a wide temperature range, something which is a real problem with aluminium electrolytics.

Usually it is necessary to fit much larger capacity types to ensure that a sufficiently low ESR is maintained at low temperatures. However, a trick I learnt early on is to use a value with a slightly worse ESR at low temperature. You may wonder why I chose this approach? Well, as the ESR normally drops with increasing temperature I discovered that allowing the ESR to go 'a little bad' at low temperatures causes the capacitor to heat up a bit and the result is that the capacitor temperature climbs to above 0°C at very low ambient temperatures. This takes a little time to occur but as most equipment only changes its temperature slowly due to the thermal mass it is a valid solution in most cases. This fix is one many power supply manufacturers employ if you carefully study the capacitor types used.

To give a comparison I have listed two types in **Table 6.4**. One is a very good Nichicon type intended for switch-mode supplies, the second is a Sanyo Os Con.

As you can see the Os-Con out performs the Nichicon by nearly 3:1 on ESR, only needs to be about 1/10th of the capacity and occupies a much smaller volume. However, the price difference is more than 4:1 for the Os-con. For volume critical applications the Os-Con is however much better.

Achieving even lower ripple voltage

Sometimes we need a lower ripple voltage than a simple output capacitor can provide on its own. Short of increasing the output capacitor value to excessive limits (which greatly increases the volume and cost) a cheaper alternative solution is add an extra L C filter section to reduce the ripple to acceptable levels. This can often consist of an inductor with a value of 10 to 25% of the main inductor and a low value electrolytic capacitor of typically 10µF to

	Nichicon PJ series	Sanyo Os-Con
Table 6.4: Comparison of two special types of input capacitor	2200µ / 16V	270µ / 10V
	ESR =85mΩ @ -10°C	ESR = 30mΩ @ -20°C
	Size: 12.5mm x 31.5mm	Size: 6mm x 10mm

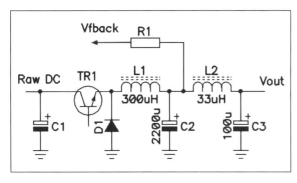

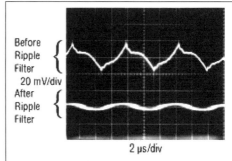

Fig 6.7: Second filter section and feedback resistor placement

Fig 6.8: The affect of adding an output filter to the circuit

220µF and a 0.1µF ceramic. This extra filter section often reduces the output ripple voltage to the order of a few millivolts which is usually more than adequate.

In certain switching regulator ICs it is a big mistake to lower the output capacitor ESR too much. This is for two reasons.

- Most control ICs need a certain amount of output ripple voltage to ensure that the voltage comparator 'trips' reliably on each cycle. Failure to supply enough ripple voltage can cause the regulator IC to lose control with disastrous consequences.

- Reducing the output ESR beyond a certain minimum introduces a destabilising pole to the feedback loop. The trend with modern very high frequency converters (those operating above about 500kHz) is to use ultra-miniature ceramic multi layer capacitors as the output capacitor. These have extremely low ESR and can cause the loop to become unstable at high current levels. Often it is necessary to include a 'lossy' aluminium electrolytic in parallel with them to preserve stability.

In cases such as these it is preferable to use a slightly higher ESR output capacitor and finish the filtering with a second L-C filter section. The point in the output network where the feedback divider is connected is also important. This *must* be taken from the first smoothing capacitor before the second inductor and final capacitor. Failure to observe this will make the control loop unstable.

Tantalum capacitors rated for high ripple current can safely be used for the output capacitors as the in rush current is inherently limited by the series inductor and many different types exist which are only marginally more expensive than aluminium electrolytics. They have similar ESR values to that of the best aluminium electrolytics so stability is often not a problem.

Selection of the recirculation diode

The maximum reverse voltage across the diode is the same as $V_{in(max)}$ and therefore the PIV of the diode needs to be chosen to be slightly higher then this. A safe choice is to set the PIV rating some 25% higher than the maximum input voltage to cater for input transients. The current rating of the diode is defined by the short-circuit current. Again it is prudent to choose a diode with approximately 25% more current rating than the calculated value.

Disadvantages of the standard buck converter

1) Leakage Current in the Series Switch

An inherent problem with the standard Buck Converter is leakage current in the series switch semi conductor when the input to output differential is high. This is especially a problem at high operating temperatures and a very small load current. If only a very small current is being drawn the leakage current can exceed the output current and the output voltage will "float up" towards the input supply voltage. The regulator IC sees this as an abnormally high output voltage and stops the switching in an attempt to bring the output voltage down to its correct value. Even though the device is no longer switching, the leakage current can cause the output to continue climbing to possibly dangerous levels for the connected equipment. In such a case it is imperative to have some minimum load resistor connected across the output at all times. Fortunately we can often save extra components by using the voltage divider resistors which supply the control IC feedback input to place sufficient load across the output. Normally these resistors can be very high values, because a very high resistance input at the control IC normally samples the divided down output voltage. Scaling these resistors so that about 1% of the total output current flows to ground via the divider resistors is usually sufficient to prevent this problem.

2) Short Circuit Series Switch Failure Mode

The standard Buck Converter bears many similarities with the linear Series Regulator as far as failure mechanisms. In both cases a shorted transistor will allow the output voltage to be the same as the input voltage and this can cause severe damage to attached equipment it is powering. A reliable over-voltage crowbar circuit needs to be fitted if this is not acceptable. For low output power often a Zener diode across the output can prevent extensive damage. In 5V supplies powering digital circuitry a common choice is a 6.8V / 1W Zener.

3) Excessive Power Loss in the Shunt Diode

Another problem is caused by the forward voltage drop in the shunt recirculation diode at high output currents. Although the standard Buck Converter works very efficiently at low to medium power levels, when the output current is increased beyond a certain point the loss in the recirculation diode starts to become excessive. To recap, the power dissipated in the recirculation diode is the product of output current times the forward voltage drop. Although a Schottky diode has a nominal forward voltage of about 0.5V, as the current increases so does the forward voltage. In fact forward voltages of up to 0.9V are common in some smaller diodes at maximum current rating. This is on par with a common silicon rectifier. The increase in forward voltage at high current, and hence the extra dissipation, is why a change to a modified Buck Converter is made. This is known as the 'Synchronous Buck Converter'.

Synchronous buck converter

If you look back to the first part of the description of the Buck Converter, you will see the basic circuit that uses two switches. The original tendency not to use a separate switching transistor for the recirculation diode was due to problems in sequencing or synchronising the two switches correctly. Today that problem has been solved and the ability to use a second low on-resistance mosfet in place of the diode means that the power wasted in a conventional diode can be avoided. In fact, with the very low on-resistance mosfets available today the efficiency can exceed 95% in some cases.

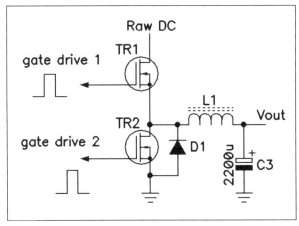

Several semiconductor manufacturers today make two mosfets combined in one package especially for Synchronous Buck Converters with the

Fig 6.9: Basic synchronous buck converter

common point being the output of the series switch. These are often a P-channel for the series switch and N-channel for the shunt switch. Some manufacturers even make complete ICs with the two switches built in, so the age of a single chip solution has arrived. These ICs are very popular with manufacturers of cell-phones and other miniature consumer equipment such as palm-tops and laptops.

One example I have recent experience with is the National Semiconductors LM-2651. This is a 1.5A output rated single chip solution operating at 300kHz and requires very little to make a working converter with efficiencies as high as 97% (measured). It comes in fixed voltage versions (1.8V, 2.5V and 3.3V) and an adjustable version. The input voltage range is between 4 to 14V. It features current limiting circuitry and a shutdown mode where it only draws 7µA. It is packaged in the TSSOP-16 outline.

The circuit shown in **Fig 6.9** uses two N channel mosfets and the top mosfet needs a gate drive voltage which is above the output voltage by approximately 10V to ensure it switches on properly. This requires a 'High-Side' driver IC. The bottom mosfet only requires a gate voltage of approximately 10V to work.

The synchronous converter is especially popular where very low output voltages are required, for example a 3.3V logic supply for processors in laptop computers. Usually the battery life is severely degraded by excessive power dissipation in the step-down converter powered off the internal battery. Using a conventional Schottky diode with a 0.5V nominal forward voltage, this is about one-sixth of the output voltage and hence efficiency suffers. Using a shunt mosfet to replace the diode makes a significant improvement in the total efficiency. This equates into extra user time before the battery is exhausted.

Some modern microprocessors can run at the 0.9V level, or even at 0.7V at reduced clock speed. The 0.6V barrier is expected to be broken soon. As the trend for lower supply voltages gains pace the Synchronous Converter will become the preferred method of achieving high efficiency and longer battery life between recharges. With these very low output voltages the forward voltage drop of a Schottky has a severe impact on the total efficiency in a standard Buck Converter, in fact in a 0.9V output supply the theoretical efficiency cannot be greater than 55%, which is worse than a linear regulator.

The very low on-resistance mosfets available have figures of about 3mΩ and better devices are announced on a regular basis. Using one of these in a typical supply where the output current is, say, 10A represents a vast dissipation saving.

Taking an example: A 10A standard Buck Converter using a Schottky diode will dissipate at least a minimum of 5W in the diode alone. The diode will most likely be one of the types in a modified TO-220 package and will require adequate heatsinking.

A Synchronous Buck Converter of the same output current, but with a 6mΩ mosfet instead of the diode, will dissipate only 0.6W. (By paralleling two mosfets the on-resistance and the power loss drops to half). This means a small surface mount mosfet with little heatsinking can safely replace the conventional diode at a cost and size saving and give extended battery life. The saving here is 4.4W, which if the battery nominal voltage is 4.8V allows 55 minutes extra operating time.

I mentioned earlier my modification of a Japanese 12A-power supply in which I was not only able to extract up to 20A from the existing transformer-rectifier-capacitor combination, but also obtain an efficiency of around 90%. This improvement was using a Synchronous Buck Converter. The control IC used was the Linear Technologies Corporation® LT-1339 which drives external N channel mosfets.

The circuit for the LT-1339 is presented in **Fig 6.10**. In this application a 100W converter supplying a 5V digital rail is illustrated. The efficiency curve shows the supply maintains 90% efficiency from 5A to 20A. A low value resistor in series with the output performs current sensing. The output inductor L1 is an off the shelf ready-wound part. Note the use of Schottky diodes to clamp the mosfet gate voltages and prevent them from swinging negative more than 0.5V.

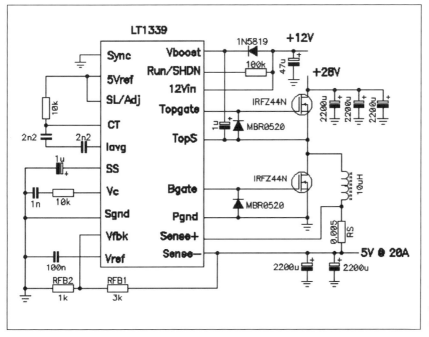

Fig 6.10: A synchronous buck converter using the LT1339 (Reproduced with permission of Linear Technology Corporation)

Incidentally the circuit in Fig 6.10 would make a really nice heater supply for those of you using 3-500Z triodes. It could save a big and expensive heater transformer to feed the filaments.

Note that the top switch gate voltage is supplied by a voltage boosted supply, VBOOST, this is because the top switch gate voltage needs to be approximately 10V or more than the source voltage to ensure low on resistance. The source voltage is at the output voltage. The diode and capacitor provide a voltage that is 12V above the source voltage of the top switching mosfet. This capacitor is boosted in voltage by the switching pulses on the source and added to the 12V secondary supply that the IC uses for its operation. The typical operating frequency can be 150kHz maximum, which makes the inductor value relatively small, only 10µH in the example shown.

The design of the output inductor and capacitor follows normal practice and only the ripple current in the inductor and the physical size of the core chosen should present any difficulties. In my supply I decided to experiment a little and try a slightly different approach to the normal design. I selected an operating frequency of 100kHz to keep the inductance size reasonable.

The output filter for my version uses three separate inductors and six low cost IRFZ44N mosfets. Effectively what I did was to construct three separate Synchronous Converter output stages and paralleled the outputs of the inductors into a common capacitor bank. This was in the interest of keeping the inductor sizes physically small to fit in the available space. All the top switch mosfet gates were connected in parallel and all the bottom switch mosfet gates were connected in parallel, and the top mosfet drains were all supplied from the mains transformer-bridge-smoothing capacitor output. These were the original ones used in the supply and proved to be more than adequate. The output inductors were each sized for one-third of the total current, about 6A per inductor, and this allowed the use of low cost powdered iron cores and wire gauge of 18SWG. I set the ripple current to 30% and this determined the inductor value of approximately 80µH. The output capacitor utilised 4 x 2200µF / 35V electrolytics connected in parallel to achieve a low ripple voltage. The final filtering was performed by another powdered iron toroid and several 47µF and 0.1µF capacitors in parallel. The ripple voltage at full load current was only 20mV. Maximum duty cycle was of the order of 70%.

Some calculations I did before finalising the design may be of interest. The dissipation in each top switch is only 1W per device at low input, and the bottom switches only dissipate 0.8W each under the same condition. The overall estimated efficiency was 96%. In practice I managed only 92% due to the choice of core used and the winding technique. However, I am more than pleased with the results. The final efficiency is however quite a bit poorer due to the losses in the mains transformer etc but I am not changing those items unless I have to.

This design worked out better than I had expected as the six mosfets could be bolted to the original heatsink that comprised the back panel. The LT-1339 was mounted on a small board and used a 78L12 regulator to provide the 12V supply to power it. All in all, a huge improvement over the original linear design as the current limiting was very positive, something the original design left sadly wanting and why I attempted the conversion in the first place!

The internal circuit of the LT-1339 is incorporated into a 20-pin DIL or SO-20 package. The IC operates in current mode giving excellent current limiting, the value of which is determined by the current sense resistor R_{sense}. The current sensing resistor is a very low value, 0.005Ω in this case as the trip voltage is only 120mV. This reduces the power dissipation in this resistor.

Inherent problems with the synchronous converter

Although the modern synchronous converter is a mega-leap forward in performance, it has a couple of problems that can catch you out. The first one is due to the way the synchronisation is performed. You may remember that I told you that the switching of the top and bottom mosfet switches needs to be carefully controlled. What happens is that when the top switch is signalled to go off, a time delay is imposed before the bottom switch is signalled on. There is therefore a very short time period where both switches are totally off and this means that it is necessary to include an extra diode across the bottom switch to perform the recirculation current flow until the bottom switch turns on fully. This diode is inherent in mosfets and is made during the manufacturing process. The internal diode in a mosfet is a Schottky, but unlike conventional Schottky diodes the in-built diode has a much higher forward voltage. Therefore it is imperative to connect an external diode to prevent excessive dissipation in the mosfet.

This external diode only needs to be a small type, typically in a 10A supply a 1A diode is more than big enough to fill in the tiny time gap. This diode only operates for a time of a few nano-seconds until the bottom switch becomes active.

The second problem exists when the input voltage exceeds about 30V. Due to the internal parasitic capacitance inherent in mosfets (Miller effect) the charge pumped into the drain of the bottom switch when the top switch turns on causes the gate of the bottom switch to show a positive voltage spike causing the bottom switch to turn on for a brief time period. This is known as 'phantom-turn on' and causes the efficiency to be eroded as it induces a 'shoot-through' blip of high current in the bottom switch. To eliminate this problem it is necessary to connect the bottom switch gate to a negative pre-bias network of about -3V to stop this effect. This is shown in **Fig 6.11**.

Although the Synchronous converter can deliver very good efficiency compared to standard Buck converters it

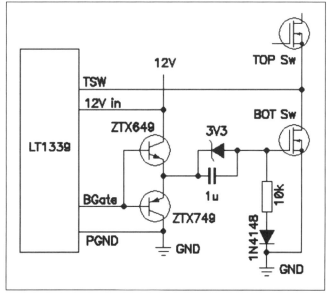

Fig 6.11: Providing negative bias to bottom switch

should not be taken for granted that dissipation is no longer a problem. As Linear Technologies Corporation point out in the LT-1339 application notes, a converter providing 500W of output power at 90% efficiency is still dissipating 55W in the conversion process.

Further developments of the synchronous converter

A recent development of the synchronous converter has seen the introduction of a multi-phase version. This uses two or more separate output switch drivers and the internal oscillator is divided down by the number of phase outputs used. The first one I came across was announced by Linear Technology and used two outputs phased at 180°. Each output drives top and bottom switches as normal but feeding separate storage inductors. The inductors are connected to a common output capacitor. The advantage of this technique is that the current in each inductor is 1/2 the total and equates to lower core losses. A further advantage is that the input and output capacitor ripple current is lower as the multi-phase ripple currents tend to cancel each other out. This means that the capacitors can be a lower value and have a higher ESR, meaning a lower cost part can be used.

A practical synchronous converter design

Here is a simple high current step-down converter that uses low cost mosfets and other components. The device is the LTC1149CN; a 16 pin DIL IC. It features a novel mode of operation when the output current falls to very low levels, this is known as 'Burst-Mode'™ where the control IC drops several cycles to maintain the output voltage in regulation. (Burst Mode is a registered trademark of Linear Technology Corporation). The circuit (**Fig 6.12**)supplies 13.8V at 10A. This would make a very nice shack power supply.

The input supply is derived from a mains transformer and bridge rectifier and produces a minimum of 16V at low line input condition. The LTC1149 can operate with up to 48V input voltage. The top switch, Q1, is a P channel mosfet and the bottom switch, Q2, is an N channel. Note the Schottky diode D2 connected across the bottom switch to fill in the dead time of Q2. Current sensing is performed in the negative supply return line with an 8.2mΩ resistor.

Transient response characteristics

A Buck Converter's response to a step change in load current is different to a linear regulator. Often getting the feedback loop to behave in a stable manner is quite hard. The task is a bit simpler in those composite ICs that contain the power stage as well as the control circuitry .

The choice of Continuous Conduction or Discontinuous Conduction mode also has a dramatic effect on the transient response. **Fig 6.13** shows some plots taken from a National Semiconductors data sheet for the LM2671 converter (**Fig 6.14**). This is a fixed voltage IC with an output current limit of 500mA.

The plots show the output ripple voltage for similar output currents. The DCM converter requires more output capacity but offers a lower ripple voltage.

The plots on the left show the output ripple for the CCM and DCM operation. As can be seen the CCM operation has a lower inductor ripple current, as would be expected because the inductor is far larger than the DCM case. In this circuit the output inductor for CCM is 100μH whereas the DCM inductor is only 15μH.

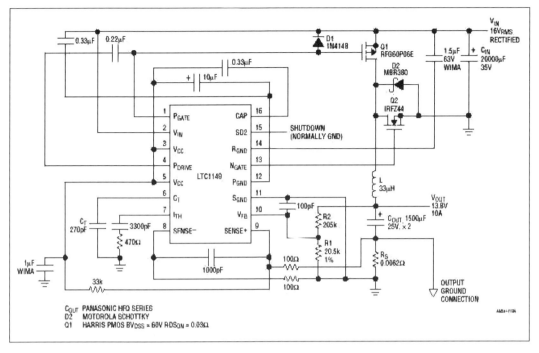

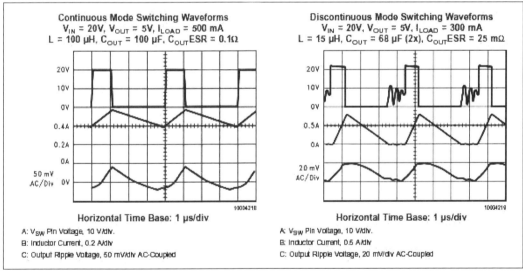

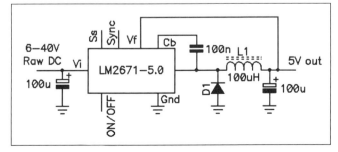

(top) Fig 6.12: A practical Synchronous Converter using the LTC1149

(middle) Fig 6.13: Output voltage ripple response plots for the LM-2671-5.0

bottom) Fig 6.14: Application circuit for the LM-2671-5.0

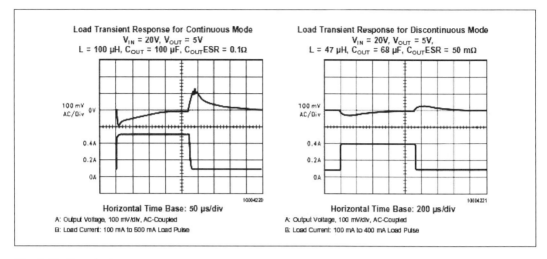

Fig 6.15: Transient response plots for LM-2671-5.0

Now look at the transient response for the two different operating modes, where the DCM converter uses an inductor of half the value of the CCM converter (**Fig 6.15**).

Here we can see that for a similar step-change in load current the transient response using DCM is superior. Not only is the output voltage dip smaller it is more critically damped when the load is reduced to the lower level.

Layout considerations

In order to make a switch mode converter that works correctly we need to be aware of some of the pitfalls when laying out a printed circuit board or bread boarding an experimental version. Because the currents flowing in the switch and rectifier can be quite high these can couple via printed circuit tracks or other wiring into the sensitive control IC. The basis of a good layout is shown in **Fig 6.16**. Ideally all ground points should be to a common point back to the input negative terminal. This minimises the circulating currents that can upset the control IC feedback input.

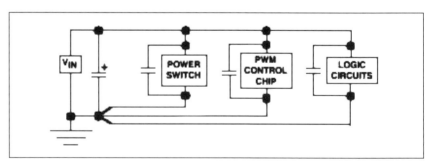

Fig 6.16: Correct grounding technique

7

~~~~~~

Inductors, Capacitors, Mosfets, Diodes etc

Mistakes: *"To err is human - to really screw up you need a computer."*
(Anon)

Some of the parameters dealing with inductors and capacitors will be used over and over again whilst discussing switch-mode power supplies. So let's get them down on paper and things will be a lot clearer.

Inductor calculations

The inductance of a coil wound on a core will depend on the permeability of the core. The higher the permeability the higher will be the inductance for a given number of turns. Because it is tedious to keep referring to permeability figures and doing the calculations to work out the inductance per turn the manufacturers of magnetic materials have rather used a different method of describing how the core effects the turns wound on it.

This is known as the A_L value. This refers to how many nH of inductance exist for each turn of wire wound (nH/turn). However, the inductance of an inductor is dependent on the square of the number of turns. Because the A_L varies as the number of turns increases, the convention is to quote the value for 100 turns or 1000 turns of a wire gauge which completely fills the bobbin or core. The gauge of wire has almost no effect on the inductance per turn, if a 30SWG wire was used the inductance would be the same as a wire gauge of, say, 20SWG.

A particular core might have an A_L value of 250nH/turn^2. It is easy to calculate what the inductance is for a given number of turns of wire. For example an inductor with 10 turns might have an inductance of 2.5µH. However an inductor with 20 turns would have an inductance of 4 times this value, 10µH. The number of turns (N) required for a particular inductor is given by:

$$N = \sqrt{L_p / A_L}$$

L_p is the required inductance in Henries.
A_L is a constant in nH/turn^2.

And hence

$$A_L = \sqrt{L_p / N^2}$$

Manufacturers list each core type with the A_L values for each different size in the range. For example a RM-10 core, although a common size, is available in many different materials, each of which has a different permeability, and hence

A_L value nH/turn	Material type	Part Number	Comment / Marking
160	N41	B65815-E160-A41	Gapped / N41-160
250	N41	B65815-E250-A41	Gapped / N41-250
1000	N41	B65815-E1000-A41	Gapped / N41-1000
5300	N67	B65815-E-R67	Un-Gapped / N67
6000	N41	B65815-E-R41	Un-Gapped / N41
8400	N30	B65815-E-R30	Un-Gapped / N30

Note: Material type N30 is not intended for power applications and is shown for information purposes.

A_L value. To confuse things even more, most of these cores are available in gapped and ungapped versions. The ungapped cores have A_L values reaching over 6000nH/turn and the largest gapped core has an A_L of as low as 160nH/turn. Fortunately, the manufacturers usually mark the core with a code so you can easily establish the A_L value. It is also nice to find out that a RM-8 core is available in all the common A_L values, as are the RM-10, RM-12 and RM-14, but each one may be made from a different material and has different air gap dimensions from the others. If the core is marked with a designation such as "N41" you know that it is an ungapped type made of N41 material. For example the different A_L values available for the RM-12 cores from Siemens are shown in **Table 7.1**.

An important thing to note about gapped core sets is that often the total gap is ground into just one half of the two piece set. This is the core, which has the marking; the other half is unmarked and is the same as an ungapped set. So make sure you don't get them mixed up. It is easy when winding several transformers at the same time to get two gapped halves together or two ungapped halves, either of which will stop the transformer from working as intended.

Table 7.2 lists some of the Siemens material types intended for power applications. Many other manufacturers make similar cores and their data is similar.

Table 7.2: Some Siemens material types intended for power applications

Material type	N41	N49	N53	N59	N62	N72
Base Material	MnZn	MnZn	MnZn	MnZn	MnZn	MnZn
Initial Permeability @ 25°C	2800 ±25%	1300 ±25%	1700 ±25%	850 ±25%	1900 ±25%	2500 ±25%
Flux Density - Bmax mT @ 100°C	390	370	420	370	410	370
Optimum frequency (kHz)	25-150	300-1000	16-200	500-1500	16-200	25-300
Curie Temperature °C	>220	>240	>240	>240	>240	>210
Relative core losses - mW/cm³						
25kHz, 200mT, 100°C	180	-	100	-	80	80
100kHz, 200mT, 100°C	1400	-	625	-	525	540
300kHz, 100mT, 100°C	-	600	670	-	-	-
500kHz, 50mT, 100°C	-	120	-	180	-	-
1MHz , 50mT, 100°C	-	560	-	510	-	-

How to gap a core correctly

I have seen many methods of generating a gapped core from ungapped core sets. In one company I worked in, when I joined the standard method was to insert some sort of non-magnetic insulating material between the two outer limbs or faces of E cores. This is acceptable as long as the material chosen is able to withstand the high operating temperatures and clamping pressures. In the original designs of a flyback converter a thin shim of paxolin (SRBF) was specified which had half the thickness of the total gap required, the total gap is the sum of the two gaps. This works well except strictly speaking the gap should be in the centre limb of a E, ETD, EFD, RM or similar core so the magnetic field does not 'spew out' everywhere and cause EMI problems. (The gapped cores have the gap ground in the centre limb for this reason; the windings on the bobbin form an efficient EMI shield).

The problem arose when thin paxolin sheet became difficult to obtain. A change was made to Mylar™, which electrically is very similar to paxolin. However, Mylar™ is a deformable thermoplastic that flows under high pressure and temperature, SRBF is a thermosetting plastic, which once cured at high temperature, does not change. The clamping pressure exerted by the clips or bolts holding the core halves together is quite high. Consequently, when the equipment under test was subjected to a high ambient temperature, the Mylar™ decreased in thickness and the gap closes up by a value of twice that of the deformation. This pushes up the inductance by a radical amount and reduces the air gap by the same amount. Because the amount of energy to be transferred is determined by the air gap (high power requires a large gap) the transformer core would go into violent saturation and over heat badly. When the unit cooled down again the gap was still too small and it would over heat even at room temperature. This caused much head scratching amongst the test personnel, as the unit would appear to behave correctly when first assembled and tested at ambient temperature. During the high temperature 'burn-in' to identify any early failure modes, the majority of units would fail, sometimes with lots of 'magic smoke'.

It took a while to figure out what was going on. Once the Mylar™ was identified as the culprit the change to a correctly ground gapped core solved the problem for once and for all. As you may have surmised by now I am not at all in favour of gapping cores with things like Mylar™, or other plastics or even paxolin for the reasons already stated. In some cases you have no choice, as a suitable ground gapped core set is not available from a manufacturer. In cases such as this, I have had the larger types of core of standard core sets ground using a surface grinder fitted with a magnetic chuck. (An alternative is to use aluminium or brass shim as this works just as well and does not suffer from high temperature problems, but I got fed up with gashing my fingers on the sharp edges).

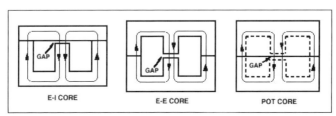

Fig 7.1: Gapped ferrite cores

Sometimes when I am designing a new transformer or Buck Converter storage inductor I will take two gapped halves of a particular core type and increase the gap to twice the normal to see the effect this has on the performance. The reason I do this is to ascertain if I can use a lower value of inductance (less turns on a particular inductor), this translates into a lower cost part as the number of turns has a direct influence on the cost of a wound inductor. It is easier than winding several inductors with different turns. I sometimes use different AL values of the same core size for the same reason to see the effect this has on the overall performance.

The one very nice feature of gapped core sets is that the reproducibility is very constant. This is because the air gap is precisely controlled and the variation of inductance between several inductors wound with identical turns is rarely more than a couple of percent. Ungapped core sets on the other hand can exhibit many hundreds of percentage variation from unit to unit. I often used to get called into to perform a *post-mortem* on a problem design using ungapped core sets. Even a tiny speck of dirt between the mating faces can cause the inductance to vary a large amount. The core sets have a waxy film to protect the ground faces, which need to mate with absolute precision to achieve the correct magnetic properties. I have found by experimenting that if I take a piece of ordinary photo-copier paper laid on a flat surface and lightly rub the ground faces on it the inductance when re-assembled will often increase by as much as 40%.

Toroidal cores

Many power supplies can use a toroidal core for the inductors, particularly low power Buck and Boost converters. These are made from powdered iron-dust, which is held together with an epoxy binder. These cores are inherently air gapped due to the construction. They are also designated with an A_L value.

Toroidal cores have certain advantages over other types. They are inherently 'self-shielding', that is they do not radiate magnetic fields quite as strongly as some other types such as rods or bars (slug coils) used in low cost applications (**Fig 7.2**).

The cores are normally colour-coded with either one or two colours to identify the material used by the manufacturer. One well-known manufacturer is Micro-Metals™ who manufactures not only powdered iron cores for switch-mode supplies but also ferrite and other types for RF applications. Don't mix up the RF cores with power supply types or vice versa, as they won't work too well!

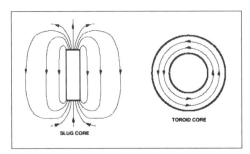

Fig 7.2: Magnetic field in slug core and toroid core

Fig 7.3: Pulse Engineering wound cores fitted with optional KlipMount™ base. *Picture reproduced with permission of Pulse Engineering*

Also several manufacturers make ready wound toroidal cores in different materials and several inductance and current rating values and can be supplied having a plastic 'boat' fitted to the base for easier mounting on a PC board. One such manufacturer is Pulse Engineering™ (see **Fig 7.3**) although there are several others with similar products.

Toroidal cores are most commonly used as the second filter section to reduce ripple voltage to low values, although in low current Buck & Boost Converters they can readily perform the function of the main energy storage inductor as well. In these applications, the wire gauge used is often substantial and the lead-out wires are able to support the coil on a printed circuit board without any other means.

In equipment destined for high G forces or vibration the leadout wires become a problem as they can fatigue and cause intermittent contact problems. Another common method of mounting toroidal coils is to fit them flat onto the printed circuit board with an insulated spacer underneath and a screw (nylon) or a plastic spacer with standard screws tapped into each end. In low cost equipment, I have observed the use of nylon cable ties through a hole in the board to retain the coil in place.

The important thing to watch out for is that the enamel on the wire is not scraped on any mounting surface or short circuits can occur. A more expensive mounting method is to provide a slot cut in the PC board and to fit the wound core into this and then apply a quick setting epoxy resin.

How to count the number of turns on a toroidal core

This is a common source of confusion. There is a convention for toroidal inductors, which differs from other types of coils. In a solenoid wound coil the number of turns refers to how many times the wire passes through a full 360 degrees. Consequently you can have fractions of a turn. If the wire only goes around the former 90 degrees, the coil has a quarter of a turn. If the wire is wound five complete turns plus a further 180 degrees, it has a total of five and a half turns.

A toroidal coil is different as it can only have complete turns and no fractions are possible. Each time the wire passes through the centre hole it is taken as one complete turn. So, if you thread the wire straight through the centre it has 1 turn. Counting the number of crests on the outside of the toroid gives a different result. If a toroidal coil has four crests on the outside, it has a total of five turns, as the number of turns is the number on the outside plus one.

Normally the core has a tolerance in the A_L value of around 10 to 20%, so if the turns vary by one turn from the correct number it has little effect provided the total number of turns is more than 10. Normally during the calculations of a particular inductance, we are finding the minimum inductance value or critical inductance.

So, if you are winding a toroidal coil it is better to err on the plus side than the minus side, ie more turns than less is preferable.

When I write the specification sheet for an 'in-house wound' inductor, I usually use a tolerance of -10% and +20% for the measured inductance, as I would prefer the inductor to be a bit bigger than nominal rather than lower than the design value. The minute extra copper loss (resistance) is not usually an issue.

Fig 7.4: Pulse Engineering data sheet

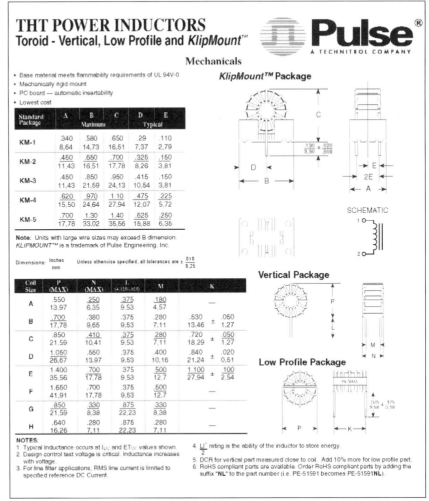

THT POWER INDUCTORS
Toroid - Vertical, Low Profile and *KlipMount™*

Mechanicals

- Base material meets flammability requirements of UL 94V-0
- Mechanically rigid mount
- PC board — automatic insertability
- Lowest cost

Standard Package	A	B	C	D	E
	\multicolumn{3}{Maximum}		Typical	
KM-1	.340 / 8,64	.580 / 14,73	.650 / 16,51	.29 / 7,37	.110 / 2,79
KM-2	.450 / 11,43	.650 / 16,51	.700 / 17,78	.325 / 8,26	.150 / 3,81
KM-3	.450 / 11,43	.850 / 21,59	.950 / 24,13	.415 / 10,54	.150 / 3,81
KM-4	.620 / 15,50	.970 / 24,64	1.10 / 27,94	.475 / 12,07	.225 / 5,72
KM-5	.700 / 17,78	1.30 / 33,02	1.40 / 35,56	.625 / 15,88	.250 / 6,35

Note: Units with large wire sizes may exceed B dimension.
KLIPMOUNT™ is a trademark of Pulse Engineering, Inc.

Dimensions: Inches / mm   Unless otherwise specified, all tolerances are ± .010 / 0.25

Coil Size	P (MAX)	N (MAX)	L (+.125/-.025)	M	K
A	.550 / 13,97	.250 / 6,35	.375 / 9,53	.180 / 4,57	—
B	.700 / 17,78	.380 / 9,65	.375 / 9,53	.280 / 7,11	.530 / 13,46 ± .050 / 1,27
C	.850 / 21,59	.410 / 10,41	.375 / 9,53	.280 / 7,11	.720 / 18,29 ± .050 / 1,27
D	1.050 / 26,67	.550 / 13,97	.375 / 9,53	.400 / 10,16	.840 / 21,24 ± .020 / 0,51
E	1.400 / 35,56	.700 / 17,78	.375 / 9,53	.500 / 12,7	1.100 / 27,94 ± .100 / 2,54
F	1.650 / 41,91	.700 / 17,78	.375 / 9,53	.500 / 12,7	—
G	.850 / 21,59	.330 / 8,38	.875 / 22,23	.330 / 8,38	—
H	.640 / 16,26	.280 / 7,11	.875 / 22,23	.280 / 7,11	—

NOTES:
1. Typical Inductance occurs at I_{DC} and ET_{DC} values shown.
2. Design control test voltage is critical. Inductance increases with voltage.
3. For line filter applications, RMS line current is limited to specified reference DC Current.
4. $LI^2/2$ rating is the ability of the inductor to store energy.
5. DCR for vertical part measured close to coil. Add 10% more for low profile part.
6. RoHS compliant parts are available. Order RoHS compliant parts by adding the suffix "NL" to the part number (i.e. PE-51591 becomes PE-51591**NL**).

KlipMount™ Package

C
.130 / 3,30 ± .020 / .508
D
B
E
2E
A

SCHEMATIC
1 O
2 O

Vertical Package
P
L
M
N

Low Profile Package
.375 / 9,58 ± .125 / 3,18
P
K

Winding inductors on core sets

My particular favourites for high current inductors or transformers are RM cores, EFD or ETD types. RM stands for 'Rectangular Module' and these are available in sizes from RM-4 up to RM-14, the larger the number the larger the core is. They are available with either circular bobbins with the pins on a circle or for the larger sizes from RM-8, they are also available in 'Power Pin' bobbins that are a 'Dual-In-Line' pin-out. For high power transformers or inductors the Power Pin bobbins are preferred as several wires can be paralleled to achieve the required low resistance needed for these applications.

EFD stands for 'Extremely-Flat-Design' and they all have bobbins similar to the RM Power Pin types with DIL pin-outs. ETD stands for 'Extremely-Thin-Design' or 'Economical Transformer Design' and is similar to EFD types with similar bobbins.

Both the EFD & ETD bobbins as well as the RM bobbins can be obtained with sectioned bobbins for mains off-line switchers. Because of the high voltages used with these, the separation of the primary and secondary windings is

Fig 7.5: RM-8 core set using a Power-Pin bobbin. The bobbin at the rear is a partially wound inductor for a Buck Converter

Fig 7.6: (a) An ETD core set with dual-in-line pins on the bobbin. (b) A high voltage flyback transformer for the authors CDI system wound on a RM-12 core

(below) Fig 7.7: A selection of the various core types available - (a) E core, (b) EFD core, (c) ETD core, (d) Toroidal core, (e) Toroidal core mounting base, (f) RM core

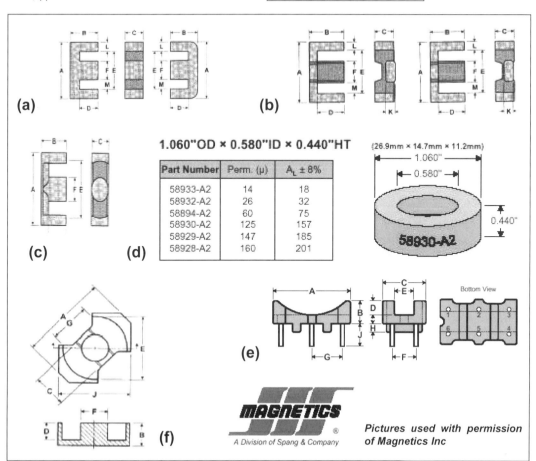

(a)

(b)

(c)

(d)

1.060"OD × 0.580"ID × 0.440"HT

Part Number	Perm. (μ)	$A_L \pm 8\%$
58933-A2	14	18
58932-A2	26	32
58894-A2	60	75
58930-A2	125	157
58929-A2	147	185
58928-A2	160	201

{26.9mm × 14.7mm × 11.2mm}

(e)

(f)

MAGNETICS
A Division of Spang & Company

Pictures used with permission of Magnetics Inc

93

especially important from a safety viewpoint. The bobbins have a central plastic ring to ensure adequate voltage isolation. This is referred to as 'creepage-distance' and is the distance between adjacent turns on the primary and secondary. A typical distance is usually 3 to 4mm, which is adequate for about 1kV.

The various core types are standardised in IEC documents. RM cores are covered in IEC-60431, ETD cores in IEC-61185. EFD currently does not have a corresponding IEC document at the time of writing.

Capacitors

Many of the capacitors used for power supplies are aluminium electrolytics. They are relatively low cost and occupy a small volume. We touched on capacitor parameters in an earlier chapter, now we need to look at them in more detail as they have a profound effect on how the switch-mode power supply operates. However, it is as well to be aware that many electrolytics intended for linear power supplies or audio applications are not suitable for switch-mode supplies.

ESR

We have already mentioned this before but we need to understand how the ESR effects the operation of a typical switch-mode power supply. A typical aluminium electrolytic capacitor is not a perfect device. It consists of internal parasitic series resistance and inductance (**Fig 7.8**), which makes it capable of dissipating power and adversely affects the ripple voltage at the output. The ESR and ESL of most types of capacitor varies with frequency. The lower the frequency the worse the ESR becomes and the ripple current rating falls off.

To give an example, let us look at a typical capacitor. The Nichicon™ data book lists many types suitable for power supply applications. I have selected a relatively low cost part to show how the ESR varies. The particular series is the PJ series, which is rated to operate at up to +105°C case temperature. These are characterised as having low impedance and intended for switch-mode power supplies. There

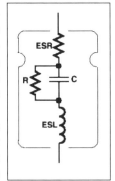

Fig 7.8: Equivalent circuit of a capacitor

are so many listed that it is necessary to narrow the range down to get a perspective. I have selected two values to show the general trend common to all aluminium electrolytics suitable for switch-mode supplies.

I have selected 2200μF and 3300μF capacitors with working voltages of 6.3V, 16V and 35V to illustrate the facts. The characteristics are listed in **Table 7.3**.

Value	Working Voltage	Size Dia x Height (mm)	ESR Ω @ 20°C	Allowable Ripple Current (Amps) @ 105°C & 200kHz
2200μ	6.3V	10 x 31.5	0.066	1.47
2200μ	16V	12.5 x 31.5	0.034	2.01
2200μ	35V	16 x 31.5	0.024	2.68
3300μ	6.3V	12.5 x 25	0.045	1.71
3300μ	16V	12.5 x 40	0.028	2.41
3300μ	35V	18 x 40	0.021	3.04

Table 7.3: Characteristics of Nichicon PJ series capacitors

There is an odd phenomenon unique to aluminium electrolytic capacitors. They are capable of 'learning' the environment they are used in. If a high voltage electrolytic is used for any appreciable time connected to a lower working voltage the capacitor 'grows' in capacitance. Therefore if a 35V capacitor is used for an appreciable time at a much lower voltage the capacitance grows larger and the apparent working voltage falls to the applied voltage. This improves the ESR, but if you now take this capacitor and apply its nominal rated voltage it will act the same as a lower voltage capacitor and exhibit excessive leakage current. This causes the internal temperature to rise and the pressure builds up until it vents. In simple terms it fails! To restore it to its correct working voltage requires us to re-form it with a current limiting resistor connected to a supply of the rated voltage. This process takes several days.

You can clearly see that the allowable ripple current rises with working voltage and the ESR falls by a corresponding amount. Hence, we normally use a much higher voltage capacitor than dictated by the output voltage required. It is not unusual to use a 35V rated capacitor with a 5V output because the ESR and ripple current are much enhanced. In a conventional power supply we would use a voltage rating about 25% more than the output voltage. In a switch-mode supply we need to use the higher working voltage to gain the extra ripple current performance and hence lower ESR. This is at the expense of the larger volume that the higher voltage capacitor occupies.

If we compare these figures with a relatively new capacitor type, the Organic Semiconductor or Sanyo Os-Con™ capacitor we get another perspective. (**Table 7.5**). The Sanyo Os Con™ series are very small in volume compared to conventional electrolytic capacitors and offer superior performance, at a higher cost. Typically the SA series is about four times the price of comparable aluminium electrolytics of similar ESR performance, but considerably smaller. Currently the maximum voltage available is 25V. The SA series is a good trade-off between performance and cost.

It can be seen that a 470µF/16V Sanyo Os-Con™ in the SA series is better than the Nichicon PJ 3300µF/16V being about twice the allowable ripple current and about half the height for the same diameter. Comparing other types, the 100µF/16V Sanyo is about the same performance as the Nichicon 3300µF/16V which occupies a case size of 12.5 x 40mm, whereas the Sanyo only occupies a case size of 8 x 10.5mm. The significant volume saving by using the Sanyo Os-Con™ is often very important to get the size down to fit into a particular set of mechanics.

Value	Working Voltage	Size Dia x Height (mm)	ESR Ω @ 20°C	Allowable Ripple Current (Amps) @ 105°C & 200kHz
47µ	6.3V	6.3 x 6.8	0.060	1.43
47µ	16V	6.3 x 9.8	0.060	1.83
47µ	20V	8 x 10.5	0.040	2.45
100µ	16V	8 x 10.5	0.030	2.74
100µ	20V	10 x 10.5	0.030	3.21
470µ	16V	12.5 x 22	0.020	6.08

Table 7.5: Characteristics of Sanyo Os-Con™ SA series capacitors

This in itself is impressive but we are only looking at the performance at +20°C. When the low temperature performance is examined the figures look even more spectacular. You will recall that I mentioned earlier that with most aluminium electrolytics the ESR gets worse when the temperature falls below 0°C. The Sanyo Os-Con™ ESR does not significantly change until the temperature falls to around -40°C where most aluminium electrolytics have ceased to work!

Here are the facts. The Sanyo Os-Con ESR increases by a factor of around 1.25 of the +25°C value when the temperature falls to -55°C, a Nichicon PJ series ESR has increased to about four times at -10°C and at -40°C - for all intents and purposes you might as well put a piece of lamb chop in the circuit for all the good it will do! I know this for a certainty as I have measured both types of capacitor over the operating temperature range and this is confirmed by the manufacturer's independent measurements on selected samples. The Sanyo Os-Con™ SA series is about as close to a perfect capacitor we are likely to get at a sensible price. However, at present the limited working voltage rather detracts from its universal acceptance. This may change in the future as the technology improves.

This means that if you want to use conventional aluminium electrolytics, the value of the capacitor needs to be greatly increased to obtain a sufficiently low ESR at low temperatures. This is often a nuisance as the volume required becomes excessive and at normal operating temperatures the stability criteria can become compromised due to the increase capacitor value.

Resistors

In common with VHF and UHF construction projects, the type of resistors used in switch-mode power supplies need to chosen carefully. In most cases the use of metal-film or carbon-film resistors are the preferred option. Wire wound resistors are generally too inductive to use, but this depends very much on the value. An acceptable low value which is used for current sensing should not exceed about 0.22Ω. There are special very low ohmic value SMD resistors made for current sensing and these are made in values from 10mΩ to 100mΩ.

The peak current which flows in some of the resistors can be quite high and this needs to be taken into account when choosing the power rating of the resistors.

Switching transistors

Today the preference is to utilise mosfets where practical. In the early days, before mosfets became available, the only choice was Bipolar Junction transistors (BJT). Nowadays these are becoming less popular except for high voltage application where mosfets still have some way to go to better the BJT cost and performance.

The chief advantage of the mosfet over the BJT is the very small amount of power required to drive them, and the lower on-resistance. In a BJT device the base current to switch them on can be substantial, the current gain (h_{fe}) of a large BJT is only around 20 so this means a large base current must be forced into them to get them to switch reliably. Failing to completely saturate the base-emitter junction with current means that the device does not turn-on fully and exhibits a higher collector emitter saturation voltage that causes a high dissipation. A high base current drive means that the conduction losses in the driver IC during switching can become excessive. A further problem arises when the transistor needs to be turned off. If the base-emitter charge is not removed fast enough the transistor will be slow to turn off causing more power to be dissipated. All sorts of extra circuitry is needed to make a BJT switch fast enough, which requires a higher current being drawn from the input supply.

A mosfet by contrast being a voltage driven device would appear to overcome all the shortcomings of the BJT. However, although a standard MosFet can be turned on with as little as 5V via a high resistance, the device cannot be made to switch fast using a current limited source. Many of the control ICs designed for use with mosfets can drive currents of over 1A into the gate of a mosfet, and sink the same kind of current level when the mosfet is being turned off.

To understand the complexity of a mosfet designed for switch-mode supplies we need to look at the limiting factors.

Mosfet gate charge and discharge

A mosfet consists of a high resistance insulated gate structure with substantial capacitance, typically 1nF or more, between the gate and source and a smaller parasitic capacitance between the gate and drain terminals. When the driver IC tries to charge the gate, to turn the device on, the large capacitance means that initially the gate appears as low impedance. We have a very short time to switch the mosfet on, because a slow switch-on dissipates excessive power in the drain-source junction. The initial gate current can be several amps for the first few nano-seconds, and then as the gate voltage rises the gate current falls to a very low value. The gate voltage needed to just turn on the mosfet is known as the threshold voltage and is usually about 2V to 4V, however this condition is for a very small drain current, typically a few hundred microamps. To get the mosfet fully conducting normally requires between about 8V to 10V. Manufacturers, such as International Rectifier, usually specify the on-resistance with a gate voltage of 10V.

If you observe the gate voltage with a very fast 'scope you will see a voltage which initially ramps upwards and then flattens out for a short time period before ramping upwards again to the final gate voltage. The flat portion seen is the transition between the mosfet turning on partially and then later fully conducting. This 'gate voltage plateau' is the result of the drain-gate parasitic capacitance, the Miller effect. As the mosfet starts to turn on, the drain voltage begins falling towards zero. The drain, via the Miller capacitance, dumps a negative charge into the gate that tries to oppose the driver voltage. We need to use a brutal amount of drive

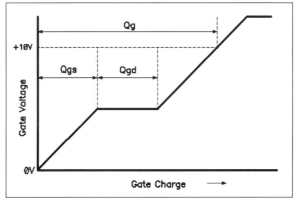

Fig 7.9: Mosfet gate charge voltage plot

current to reduce this dangerous plateau to as short as time as possible. During the plateau period the drain is only partially conducting and the dissipation in the drain-source junction is excessive. Only when the gate voltage has reached approximately 8V or so is the drain-source junction near fully conducting. To ensure an acceptably low on-resistance the gate voltage needs to reach above 8V, a value of 15V is usually the safe maximum for a standard mosfet, and hence between 10V and 13V is usually aimed for to make certain the on-resistance is as low as possible.

The gate charge plateau (Qgd) can be seen in the diagram. Only when the gate voltage has reached the final voltage is the mosfet fully conducting. Mosfets normally have a faster turn on time than the driver IC does, an IRFZ44 mosfet is specified at ≈7ns with a 10V gate voltage supplied from a 12Ω source.

Discharging the gate

As charging the gate to switch the mosfet on is a problem, so is turning the mosfet off because of the stored charge in the gate source capacitance. If you take a normal mosfet and apply 12V to the gate, the drain will conduct fully. If you now disconnect the 12V source and leave the gate open circuit it will continue conducting for a long time until the gate charge leaks away. The leakage current in the gate-source junction is very small; a mosfet can carry on conducting for several minutes until the gate decays to below the threshold voltage. In order to stop the mosfet conducting we need to bring the gate voltage to zero as quickly as possible with a low impedance current sink, to reduce the dissipation during the turn off period.

In a typical switch-mode supply operating at 100kHz we only have around 50ns to turn the mosfet on or off. This means we have to drag the stored gate charge out by applying a solid short across the gate-source junction. The driver or control IC usually uses a substantial pair of transistors configured as a 'totem-pole' to charge and discharge the gate from a low source resistance. The control IC has a very fast rise and fall time in the output totem pole even when driving a high gate capacitance, typically 30ns. This can be seen in the 'scope trace in **Fig 7.10**. This trace is for the Motorola MC34023, but many other manufacturers ICs have equivalent performance.

Fig 7.10: Driver IC rise and fall time plot

The output stage of the MC34023 is shown in **Fig 7.11** with the NPN totem pole transistors.

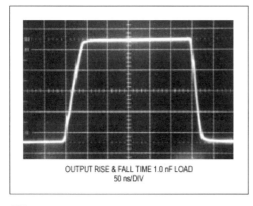

OUTPUT RISE & FALL TIME 1.0 nF LOAD
50 ns/DIV

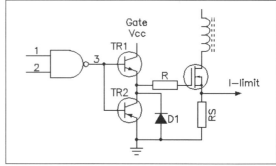

Fig 7.11: Driver IC output stage

Mosfet transfer characteristics

The gate-source voltage has a profound effect on the Drain-Source on-resistance as can be seen in a set of typical curves for an IRFZ44 device (**Fig 7.12**).

With only 4.5V gate voltage the maximum safe drain current rises to just over 10A, with 15V applied to the gate the safe drain current exceeds 160A. It is vital to saturate the drain-source region to ensure low on-resistance or

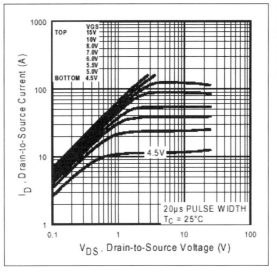

Fig 7.12: Mosfet transfer character-istics. *Used with permission of International Rectifier*

the dissipation will be high causing an excessive junction temperature, even with adequate heatsinking.

Junction temperature

The junction temperature shows a positive temperature coefficient. The graph in **Fig 7.13** shows that the on resistance increases to approximately twice the nominal at high junction temperature, which makes the device inherently self-protecting.

A mosfet has an inherent reverse biased Schottky diode across the drain-source terminals (**Fig 7.14**). This diode is part of the manufacturing process. Typically the current rating of the parasitic diode is of the same order as the Drain-Source peak current rating, but with a higher forward voltage than a normal Schottky diode. Typically the forward voltage is about 1.5 times a nor-mal Schottky diode and the breakdown voltage is comparable with the drain-

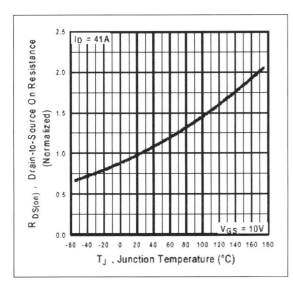

Fig 7.13: Drain-Source on-resistance versus temperature. *Used with permission of International Rectifier*

Fig 7.14: Mosfet internal body diode. *Used with permission of International Rectifier*

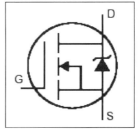

source rating. However, although the turn on time of the diode is negligible being faster than the Drain-Source, the turn off time is much slower being typically 60ns. This causes problems if the diode conducts due to a high reverse voltage being applied, which occurs in fly back and forward converters. Normally an external Schottky diode is needed in parallel to protect the internal diode. This diode can be quite a low current device, as it only needs

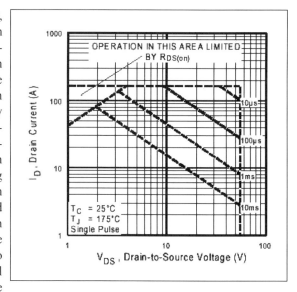

Fig 7.15: Safe operating region for a mosfet. *Used with permission of International Rectifier*

to conduct for a few nano-seconds until the internal diode turns on. For a 10A mosfet an external 1A diode is usually more than adequate.

Maximum safe operating area

Semiconductor manufacturers often give safe operating details in the form of a graph of current versus voltage. A typical graph looks like the one in **Fig 7.15** for the IRFZ44 mosfet.

The graph shows that as long as the Drain-Source voltage remains below 55V, the device rating, the Drain current can be anywhere up to 160A for pulse durations of less than 10μs.

Logic-level mosfets

Although the majority of switch-mode circuits can use the standard gate threshold mosfets, there are some applications where the standard types will not work. If the equipment is powered from a low voltage battery there is often no alternative but to use a mosfet with a lower gate threshold voltage.

There are a large number of low gate threshold mosfets available today. These are known as 'Logic-Level Mosfets' as they can be driven by PWM controllers operating from a 5V or 3.3V supply. The disadvantage of logic-level mosfets is that they have a higher on-resistance than a comparable standard gate level device and are more expensive.

Typically the gate threshold voltage will be less than 1V and the fully saturated gate voltage will be around 5V.

Bipolar junction transistors (BJTs)

Although the mosfet is preferred for most applications there are some where the cost of a mosfet becomes unacceptable. A typical case is an off-line switching supply. The BJT devices are lower cost and available to above 1kV whereas mosfets above about 800V are still expensive.

The BJT is characterised differently to a mosfet. The term 'on-resistance' is used by mosfets to specify the ohmic loss when conducting. In a BJT the term used is the 'collector-emitter saturation voltage' ($V_{ce\text{-}sat}$). In a high voltage BJT the saturation voltage can be quite high, typically 3V, but because the collector current is fairly low the power dissipation is still low. In a comparable off-line mosfet the on-resistance will be of the order of a few ohms. If the mosfet has an on-resistance of 5Ω when 1A of drain current is flowing the voltage developed between drain and source will be 5V. Often when comparing similar current rating devices the BJT is the lower dissipation device.

Insulated gate bipolar transistor (IGBT)

Another popular device for off-line switching duties is the IGBT. This is an Insulated Gate Bipolar Transistor. The IGBT is used for very high switching voltages, above 600V, and it has a gate structure similar to a mosfet and an output stage consisting of PNP and NPN transistors. The collector uses a PNP structure and the emitter uses a NPN structure, which gives a lower saturation voltage and hence lower dissipation. The gate structure makes for simple driving as the power level is comparable to a mosfet, however

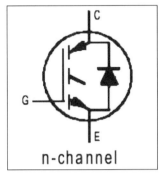

Fig 7.16: Internal structure of an IGBT device. *Used with permission of International Rectifier*

currently IGBTs are somewhat slower than mosfets and can only be operated up to about 100kHz.

Diode parameters

As the mosfet is an important part of a switch-mode supply so is the rectification diode. Most of the low output voltage power supplies will utilise a Schottky diode whereas other may use Ultra-Fast rectifiers. Schottky devices are limited to around 100V due to the manufacturing process. Ultra-Fast diodes can be made up to about 1500V but they have a typical forward voltage worse than Schottky types, usually approximately 0.8V at +25°C junction temperature.

Diodes are also rated for maximum average current and peak repetitive current. A mains rectifier, such as a 1N4007 is rated at 1A average and 40A peak non-repetitive for 8.33ms duration. Switch-mode diodes spend all their working life having to deal with high peak currents that can be many times the average current.

Diode peak current rating

Figs 7.17 - 7.20 are from International Rectifier data sheets. Figs 7.17 and 7.19 are for a 1A surface mount rectifier, the 10BQ040. The part numbering relates to a 1A average current with a 40V PIV rating. The peak current is specified as 430A, which is over ten times that of a 1N4000 series diode. The forward voltage is specified as 0.49V with 1A average current flowing.

Now look at the figures for another International Rectifier diode, the 50SQxx (**Figs 7.18 and 7.20**) which is a family of 5A Schottky rectifiers. Here the peak current is a staggering 1900A, with a forward voltage specification of 0.52V at 5A.

The 10BQ040 has a forward drop of 0.45V at 1A. The 50SQxx has a forward drop of 0.6V at 5A. Both these figures are at a junction temperature of +25°C, which is often not possible under actual operation in a typical circuit.

Major Ratings and Characteristics

Characteristics		10BQ040	Units
$I_{F(AV)}$	Rectangular waveform	1.0	A
V_{RRM}		40	V
I_{FSM}	@ tp = 5 μs sine	430	A
V_F	@ 1.0 Apk, T_J = 125°C	0.49	V
T_J	range	-55 to 150	°C

Major Ratings and Characteristics

Characteristics		50SQ...	Units
$I_{F(AV)}$	Rectangular waveform	5	A
V_{RRM}	range	80 to 100	V
I_{FSM}	@ tp = 5 μs sine	1900	A
V_F	@ 5 Apk, T_J = 125°C	0.52	V
T_J	range	-55 to 175	°C

Fig 7.17: 1A diode data

Fig 7.18: 5A diode data

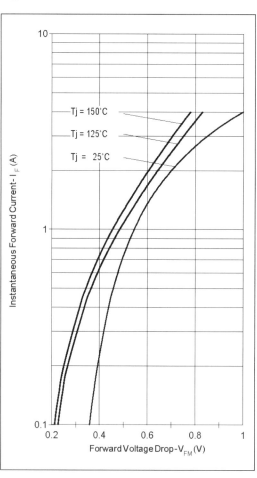

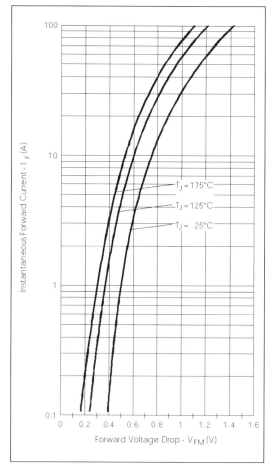

Fig 7.19: 10BQ040 data. Maximum forward voltage drop characteristics

Fig 7.20: 50SQxx data. Maximum forward voltage drop characteristics

The illustrations on this page are reproduced with the permission of International Rectifier.

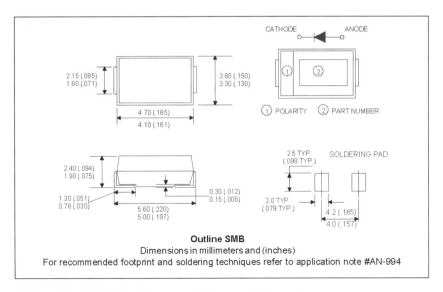

Outline SMB
Dimensions in millimeters and (inches)
For recommended footprint and soldering techniques refer to application note #AN-994

Fig 7.21: The 10BQ040 diode is supplied in the SMB plastic package

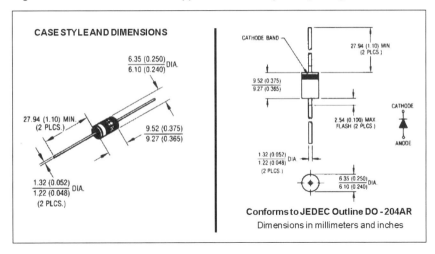

Conforms to JEDEC Outline DO - 204AR
Dimensions in millimeters and inches

Fig 7.22: The 50SQxx series is supplied in a DO-204AR package

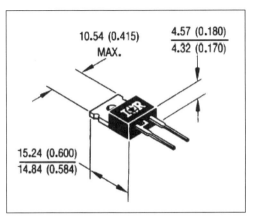

The illustrations on this page are reproduced with the permission of International Rectifier.

Fig 7.23: A single diode in the TO-220 package

Fig 7.24: Various versions of the TO-220 rectifier diodes. *Used with permission of International Rectifier*

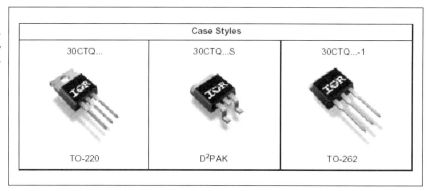

Fig 7.24: Various versions of the TO-220 rectifier diodes. *Used with permission of International Rectifier*

Figs 7.21 and 7.22 show the packages used for two popular diodes. Other styles of diodes in common use are the modified TO-220 package, which can contain either one or two devices. **Fig 7.23** shows a single diode configuration and **Fig 7.24** two diodes.

The requirement for proper heat sinking is imperative to allow the diode to operate within its safe working limits. For surface mount diodes this means using a substantial area of copper foil to get the heat away from the package as quickly as possible. For conventional diodes the lead length has a vast effect on its heat sinking. The leads should be as short as feasible and the leads connected to substantial areas of copper.

One important criterion with leaded devices is the bend radius of the leads. This must be such that no strain is placed on the package. Often a minimum bend radius of 2mm is quoted by the manufacturers to ensure the leads are not subjected to undue stress, which can damage the internal connections within the plastic moulded package. TO-220 diodes need heatsinking to a suitable metal surface with an insulating washer and bush because the tab is connected to one of the leads.

Fuses and Fusing

Finally let us take at look at the use of fuses and the correct type to use and how to connect them in the circuit.

A fuse is a weak-link deliberately placed in a strategic portion of a circuit to limit the flow of excess current. Should the current exceed the rating of the fuse, the fuse link will heat up and cause the circuit to go open circuit. How long this takes will depend on several factors. For a minor overload, say 20%; the likelihood is that the fuse will not blow for some considerable time. This may or may not be a problem; it depends to a large extent on what we desire the fuse to do under this mild overload. It would be very annoying to have to keep replacing fuses because of such a minor overload condition.

There are several different types of fuses commonly used. These are the Fast-Blow, standard fuse and the Slow-Blow fuse. Each has its particular application and care must be taken to select and fit the correct one for the piece of equipment.

Generally, in house wiring applications the fuse is not designed to protect the equipment. Rather it is designed to protect the wiring within the building, and hence reduce the risk of fire.

Selecting the correct voltage and current rating is sometimes tricky and often an educated guess needs to be made. For example, an electric fire or similar appliance which draws 3kW from a 230V AC mains supply would require a fuse with a current rating of at least a 13A rating to safely survive. Fused plugs are commonly used in some countries and usually can be purchased with a selection of different ratings, or the correct fuse can be purchased separately and fitted to a plug. Common fuse ratings for this type of plug (commonly called 13A fused plug-tops) are 1A, 2A, 3A, 5A, 7A, 10A and 13A. As the 13A fuse is the highest available the appliance will need to be fitted with this value, although it should really have a 15A fuse. This is one of the failings of the '13A square-pin plug' and the older 15A type with round pins is superior in this respect. The fuses designed for the 13A plug-top are classified as Fast/Medium acting.

Fuses designed to protect AC induction motors often need to be rated at least 175% of the running current to prevent the fuse blowing on switch on. A good rule of thumb in most applications, if there are no other over riding criteria, is to fit a fuse with a current rating of roughly 125% of the calculated normal current.

The voltage rating of the fuse also needs to be carefully selected. In general, when the applied voltage is low a fuse can have a short length body. As the applied voltage rises the need is for the body length to grow longer to prevent arcing when the fuse ruptures.

A very special case is when we wish to use a fuse in the output of a high voltage supply. Because of the high voltage and the fact that it is DC extra care needs to be taken. There are special fuses made for these applications and the body length is often 100mm or more to ensure the DC arc is quickly extinguished when the fuse ruptures. A standard 230V AC fuse is totally inadequate for this purpose, in fact downright dangerous, and will cause the arc to continue passing current with little voltage drop. Even if you are lucky and the arc is eventually extinguished (which could be as long as 10s), it will be because the fuse has exploded, scattering hot glass or ceramic in all directions! Personally I prefer not to use fuses in a high voltage output, but rather rely on adequate fusing of the primary side of the HT transformer.

The voltage rating of a fuse should always be equal to or greater than the applied voltage. It is permissible to fit a fuse with a higher voltage rating than the applied voltage, but never a lower voltage rating because of the arcing problem.

Where the fuse is placed in a circuit is also important. In general it is preferable to place the fuse in a portion of the circuit carrying AC, rather than DC, as the arc will be extinguished quicker for the AC condition as the applied voltage will drop to zero every half cycle. Also as the arc is established the metal in the fuse will be rapidly 'burnt-back' away from the initial break, and the gap when it has increased to a sufficiently large value will cause the arc to be extinguished. The extinguishing of the arc is aided by the filler material that is inserted in the fuse element. AC fuses usually have a ceramic body and are packed with fine silica sand, which helps to prevent the fuse from exploding under high fault current conditions. Glass body fuses normally have no filler material and hence are harder to stop the arc and a higher possibility of the fuse exploding under high fault current conditions. If you examine a glass fuse which has blown you will often find evaporated metal coating the inside of the glass tube which can form a conducting path between the end caps.

Let us look at each type in detail.

Slow-blow fuse (Anti-surge)

The fuse is so called because it is designed not to blow if a short overload condition exists, which can be up to 200% of the fuse rating. The Slow-Blow fuse is most often used where there is expected to be a momentary overload current flowing for a short time, such as occurs with induction motors when they are first switched on. After a second or two the current being drawn drops to below the fuse rating and the fuse will not rupture. The way this is achieved is to place some sort of heat absorber in the fuse to prevent the temperature of the fuse wire from becoming too hot with a short overload.

Slow-Blow fuses are used as the input fuse for circuits containing a substantial capacitance or inductance, such as motors, transformers and capacitor input filter circuits. After the initial high starting current the running current falls to a safe value. A common application is for the input fuse of off-line switching supplies or normal transformer derived linear regulators. Another common use is in automotive lighting circuits, where the high in-rush currents due to the cold filament of the lamps cause a short period of high current to flow on switch on.

The time it takes for a Slow-Blow fuse, or any other type for that matter, to rupture is a function of the overload current. With a 500% current flowing it might be in the order of one second. With a 1000% current flowing it will be progressively less, perhaps 0.1s. The wiring can probably tolerate this for the short time the current is flowing. The important thing with any fuse is that it should not normally rupture when the rated current is flowing but should rupture when a gross fault condition exists. With some of the other fuse types, particularly the fast-blow types, if a fuse is run for a long period at the rated current it will eventually rupture, even though the current did not exceed the rated current. This is because the fuse wire is at an elevated temperature and over a long time minute particles of the metal are 'boiled off' and the wire gets progressively thinner so lowering its current capacity. Incandescent light bulbs exhibit this and will usually fail on switch-on because the filament is too thin to support the switch-on surge current.

The way the fuse is marked by the manufacturer indicates the fusing characteristics. A slow-blow fuse will have something like this: 230V AC 5AT.

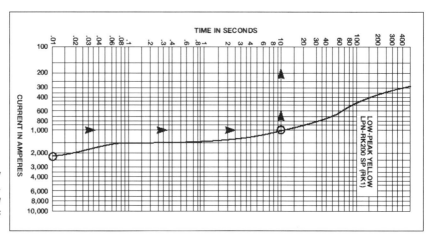

Fig 7.25: Slow-Blow fuse data. [Reproduced from Bussman Industries data sheet]

The T after the current rating denotes a time-delay (anti-surge or slow-blow fuse) with a rating of 5A.

Fig 7.26: A slow-blow fuse

Fig 7.25 gives an indication of the time required for a fuse to rupture, the fuse shown is a 200A time delay type. For minor over load currents the time delay is long, about 10s for a 500% current (1000A), but at 2200A the time required is only 0.01s

Medium speed fuses

Medium acting fuses are the most common in use. They provide a similar characteristic to the Slow-Blow types but at lower overload ratings. Typically they will carry approximately 30% over the rated current for a long time before rupturing but will rupture rapidly if the current exceeds 300%.

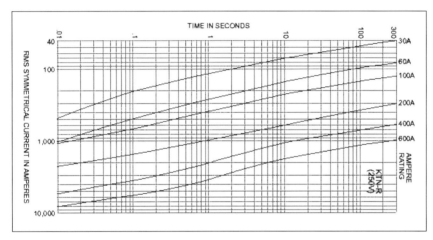

Fig 7.27: Medium Speed fuse data. *[Reproduced from Bussman Industries data sheet]*

Fast-acting fuses

Fast-acting fuses are commonly used to protect semiconductor devices. They have a limited overload capacity and will rupture rapidly if the current exceeds approximately 150% of the rated value.

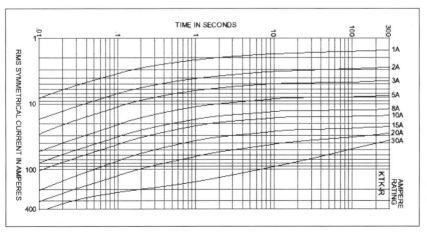

Fig 7.28: Fast acting fuse data. *[Reproduced from Bussman Industries data sheet]*

In **Fig 7.28** you can see that a 1A rated fuse will rupture in about 2s when the current has risen to 2A, and in 0.01s when the current rises to 8A. Fast acting fuses are normally designated by the symbol FB (fast-blow) after the voltage and current rating. The thinned centre portion gives the fast action.

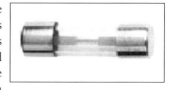

Fig 7.29: Fast acting fuse

Where to connect the fuse in the circuit

As with most things there is a correct way and an incorrect way when placing fuses in a circuit. In house wiring the fuse is always placed between the incoming mains supply and the wiring. This is to protect the wiring and prevent a fire hazard. The fact that an appliance may also be fitted with fused plug-top is incidental. If you examine **Fig 7.30** we can see some of the relevant points.

Fig 7.30: Correct

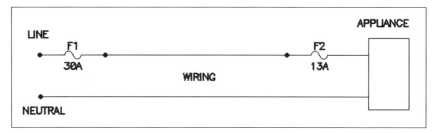

The input fuse (F1) is placed in series with the line ahead of the wiring. Should a fault develop between the line and neutral the fuse F1 will blow and protect the wiring. Fuse F2 is placed directly before the appliance and as it has a lower rating than the main fuse will blow if the appliance develops a fault between line and neutral.

Fig 7.31: Incorrect

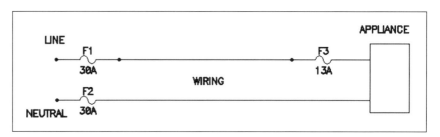

Now take a look at **Fig 7.31** which shows how *not* to do it!

Here the circuit contains a fuse in both the line and neutral circuits. I have seen this in some amateur published articles, but the author obviously hasn't considered what can go wrong.

Suppose we have a fault condition between the line and neutral which would cause the fuses to blow. Fuses have a rather loose tolerance and there is a very good likelihood of one fuse blowing before the other.

Let us assume the fuse in the neutral line was the one to blow. The fuse in the line side of the circuit would remain intact. This is extremely dangerous, as the owner does not know that the line is still connected, the appliance has stopped working because a fuse blew, but it is still connected to the line side of the

Fig 7.32: Bridge rectifier fuse placements

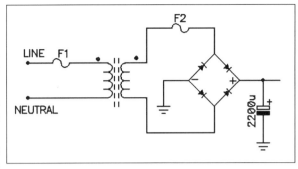

mains. This presents a serious electric shock hazard.

Never put a fuse in the neutral side of the mains supply.

The only time it is permissible to use two independent fuses is the case of the secondary winding of a bi-phase full wave rectifier. In the bridge rectifier the only safe place to place the fuse is in one leg of the transformer secondary. **Fig 7..32** shows the preferred placement. A single fuse in one leg of the transformer primary and secondary provides protection from all failure modes. Failure modes are:

- Primary shorted turns
- Secondary shorted turns
- Bridge failure
- Capacitor failure
- Short on DC output

A second secondary fuse can be fitted in the other leg but serves no purpose, one secondary fuse provides all the protection necessary.

Fig 7.33 shows how not to place a secondary fuse in a bi-phase rectifier. The fuse placed in the transformer centre tap to ground only protects against a shorted DC output. If one of the diodes should become short circuit the circulating current in the secondary can rise to excessive levels and only the primary fuse provides any protection. The correct way to place the fuses is shown in **Fig 7.34**.

With the secondary fuses as shown all fault conditions are taken care of and the rectifier could continue operating as a half-wave circuit if one diode went short circuit.

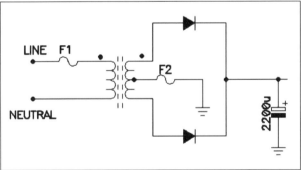

Fig 7.33: Incorrect placement of secondary fuse in the bi-phase rectifier

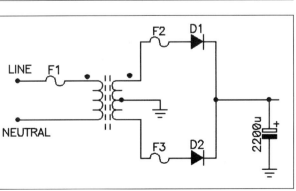

Fig 7.34: Correct method of placing fuses in the secondary circuit

You may think I being a little picky going into this much detail. Well, if it saves someone's life it will be worth it.

Some amateurs might just prefer to fit a fuse in the primary of a transformer and forget about the secondary fuse. In a gross fault condition this can sometimes work. However, consider this scenario.

A large mains transformer has several secondary windings. The transformer is rated at 500VA and therefore the primary fuse selected is a 3A anti-surge type. One of the windings feeds a small 12V supply for control purposes. The secondary winding is rated at 500mA and the bridge rectifier uses 1N4002 diodes. During operation a fault in an attached piece of circuitry causes the 1N4002 diodes to go short circuit.

The question is: Will the primary fuse blow because of this? The answer is: Very unlikely!

What will most likely happen is that the 12V secondary winding will burn out and the transformer will be at the very least a candidate for a rewind. In the worst case scenario it could suffer from total failure and will need replacing. All this was risked to save a few pence on a fuse.

The Boost Converter

The Boost Converter is one of the simplest types where the requirement is a single output voltage, higher than the input voltage. The output can be either a positive or negative voltage. The disadvantages of the positive output boost converter are (a) that this type of converter is not inherently short-circuit proof and will still supply an output voltage even when the switching transistor is turned off, and (b) the output is not isolated from the input. Because of this fact the current limiting must be performed on the input side of the switching transistor. A further disadvantage is that the input voltage is limited to about 50V DC due to safety aspects.

The converter's uses are many. One unusual application I came across recently was to supply a 24V vehicle trailer lights from a 12V truck. In many countries, the commercial truck market has used 24V vehicle systems for many years. However, America still utilises 12V on its commercial vehicles. The problem arises when an imported American articulated truck has to be coupled to a locally manufactured trailer. This problem is simply got around by using a number of boost converters that are powered from the 12V truck.

Another use, for amateurs, is to power 24V transceivers from 12V. These are often found on the surplus market for very little cost because many think it is difficult to make a 24V converter. A further common use is to supply a low current varicap tuning voltage of about 30V from a 5V supply. A supply I made

Fig 8.1: Laptop computer power supply using a Boost Converter

recently was to power my lap-top PC when installed in a motor vehicle that I was test driving or tuning. My laptop required a 19V DC supply at around 2.5A to power it and recharge the batteries. As the batteries are rather old and liable to go flat without much warning this was a problem. The Boost Converter fitted into a small plastic box (**Fig 8.1**) and was powered by plugging into the vehicle's cigarette lighter socket.

The DC input is by a 2-pin polarised connector that caters for either a cigarette lighter plug or the long leads with crocodile clips to suit car battery terminals.

Principle of operation

The boost converter works by storing energy in the form of magnetic flux in an inductor during the switch on-time and then releasing it when the switch turns off. The boost converter is often called a 'non-isolated fly-back converter' because of the way it operates.

The circuit of a simple boost converter is shown in **Fig 8.2**. This IC, the LT1370, is manufactured by Linear Technology Corp, and is packaged in a 7 pin TO-220, or SMD 220 type format. It contains the switch transistor with a maximum peak current of 6A and an on-resistance of 0.065Ω. The IC operates at a frequency of 500kHz, which makes the inductor value very small. It is the latest in a series of ICs from LTC, others in the series are the LT-1070, LT-1170 and LT-1270 which switch at 40kHz, 100kHz and 60kHz respectively.

The particular application circuit shown is an example often found in small laptop computers where the 12V disk drives require a positive supply of around 1A maximum and the rechargeable battery consists of 4 Ni-Mh cells. The nominal voltage of a Ni-Mh cell is 1.2V, and the fully discharged voltage is normally limited to 1V/per cell to prevent damage. The fully charged voltage is usually limited to 1.5V/per cell therefore the battery voltage limits are from 4V to 6V in this application with a nominal voltage of approximately 5V. Very few external components are needed to build a reliable design with high efficiency of around 90%.

The very high switching frequency means that both the magnetic component and the output filtering capacitor can be very small to suit the limited volume

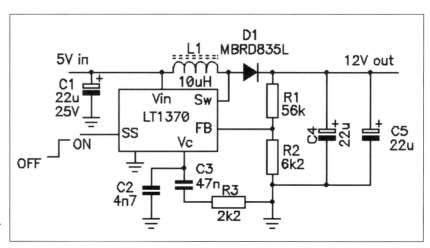

Fig 8.2: Boost converter

available in this type of application. However, the 500kHz switching frequency might pose problems in a radio receiver using a 455kHz IF system and extra precautions would be needed to screen and filter the converter in this case.

The switch current sensing is performed by an internal 50mΩ resistor in series with the ground return of the emitter of the power switch. The output voltage is stabilised by sensing the output voltage with a potential divider as shown. The LT1370 develops a 1.245V reference voltage (VREF) from the FB pin to ground. Output voltage is set by connecting the FB pin to a potential divider. The FB pin bias current represents a very small error and can usually be ignored for values of R2 up to 7kΩ. The suggested value for R2 is approx. 2k2Ω to 6k8Ω.

Duty cycle

The Boost Converter has a non-linear transfer characteristic. To achieve high step-up ratios requires a high duty cycle. The formula for output voltage is:

$$V_o = \frac{V_{in}}{1 - D}$$

And the formula for the peak switch and inductor current is:

$$I_{pk} = I_o \; x \; \frac{V_o}{V_{min} \; x \; \eta} \; + \; \frac{V_{min} \; x \; (V_o - V_{min})}{2 \; x \; f \; x \; L \; x \; V_o}$$

Where η is the efficiency assumed.

Average diode current is equal to I_O and average switch current is equal to:

$$I_{SW} = I_O \; x \; (V_O - V_{in}) \, / \, V_{in}$$

From these two formulas we can see that high step-up ratios will require a high input current and a high duty cycle. In practice a step-up ratio of about 8:1 is about the maximum we can achieve without excessive inductor and switch current.

If the duty cycle was set to 90%, the step-up ratio is 10:1. In practice is it prudent to limit the duty cycle (and hence the peak switch current) to a maximum of about 80%; this gives a step-up of 5:1.

Taking the application circuit, where the 5V input is stepped up to 12V at 1A with an estimated efficiency of 90% using a 10μH inductor, we can solve for D and the input current I_{pk}.

$$Ipk = 1 \; x \; \frac{12}{4 \; x \; 0.9} \; + \; \frac{4 \; x \; (12 - 4)}{2 \; x \; 500kHz \; x \; 10\mu H \; x \; 12} \; = 3.599A$$

this is less than the 6A transistor limit of the LT1370.

> Always keep in mind that the input current must be able to be sourced by the input supply, which are often rechargeable batteries. As the battery voltage drops under discharge the input current will need to increase to provide the same output power. A boost converter providing a 3:1 voltage step-up with an output current of 1A will draw a minimum of 3A from the input source.

$D = 1 - (V_{min} / V_o + V_d) = 1 - (4 / 12 + 0.5)$ $= 0.68$

this is less than 0.8 (80%)

where:

V_{min} = lowest input voltage, 4V

V_o = output voltage, 12V

V_d = diode forward voltage, a Schottky diode of 0.5V is assumed

This application requires a maximum duty cycle of 68% (step-up 3:1) at the lowest input voltage of 4V.

The average input current is given by:

$I_{avg-in} = P_o / (V_{in} \times \eta)$

where η is the efficiency assumed, typically about 90% (0.9) and the input voltage at the nominal value of 5V.

$I_o = 1A$

$V_{in} = 5V$

$I_{avg-in} = 12 / (5 \times 0.9) = 2.66A$

As the input voltage is raised the average input current falls, and so does the duty cycle, until when the input voltage reaches $V_o + V_d$ the switching stops as the duty cycle has fallen to 0%. Hence the input voltage always has to be lower than the output voltage plus the diode forward voltage drop. If the switching is stopped with the input still being fed from the supply, the output voltage will be $V_{in} - V_d$.

Inductor calculations

The selection of a suitable inductor involves trade-offs concerning the size, maximum output power and peak inductor ripple current. In the same way as the Buck Converter has this same choice the Boost Converter is very similar. Higher inductor values provide maximum output power and lower ripple inductor current, but are physically larger and degrade transient response. Low inductor values have high ripple current, which reduces maximum output power and increases the peak current in the inductor and switch. Many of the ICs designed for this application have limited switch current, in the case of the LT1370 the limit is 6A maximum.

With these facts in mind we can derive a formula which should suit the majority of applications. This equation is based on the maximum allowable inductor ripple current. As in the Buck Converter the use of a large ripple current reduces the inductor value but also increases the peak inductor current, which makes the core losses higher. An increase of the inductor ripple current decreases the possible output power; a good choice is to limit the inductor ripple current to not more than 40% of the output current.

$$L = \frac{V_{in} \times (V_O - V_{in})}{(\Delta I_L \times f \times V_O)}$$

Gives the minimum inductance value, which can transfer the required power.

Where:

f = switching frequency in Hz

I_L = inductor ripple current in Amps

Let $\Delta IL = 0.4A$ (40% of output current)

$$L = \frac{4 \times (12 - 4)}{0.4 \times 500 \times 10^3 \times 12} = 13.33\mu H \text{ (select a 15}\mu H \text{ or 18}\mu H \text{ inductor)}$$

Note: The inductor selected must be able to handle a minimum of $2.4A + I_L/2 = 2.6A$ without saturating therefore a 3A inductor is the smallest practical.

For many low current applications the use of a toroidal inductor is the best choice. This can be wound by the constructor using a suitable powdered-iron core made by Micrometals or a ready wound inductor can be purchased from several suppliers. I often use wound inductors made by Pulse Engineering and these can be obtained with a plastic 'boat' for direct mounting onto a board.

Diode selection

The diode needs to be rated for the average output current with an adequate PIV. The peak current flowing in the diode is higher than the output current and a type rated for high peak current needs to be selected. A Schottky diode is preferred because of its low forward voltage and fast switching speed. The PIV of the diode is the same as the output voltage. For most applications a good choice would be a 3A diode with a PIV of 35V. In their LT1370 application notes, Linear Technology Corporation recommend a Motorola MBRD835L which is an SMD diode with an average current rating of 8A and a PIV of 35V.

Output capacitor selection

The output capacitor in a Boost Converter has a hard time because the ripple current flowing in it is fairly high. It therefore needs to be a low ESR type with adequate ripple current rating. Often two or more aluminium electrolytics need to be paralleled to achieve a low enough ESR.

Input capacitor selection

The input capacitor has a much easier life as the input current is being drawn through an inductor. This means that the input ripple current is triangular in waveform and relatively low in value. A single large value electrolytic is usually adequate with a $0.1\mu F$ multi-layer ceramic in parallel mounted as close to the input of the inductor as possible.

Layout considerations

As with all switch-mode supplies the correct performance relies heavily on a good board layout. Tracks should be short and fat due to the high peak currents flowing.

Linear Technology Corp recommends following the layout parameters shown overleaf. The tab of the package is ground and should be soldered to a large area of copper to get the heat away from the IC as efficiently as possible. The output capacitors should be grounded to this same copper area with very short leads; SMD components offer the best performance in this aspect. However, if using leaded components make the leads as close to zero length as possible.

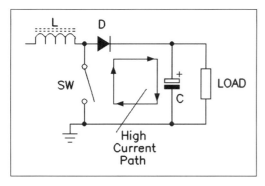

Fig 8.3: High frequency circulating current diagram

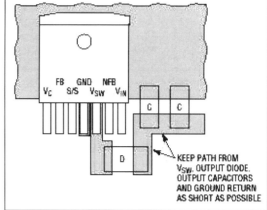

Fig 8.4: Recommended layout

The high frequency circulating current path should use substantial tracks and be kept as short as possible to reduce EMI. A suitable layout is shown in **Fig 8.4**.

The buck-boost converter

This is a variation of the normal Boost Converter. However in this case the output voltage is negative when the input voltage is positive. This is what the Buck term refers to; the voltage is below the input ie it is below ground or negative. The Boost part refers to the fact that a higher voltage (numerically at least) can be obtained. It is possible to develop the same voltage step-up as the normal Boost Converter and the same sort of equations apply. **Fig 8.5** shows the arrangement.

This converter requires a device with a high-side switch, the same as a normal Buck converter. The negative voltage often presents a problem with ICs which only cater for feedback from a positive output. In many cases a scheme to use a resistor from the V_{ref} pin to the FB pin can be used with another resistor from the output to the FB pin. The V_{ref} pin via the first resistor tries to pull the FB pin positive, but the negative voltage from the output resistor pulls it down towards ground. By scaling the resistors correctly the IC will regulate with the FB pin being held at the nominal feedback input voltage.

Here the inductor is connected between the output of the switch and ground. The output diode allows only the negative voltage pulses to be directed to the output reservoir capacitor. This converter is not inherently short circuit proof, as the Boost Converter is, but no output current flows when the switch is not operating.

The formula for the output voltage is similar to the normal Boost Converter except the sign of the output voltage is negative.

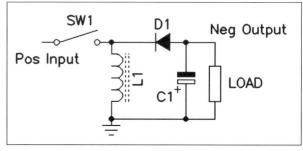

Fig 8.5: Buck-Boost Converter

$$V_o = -V_{in} \text{ x } \frac{D}{1-D}$$

The peak inductor current is given by:

$$I_{pk} = \frac{I_o}{1-D} = I_o \text{ x } \frac{V_O + V_{in}}{V_{in}}$$

The Buck-Boost Converter is often used to provide the negative supply for op-amps in battery powered equipment where a plus-and-minus supply is required. The positive supply being supplied from the raw battery voltage and the negative supply from the Buck-Boost supply.

12V to 24V boost converter

For those applications where a simple step-up DC converter is required, the Boost Converter is a good choice when the output current required isn't too high. A Boost Converter can deliver an efficiency of around 90%. The output is not inherently short circuit proof because of the topology and hence adequate fusing should be fitted to the input. The circuit shown is dimensioned to provide a maximum of 1A of output current.

A basic Boost Converter is shown in **Fig 8.6** using the UC3843B and a low cost mosfet. The UC3843B is an 8-pin DIL IC containing everything except the power switch. The mosfet chosen is the International Rectifier IRFZ-24N that has a suitably low on-resistance and can safely handle up to 17A of rms current and 68A of peak current. At 24W power output it requires little heatsinking. The circuit will operate from approx. 9V to 16V and provide an efficiency of about 90% at 1A output current.

The UC3843B features an under-voltage lockout threshold of 8.4V so if the input supply voltage falls to less than this level the circuit will be shut down and restart when the supply voltage rises above the threshold. In automotive

Fig 8.6: 12 to 24V Boost Converter

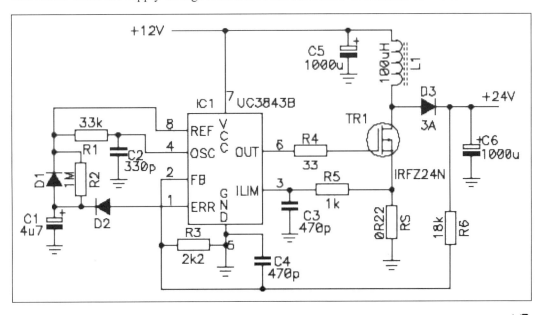

Fig 8.7: Boost Converter inductor wound on T106-26 core

Fig 8.7: Boost Converter inductor wound on T106-26 core

applications this provides protection should the battery voltage fall below 8.4V whilst the engine is being cranked. Another device in the series is the UC3842B and this has an under-voltage lockout threshold of about 16V so it is unsuitable for 12V automotive applications.

The Boost Converter operates in a flyback mode by alternatively storing energy in the form of magnetic flux in an inductor when the mosfet is turned on and then releasing it to the output when the mosfet is turned off. Because the switching frequency is high, the value of inductor required is quite small and occupies very little volume. The inductor is wound on a powdered iron core made by Micrometals and able to supply up to 1A of output current. The core material is type 26 and its diameter is 1.06in (27mm) - part number T106-26, colour coded white/yellow. The storage inductor is wound with 22SWG enameled copper wire with 33 turns (**Fig 8.7**). The boost converter operates at about 100kHz, which is set by R1 and C2 on the oscillator input (pin 4)

Feedback resistors R3 and R6 set the output voltage. The internal reference voltage is 2.5V. The converter features a soft start circuit to reduce the inrush current on switch on. Components D1, C1, D2 and R2 form the soft start circuit. D1 and D2 are 1N4148 or 1N914 types. C1 should be a low leakage tantalum capacitor. The inductor peak current, and hence the maximum power output, is set by the low value resistor Rs in the source of TR1. The voltage developed across Rs is a replica of the triangular waveform drain current, and is filtered by R5 and C3 then fed to the current limit input of IC1. Rs needs to be a high wattage resistor and a 2W wire-wound would be the best choice for this component. The gate drive to TR1 is via R4 to suppress ringing caused by the Miller effect in the mosfet.

The output rectifier diode D3 should be a Schottky for the best efficiency. A type rated at 3A average current is the optimum choice with a PIV rating of at least 30V. A suitable device would be the International Rectifier 31DQ03. Ultra-fast diodes will also work with a slightly lower efficiency. A suitable device would be a BYV28-50 or MUR310. Normal silicon rectifier diodes such as 1N4000 or 1N5400 series are far too slow to work effectively at 100kHz and should not be used.

The output smoothing capacitor C6 needs to be a type designed for switch-mode supply applications and having a low ESR to reduce the output ripple voltage and able to sustain high peak ripple current. An ESR of less than 0.25Ω is needed if the output ripple voltage is to be less than 100mV p-p. The peak charging current into C6 is approx. the same as the average input current and so a diode and smoothing capacitor capable of handling high peak current is required. A suitable type would be a Nichicon PJ series rated at 35V and having a value of at least 1000µF. The input capacitor C5 can also be a Nichicon PJ type or a normal electrolytic because the ripple current it experiences is not as severe as C6.

All the resistors except Rs can be quarter watt or half watt types. TR1 will require a small heatsink with an insulating washer and mounting bush to prevent the drain shorting to ground. Because of the high circulating currents the grounding of components around IC1 and the mosfet is critical. Although the frequency is only 100kHz the construction should use short leads and low inductance grounding similar to VHF construction techniques.

One or two points about boost converters need to be appreciated. The first is that the power to be converted has to come from the input supply. For a converter with an input voltage range of 9 to 16V the input current will be highest when the input voltage is 9V. With an efficiency of 90% the input power required is 1.1 x 24 = 26.4W and with a 9V supply this is an average current of 3A. When the input voltage is 16V the average input current is about 1.7A. If the input supply cannot deliver the required current the converter will not operate correctly. Many linear regulated power supplies, although capable of supplying the average current, are not able to supply the high input current pulses that a boost converter draws. Although the average input current is only 3A the peak current can be several times this figure for a short period when the mosfet turns on. If the linear supply runs into current limit the converter will hiccup and behave erratically. When testing a boost converter using a linear regulated bench supply as the input source, it is often necessary to connect a large electrolytic capacitor (10,000µF or more) across the bench supply output to help supply the pulsing peak current.

If the output ripple voltage needs to be less than 100mV, then rather than increasing the value of C6 it is better to insert an additional filter LC network in series with the output (**Fig 8.8**). This can be a small inductor also wound on 26 material (T50-26) as in **Fig 8.9**, and having a value of about 10 to 20% of the main switching inductor. This with an electrolytic capacitor of about 100µF will reduce the ripple voltage to about 10mV.

For applications requiring more output current the value of Rs can be reduced. If Rs is set to 0.1Ω the converter can supply up to 2A. The rectifier diode will

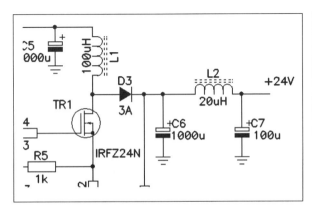

Fig 8.8: Additional output filter

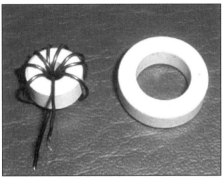

Fig 8.9: Output filter inductor (left) and T106-26 core (right)

Fig 8.10: Drain waveform of Boost Converter

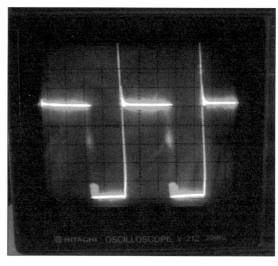

need to be a 5A device and the value of C6 will need to be larger; a value of 2 x 1000µF PJ types in parallel will suffice.

In **Fig 8.10** the Boost Converter is running at approximately 40% duty cycle and supplying about 35W output. The mosfet drain voltage swings between approximately 0.25V above ground up to 25V and the steep transient seen is when the drain current is switched off. This peaks at about +40V. This transient is clamped by the reservoir capacitor to less than 1V peak. The second stage L-C output filter reduces this to approximately 5mV peak.

Fig 8.11 shows the Boost Converter used in a supply for my TS-700 transceiver. The original Kenwood power supply used a crude DC-DC voltage doubler converter for the PA transistor supply. The original design supplied only 20V and it was renowned for causing spurious sidebands on transmit because it ran at approximately 600Hz. The PA transistors are 24V types and running below the 24V supply causes a loss in gain and linearity. I designed a replacement board using a 12V to 24V Boost Converter with extra filtering. The PA transistors now have a full 24V supply that improves the power output and linearity. The efficiency of the new PSU module is much higher; around 85% as opposed to not more than 50% for the original design. This allows cooler

Fig 8.11: Boost Converter used in a replacement PSU module for the writer's Kenwood TS-700G 2m transceiver

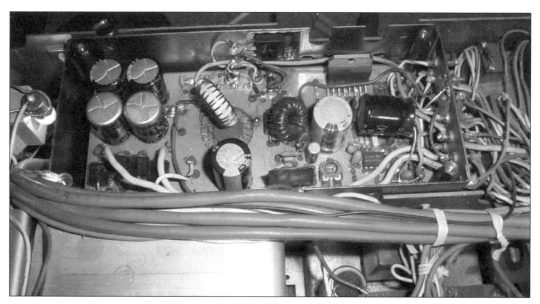

operation and more output current for the same DC input from the 12V supply. The mosfet used was a much larger type than necessary because one was to hand. The boost inductor is wound on a Micrometals T106-26 powdered iron core and the supply runs at about 110kHz. Second stage filtering reduces the output ripple voltage to less than 5mV p-p. This supply is filtered further in the PA module and the ripple at the PA transistor collectors is less than 1mV p-p.

Amongst the other modifications made was a better 9V stabilised supply and an additional 28V/150mA supply to power the 24V antenna relay. The 24V converter is now switched off during receive, saving power and eliminating spurious signals. A transformer and bridge rectifier supplies the main DC input for the PSU or it can be powered from a 12V vehicle supply for mobile or portable operation.

The Boost Converter follows an application note for the SGS-Ates L-296 integrated circuit. The 9V supply uses another SGS-Ates IC, the L-200 adjustable linear regulator that features low noise and ripple voltage. The low current 28V supply for the antenna relay uses a TBA-820M audio amplifier IC to form a voltage doubler from the raw 12V input. This is powered up during receive and switched off during transmit, because the same 28V supply powers the mast head preamplifier and it was prudent to switch off the main 24V boost converter on receive to prevent 'birdies'. An additional board that controls the power supply and the linear amplifier PTT lines performs transmit / receive sequencing.

Fly-back Converter Basics

The isolated Fly-Back converter is a natural extension of the Boost Converter and one of the most popular types in use today in the range of 20 to 200W. Above approximately 200W the core losses and switching transistor peak currents can start to become a problem so other types of isolated converter are a better choice. However, because of its simplicity and relative ease of design and construction it has many applications both for off line converters and DC-DC converters within this power range. One of its major claims to fame is that it can produce an output voltage that is either lower than the input voltage or higher than the input voltage (a capacitor discharge ignition system I designed for racing cars used a flyback converter to generate the +400V required at 100W output). It can also tolerate a fairly wide input voltage range and operate with reasonable efficiency, typically 75% or higher across this wide input voltage. Another unusual application, which is becoming very common, is to supply the high voltage required by High Intensity Discharge lamps now being used for automotive headlights.

Operating principle

The Fly-Back Converter operates on the same principle as the Boost Converter but uses an isolation transformer to separate the primary and secondary windings. Because of this it is very often used for off-line supplies where the input voltage can be as high as 400V and the output voltage can be anything desired, within reason.

Another major advantages it has is that it is easy to design a supply with multiple outputs, such as the PC supply mentioned earlier. All the secondary windings are wound on a common transformer core with individual rectifier diodes and smoothing capacitors for each output voltage. Typically a desktop PC power supply uses the fly-back converter to develop +5V, +12V & -12V from the rectified mains.

Now to the facts about fly-back converters. The fly-back converter uses a 'transformer' with a primary winding and one or more secondary windings depending on how many different output voltages you require. But although it looks like a transformer and even I sometimes refer to it as 'transformer' in actual fact it is not a transformer in the true sense. It is in fact a coupled inductor. It works in exactly the same way as the Kettering ignition coil used in a motor car, as is illustrated in **Fig 9.1**.

Kettering was one of the great American inventors of the 20th century; many people put him at a higher level than Thomas Alva Edison. Kettering was a graduate of Ohio State University and obtained a degree in engineering in 1903. Both Edison and Kettering had very similar approaches when developing a new idea; they did the bulk of the work themselves and the other team members served a minor role. By contrast Edison had no formal engineering training or a proper school education.

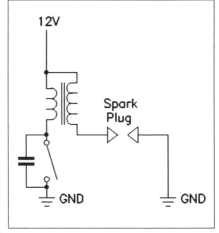

Fig 9.1: Kettering Ignition system using contact breaker points

However, back to the story. As you are probably aware the ignition coil in a car produces a very high voltage, typically around 20kV or more. The fly-back converter can also be used to produce similar voltages, in fact almost all television sets and computer monitors use a type of fly-back converter to produce the high voltage for the cathode ray tubes used in these items.

Charles Franklin Kettering

Charles Kettering, (born 28 August 1876 in Ohio), patented the automotive ignition coil and was very particular in his patent application (*US Patent 1,150,523*) to call it a "coil" and not a transformer, because it isn't a transformer at all.

Kettering was a prolific inventor. His first invention was when he was employed by the National Cash Register company (NCR), shortly after graduating, and he developed the first electrically driven cash register. Later he left NCR and formed Dayton Engineering Laboratories Company (DELCO) where he and his team first invented a gasoline powered portable electric power plant used on thousands of Midwest farms to generate electricity. But it was in the automotive world where Kettering work was most felt.

Kettering invented the electric starter, DC generator for charging the battery and the ignition system for cars between 1907 and 1911 and these were first fitted to the 1912 Cadillac, by that time owned by General Motors. Later Delco was bought by GM, and Kettering's long association with that company, in charge of new developments, continued to his death in November 1958. Some of his other inventions include safety glass, four-wheel servo-assisted brakes, automatic transmissions, alternators and spark plugs.

The new ignition system, because the spark could be fired at the correct time in relation to the crankshaft position and therefore the fuel was burned more efficiently, showed up a hitherto unnoticed defect in the combustion process because of the poor octane fuel then available. (In those days the **>**

The name 'Fly-Back' comes from what happens when you suddenly stop the flow of current in an inductor (see **Fig 9.2**). In the same way as the Boost converter works, the Fly-Back converter utilises the large voltage generated as 'Back EMF'. An

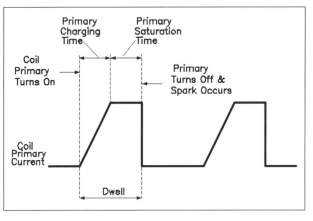

analogy can be drawn with a simple compression spring. The spring is compressed over a relatively long time period and when fully compressed can be released suddenly to use the energy it now contains. An air rifle or 'pellet-gun' uses this principle.

In the Fly-Back converter, when the primary switch is turned on the secondary voltage rises very rapidly to a negative voltage several times the normal positive secondary voltage. In a supply designed to give a 5V output the reverse secondary spike voltage can often exceed 20V. In a conventional supply using a mains transformer, the rectifier diode PIV required is usually twice that of the

compression ratio of the engine was only about 5:1). This was a pronounced 'knocking' sound when the engine was labouring. Today we know this as detonation or 'pinking' or 'pinging' to give it its common name.

During experiments to try to find a solution, one of Kettering's team injected iodine into a running engine to see if the dye would give a clue as to why the engine 'knocked' so badly. He was very surprised to find that the knocking was greatly reduced. Iodine being expensive and a toxic substance was not a suitable method of raising the octane but a substitute was soon found - tetra-ethyl lead. Kettering and his team where the inventors of modern leaded fuels which are still used today. Today the use of lead in fuels is not considered good environmentally.

Further inventions included the development of a diesel-powered locomotive and the invention of a compact air-conditioning system for cars. This required the use of a better refrigerant than ammonia which was used in domestic appliances and hence the birth of Freon, which today we now know causes ozone depletion. (So Kettering made at least two negative contributions to the environment).

Towards the end of his long career with GM Delco Kettering's team (he never actually retired as he was always involved with the day to day running of his laboratory and was affectionately knows as Boss Kett) invented synthetic aircraft fuel for the Allied Forces as the German war machine had cut-off supply routes and this invention took place before the American Forces direct involvement in WW2. At his death, Kettering had held over 130 patents world-wide and more than twenty honorary doctorates from various educational establishments.

output voltage, in a Fly-Back converter it is vastly different. This makes the choice of the PIV rating of the diode critical to prevent failure because the maximum secondary voltage is the sum of the output voltage plus the induced negative voltage. In the example quoted this would be at least 25V and when the additional spikes are considered we would need a 35V or 40V PIV diode for a 5V output to survive safely.

A second problem with the fly-back converter that has a large step-down ratio, typically an off line supply delivering 5V or so, is

Fig 9.3: Typical fly-back EHT transformer from a small TV or computer display, the primary is the left-hand side and the heavily insulated high voltage secondary is the right-hand side

when the secondary current switches off (because the switch has been turned on again). It acts just like the ignition coil primary and induces a large voltage in the transformer primary. (In this mode the secondary becomes the 'primary' and the primary becomes the 'secondary'.

In the ignition coil we have a primary, which connects to the 12V battery and the contact breaker points or electronic control module. The number of turns on the primary is usually around 100 ($N_p = 100$). The secondary has about 10,000 turns ($N_s = 10,000$) and this step-up produces the very high voltage.

$(V_o \approx V_{in} \times N_s/N_p)$

In the low output voltage off line fly-back converter the secondary will be only a few turns, typically around 2 to 4 turns for a 5V output, but the primary can have as many as 200 or more turns. So the back EMF will add to the voltage developed across the primary when the switch turns on again (from the secondary transferred through the flux to the primary) as the flux abruptly reverses again. In practice the switch voltage in the off line converter will jump up to at least twice the input voltage (800V or more) if steps are not taken to limit this voltage spike with a 'snubber' or clamp circuit. Failure to clamp the spike on the switch transistor will cause it to fail - dramatically! A loud bang and a blinding flash as the full weight of the mains is behind it produces lots of magic smoke.

Switching transistors intended for use in off line fly-back supplies normally need to be rated at least twice the input voltage because of this.

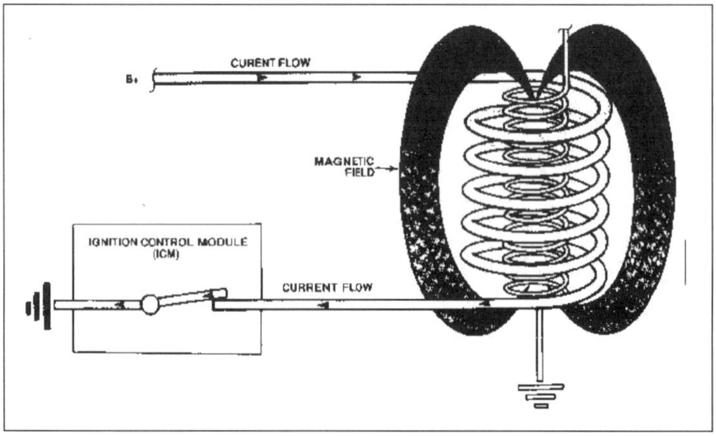

Fig 9.4: Construction of a typical ignition coil. Note the open magnetic path; the flux produced in the windings has no direct path other than through the air. The laminated soft iron core is not shown

CURENT FLOW

B+

MAGNETIC FIELD

IGNITION CONTROL MODULE (ICM)

CURRENT FLOW

Incidentally if you have one of those 'dinosaur' cars that still uses contact breaker points to switch the ignition coil and you have an oscilloscope, you can hook the 'scope to the points and measure the voltage across the points with the motor running.

What sort of voltage would you expect to see when the points open? If you said 12V you would be totally wrong! You will typically see anything up to a 300V spike, caused by the back EMF in the primary as the flux does its 'about turn'. The capacitor (known as a 'condenser' in the automotive industry - quaint name that) fitted across the contact breaker is there for two reasons. The first and most important reason is to provide a discharge path to ground for the high frequency primary oscillatory current, which flows when the points open and the spark occurs. The second reason is to slow down the rate of rise of the primary reverse voltage and so limit the spike voltage to safe proportions, this reduces the contact burning. Removing the condenser will reduce the high voltage output dramatically and cause the contact breaker to soon expire.

Even if you have a modern car that utilises a transistor in place of the points, (in which case there is no capacitor fitted) you will see similar voltages induced when the transistor switches off. The transistor used to switch the coil on and off needs to have a very high breakdown voltage of around 300V and usually a form of Zener clamp is incorporated within these special transistors - from collector to base - to limit the collector voltage to safe levels.

Principle of operation

The Fly-Back Converter (**Fig 9.5**) works by storing energy in the form of magnetic flux in the core. This is developed by current flowing in the primary winding, in exactly the same way as the Boost Converter and the ignition coil works. After the primary current has built up to a certain level the switch is turned off releasing the energy to the secondary. When this occurs, the primary current abruptly falls to zero and the flux reverses its polarity in the core. During the period when the switch is on, the secondary winding, (because of the phase of the windings) develops a large negative voltage which reverse biases or blocks the rectifier diode from conducting. It is the 'shuttling' of the flux backwards and forwards in the core that transfers the energy.

During the switch off time the secondary voltage also reverses and becomes positive and the rectifier diode now passes current to the capacitor and load. The secondary current (I_s) at the instant the switch turns off jumps up to a value which is

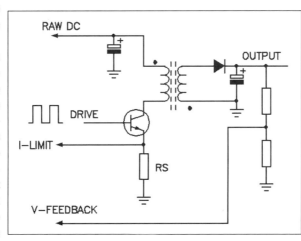

Fig 9.5: Basic Fly-Back converter circuit. Note the 'dot notation' on the transformer that indicates the phase of the windings. The dot normally indicates the start of the winding

determined by the value of the primary current (Ip) at switch-off and the ratio of the primary to secondary turns. If the primary has four times the turns of the secondary then the secondary current will start at 4 x I_p and then ramp downwards towards zero.

One important point, which needs to be understood about this type of converter, is that it is essential that the core must have an air-gap in the magnetic circuit. The cores for fly-back transformers (there I said it again) are normally made from a high permeability ferrite.

Ferrite is unable to store energy to any great extent without saturating. Air on the other hand can store lots of energy. In fact in a fly-back transformer 99.9% of the energy is stored in the air gap. Just as the ignition coil has an open magnetic circuit with a large air gap, so the fly-back transformer must have an air gap to operate safely.

Manufacturers of ferrite cores intended for fly-back transformers make a variety of gapped cores with a selection of different size gaps. A large gap will enable a large amount of energy to be stored. These gapped cores have a much lower inductance per turn than an ungapped core and so require more turns to achieve the required inductance. Gapping the core reduce the permeability and hence the A_L value.

The current and voltage waveforms occurring in a fly-back converter are shown for DCM and CCM operation in **Figs 9.6 and 9.7**.

Now we can look at some of the equations relating to the fly-back converter:

Energy Stored In the Primary:

$$E = 1/2 \times L_p \times I^2_p \times \eta \qquad \text{in joules} \qquad (1)$$

Where: L_p = inductance of the primary in Henries.

I^2_p = peak primary current in Amperes squared.

η = Efficiency of transformer coupling, usually very close to 100%

Note: This amount of energy is transferred on each switching cycle.

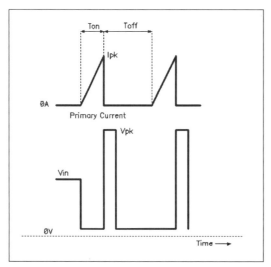

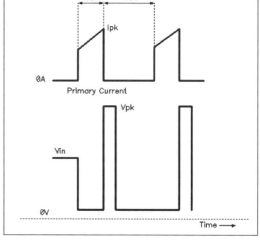

Fig 9.6: Primary current and voltage waveforms for discontinuous mode

Fig 9.7: Primary current and voltage waveforms for continuous mode

Power output

Note: Power is energy transferred in a unit of time. The factor f_s, the switching frequency (in Hz) converts the previous equation to power.

$$P_o = 1/2 \times L_p \times I_p^2 \times \eta \times f_s \qquad \text{in watts} \qquad (2)$$

Note: This amount of power is transferred continuously. To increase the power output we can either increase the inductance, the primary current or the switching frequency. The current is the most effective as we can see from equation 2 that it has a square law. Doubling the primary current will quadruple the output power.

Therefore by reducing the primary inductance by, say, 25% allows the primary current to increase by the same amount but the power output increases by 50%.

If the primary current were increased without reducing the inductance we would eventually run into a problem with the switching frequency. The time, T, for the current to rise in an inductor is dependent on the inductor value and its resistance:

$$T = L / R$$

The peak primary current in a Fly-Back Converter can reach unacceptably high values. The formula below clarifies this:

$$I_{PK} = (5.5 \times P_O) / V_{in(min)}$$

where: P_O = required output power - watts

$V_{in(min)}$ = minimum input voltage

Note: The above formula assumes 100% efficiency, we normally will end up with an efficiency of somewhere between 65 to 85%.

Let's take a couple of typical cases to illustrate the problem:

In an off line switcher the input voltage is the rectified mains. For a 230V supply the minimum AC input might be 200V, this gives a rectified DC voltage of around 280V, this is the figure for $V_{in(min)}$ to be used in the above formula.

Assuming 100W-output converter the peak primary current works out to be 1.96A. For a modern switching transistor this is not a problem.

Now take the case of the same output power but operating from a 12V-vehicle supply. The minimum battery voltage would be ≈10V and this gives a peak primary current of 55A. This is starting to become a problem. Whereas there are many suitable devices which can accommodate these sort of peak currents, the EMI aspects make it prudent to lower the peak currents to ease the EMI filtering aspects. Incidentally this peak current is supplied by the stored charge in the input reservoir capacitor, so this needs to be quite a large value and have a low ESR.

When using this general formula it is often found that the switching device current rating becomes a problem. This is especially the case for composite ICs made by several manufacturers where the switching transistor is incorporated in the IC. Here a different design approach needs to be made. In such a case the manufacturer normally states the safe peak device current in the data sheet.

Where the peak current is limited the only alternative is to either find a higher rated device (not often possible) or to increase the primary inductance.

I address this problem in the suite of programs shown in Appendix 2. A first attempt is made with the standard set of formulas and the peak primary current

Too high an inductor value means the current cannot rise high enough in the time available. This is exactly what happens with the Kettering ignition system at high engine speeds. The coil primary current cannot attain the full peak value in the time before the contact breaker points open. Consequently the power of the spark falls off at high RPM and the engine cannot produce the possible output power due to this.

This is one of the reasons the automotive industry has over the years discarded the contact breaker points system in favour of electronic ignition systems with a transistor replacing the points. With modern ignition control ICs, the primary current can be adjusted to better suit the operating conditions of the engine and reduce emissions caused by poor combustion. A lower primary current is selected for idling and low RPM use and an increase in the primary current is provided for acceleration and high RPM use. This prevents the coil from overheating during extended periods of idling in stop-go city driving, (where little cooling air is flowing under the bonnet of the vehicle), and it also provides an adequate spark for periods of high speed driving and acceleration.

is calculated. The user then has the option to either accept this or select a lower peak primary current and the program then recalculates the required primary inductance to achieve the same output power. This option needs to be used with caution for the reasons stated below. Too low a peak primary current or too high a primary inductance means that the converter will fall out of regulation at full load with minimum input voltage.

Another formula takes into account the duty cycle (D) and the input voltage.

Note: This formula only applies to Discontinuous Conduction Mode converters.

$$Po = \frac{V_{in}^2 \times D^2 \times \eta}{2 \times L_p \times f_s} \quad watts \qquad (3)$$

where:

V_{in} is the minimum input voltage

η is the efficiency, 1 = 100%

L_p is the primary inductance, in Henries

f_s is the switching frequency in Hz

D is the duty cycle, 1 = 100%

Duty Cycle (D) is defined as:

$$D = t_{on} / (t_{on} + t_{off}) \qquad (4)$$

and

$t_{on} = D / f_s$

where the time for one cycle $t_{on} + t_{off} = 1/ f_s$ \qquad (5)

The value for D must lie be between 0 and 1 (0 to 100%)

In equation 3 we can see that L_p has an inverse effect on the power output. To increase power output we need to reduce the value of L_p to allow a higher peak primary current to be reached and hence more power to be transferred.

Continuous & discontinuous conduction modes

Fly-Back Switch-mode converters, like the previous types already described, can operate in two different modes. These are known as Continuous Conduction Mode (CCM) and Discontinuous Conduction Mode (DCM). Each mode has certain advantages and disadvantages.

Voltage mode & current mode converters

A distinction is also made between two different types of operating conditions. These are Voltage Mode and Current Mode. In the Voltage Mode Converter the output voltage is regulated but no attempt is made to provide current limiting in the event of a short circuit being placed across the output. For low power switch-mode converters Voltage Mode is often acceptable. However, when the output power exceeds a few watts it is essential to provide a form of current limiting to protect the switching transistor, the transformer and output diode, especially if the input supply is able to source large amounts of energy - such as an automotive system driven from a lead-acid battery. In this case the Current Mode Converter is preferred.

Current mode monverter

In the current mode converter the peak output power, and hence how much short circuit output current can flow, is determined by the peak primary current during the switch on-time. By terminating the primary current when the maximum allowable primary current has been reached, the current limiting is very predictable and able to withstand a prolonged short-circuit across the output with little risk of damage to the converter. In practice a 'fudge-factor' of 1.25:1 is often used to ensure the converter can deliver full output power with minimum input voltage without the limiting causing the power to back-off.

Current mode converter in discontinuous conduction mode

By far the majority of Current Mode fly-back converters designed today operates in discontinuous mode. In DCM the current in the primary always starts ramping up from zero when the switch is turned on. After the current has risen to some maximum value, which is sensed by the control IC, the switch is turned off. During the time the switch is on the diode connected to the secondary winding is reverse biased and no current flows via this path. All the output current is supplied by the output reservoir capacitor during this period, whose output voltage decays to a lower level.

This variation in the output voltage is the output ripple. With a large value capacitor the voltage sag between the switch on and off states will be less, however the charging current when the switch turns off will be much higher due to this. The value of the output capacitor required in a fly-back converter operating in DCM needs to be made approximately two times larger than most other types of switch-mode converters. This is because the charging current is very much larger than other types and the ESR of the capacitor has a pronounced effect on the value of the output ripple voltage.

When the switch turns off, the primary current is abruptly terminated and it falls to zero very quickly. The flux in the core now reverses in polarity and so does the secondary winding induced voltage polarity, and so now the diode is forward biased. Current now flows into the reservoir capacitor and the load as the flux is discharged in the core. The output voltage across the reservoir capacitor ramps upwards until all the energy in the core is used up.

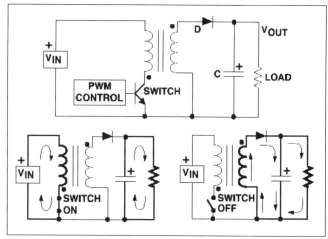

When this occurs, the secondary current

Fig 9.8: Basic Flyback Converter operation

will have dropped to zero and can no longer charge up the capacitor or supply any current to the load. The whole cycle then repeats. **Fig 9.8** illustrates this.

A low value resistor placed in the ground return of the switching transistor is usually used to sense the primary current. Other techniques used are a current transformer inserted between the primary and the transistor collector, this however only works whilst the transistor is switching and is useless for DC fault conditions. The resulting voltage developed is fed back to the control IC (I_{sense} input) and used to trip a comparator. When the current sense comparator is tripped the switch is turned off.

Discontinuous or Continuous Mode is easy to see by using a 'scope connected to the current sensing resistor connected between the switch transistor emitter, or mosfet source, and ground. The resistor has a voltage developed across it (due to the primary current flowing in it) that is an exact replica of the primary current flowing during the switch on-time.

The voltage sensed is filtered, to remove the switch-on transient spike, caused by the transformer inter-winding capacitance and diode reverse recovery time, and fed-back to the control IC I_{sense} pin. The I_{sense} voltage is used to terminate the switch on-time when the primary current has ramped up to a predetermined maximum. In some applications the voltage sensed is too great and in these cases a potential divider is used to lower the voltage to that required by the IC.

This is what makes the Current Mode controller IC such a good device. By setting the current limit point about 25% higher than the primary current required to achieve full output power at minimum input voltage the circuit has a very well defined current limit that can safely withstand prolonged shorts across the output. When a short is placed across the output the duty cycle backs off to virtually zero and the average input current falls dramatically. It is inherently a 'Fold-Back' type of current limiting. The Voltage Mode Converter type of controller use only output voltage sensing to terminate the switching period. These under a short circuit output operate in 'Constant Current' mode - delivering maximum

> Some people are confused by the terms Continuous and Discontinuous as each time the switch turns off the primary current falls to zero. When it is said that the primary current starts from a non-zero point we really mean something slightly different. At the instant of switch on, instead of the current rising in a ramp shape from zero to some maximum, we actually mean that as soon as the switch is turned on, the current rises immediately to some value and then ramps upwards to the maximum.
>
> Continuous & discontinuous refers to how the currents in the primary and secondary behave over a complete switching cycle.

rated output current into a short circuit which is stressful to the switch, transformer and output diode - which is not as satisfactory as the 'Fold-Back' mode.

Continuous Conduction Mode

Although the vast majority of Fly-Back converters built operate in DCM there are some which use CCM. The main reason is usually due to efficiency in very small supplies. The CCM Fly-Back converter has a theoretical advantage over the DCM version, but this really only holds for miniature switch-modes where the constraint is making the supply as compact as possible.

In contrast to the DCM type, the fly-back converter designed to operate in Continuous Conduction Mode (CCM) the primary current does not start from zero every time the switch is turned on. Because the CCM converter does not completely exhaust the magnetic flux in the core every cycle, the primary current starts from a point, which is above zero. The current then ramps up from this current until the trip point is reached and the switch is turned off.

The secondary current behaves in the same manner. When the diode conducts, the current decays to a value that is greater than zero and then the cycle is ter minated by the switch being activated again. The core always has some residual flux, which could be extracted. Your could consider this as a 'reserve tank'. This is why the CCM converter can theoretically supply more output power than a DCM converter with the same core size. However, this is not without certain penalties.

In order to achieve CCM the primary inductance needs to be much higher, meaning more turns and higher copper losses but with a lower primary peak current. However, the flux density is not so high that core saturation becomes a problem due to the gapped core, so the additional losses are actually quite small. The primary current does not reach anywhere near as high a peak current as a converter operating in DCM (theoretically it only reaches half the amplitude of a DCM converter with the same power level) and this eases the EMI effects of large currents being switched.

Of the two it would be virtually impossible to tell the difference by simply monitoring the input current with a meter. The two converters have almost iden tical average input currents, the DCM being slightly less efficient because of the higher peak currents, but the CCM has slightly higher copper losses. All in all the two factors practically cancel out and there is maybe a 1% advantage in efficiency by using CCM as against DCM, but you would be unable to say for sure without using a 'scope to look at the primary or secondary current waveforms.

When a converter set for CCM has its output current reduced towards zero, it will eventually cross over into DCM at a current that is very small. There is usually no penalty to be paid and although the efficiency drops markedly, because the circuit is now operating at a very low power level, no harmful effects are normally encountered. As long as the converter is running in CCM there is no direct dependence of the output voltage on the output loading. To a first order, the duty cycle will remain constant as the load is changed, and the initial value of the primary current will change instead.

Disadvantages of DCM

The Discontinuous Mode does have a few disadvantages. In order to make sure that the magnetic flux in the core is 'run-dry' after each complete cycle the value of the inductance in the primary has to be made a smaller value, this reduces the copper losses but means a higher peak primary current flows during the switch on-time. This increases the core losses and often dictates the use of the next size larger core. The inductance value needs to be small enough so that even with light loads and small duty cycle values, it remains in DCM. This is practically impossible to attain in practice and a converter set for DCM with moderate to large loads will eventually cross over into Continuous Mode as the output current is reduced towards zero. Often a 'dirty fix' used by designers is to place a small load resistor across the output terminals to ensure the DCM converter always draws a small current, sufficient to stop the CCM taking over. This reduces the overall efficiency as the current is wasted and does no useful work. (In a typical PC switch-mode supply this load is often the cooling fan contained within the power supply box and running off the +12V rail).

One other disadvantage of the DCM converter is that the diode and output capacitor handles higher peak currents than a CCM converter. The diode current RMS rating is the same as the output current. The capacitor in particular has a tougher time and the ESR of the capacitor needs to be acceptably low to prevent excessive heating and output ripple voltage.

Advantages of DCM

Notwithstanding the above, the choice is often made to opt for a DCM converter. This is because the Continuous Conduction Mode converter has one serious problem when the duty cycle is increased to greater than 50%. The control loop becomes very difficult to stabilise, as the CCM converter has an inherent destabilising element added to the control loop once it crosses from below 50% duty cycle to above. (Continuous Conduction Mode contains a right-hand-plane-zero in its open loop frequency response; the discontinuous mode does not). The CCM converter *can* be made stable in either of these regions but maintaining stability in both operating regions is more difficult and requires a lot more trouble to design the more complex compensation components needed, assuming the control IC has this capability. Even then, satisfactory operation in CCM is not guaranteed as factors such as input supply voltage, temperature of the core etc have a direct bearing on the loop stability criteria.

Many designers (myself included) prefer to take the safer option and suffer the slightly higher core losses running in DCM than risk the problems that CCM can bring. DCM converters can cross the 50% duty cycle boundary safely without any destabilising effects existing.

Critical inductance

To determine if a converter will run in CCM or DCM depends on the value of the primary inductance. This is known as the 'Critical Inductance' (L_{crit}). If the primary has a value above the critical inductance it will run in CCM and if below it will run in DCM, for all values of input voltage and load current, down to the minimum primary current used to calculate the critical inductance. At output currents less than the minimum the converter will cross over into the opposite mode, but as has already been stated this is of no great concern for the majority of cases. If you monitor the secondary voltage waveform or the primary voltage waveform with a 'scope the signal will appear to become 'sqirrely' with spurious spikes and ringing evident at low output currents but these don't normally cause a problem. Once the load is increased the waveforms clean up.

The critical inductance is given by:

$$L_{crit} = \frac{1}{\Delta I_p \times f_{sw} \left(1/V_{min} + 1/V_o \right)}$$

where:

ΔI_p = ripple current in primary (A)
f_{sw} = switching frequency (Hz)
V_{min} = minimum input voltage
V_o = output voltage

> ΔIp causes more than a bit of confusion, as witnessed by many application notes getting tied up in errors on this parameter. In the case of CCM the ripple current is the difference between the starting current and the final peak current. In the DCM case the same holds, but the ripple current is the total current from zero to I_{pk}, because the DCM primary current really does start from zero. Refer again to the current waveforms for each type to get this fact clear.

Design tip: When the critical inductance has been calculated it is prudent to add or subtract 25%, as appropriate, to the calculated value to ensure the mode is firmly fixed in either DCM or CCM.

The most crucial converter is one designed to run in CCM. It is prudent to not only increase the calculated L_{crit} by some 25% but to also lower the minimum output current by about the same amount. For example if the minimum output current expected was, say, 0.25A I would reduce this by approximately 25% to 0.2A to be certain that CCM would exist under all variations in temperature and input voltage variations. Switch-mode power supply design of Flyback converters is a bit of a 'black magic' science at times and you only gain these things after several years of experience!

Ratio of primary to secondary turns

Unlike a conventional transformer, the flyback transformer has no set turns ratio between the primary and secondary. The secondary can have more turns than the primary or fewer turns; it depends on the duty cycle chosen for minimum input voltage. From experience gained designing many Flyback converters I usually select between 40% to 50% as the maximum duty cycle when the input voltage is at the minimum value. (The Flyback converter can however operate at up to about 80% duty cycle without any problems in some circumstances). At maximum input voltage the duty cycle will drop to around 20%.

In automotive applications this allows safe operation under abnormal operation. For example a 12V system would normally be designed for an input voltage range of ≈10V to 16V. However, during engine cranking the battery voltage can momentarily fall to as low as 6V. If the duty cycle had been selected to be, say, 75% at 10V then during cranking the duty cycle would hit 100%, the control IC could lose control and the switching transistor or transformer primary winding would be over-stressed and consequently fail.

In aeronautical applications the aircraft battery voltage is often a nominal 24V. However, there is a particular test set down in at least one international standard that requires aircraft radio transceivers to operate at battery voltages well below the normal one. This is the 'Crash-Test' and requires the transmitter and receiver to work, albeit at reduced performance, with voltages as low as 16V. Consequently the power supply designer needs to ensure that with such abnormally low input voltages the supply can still work safely.

Multiple output flyback converters

One of the nice things about the Flyback converter is that is easy to make a supply which has several outputs with different voltages, even negative voltages. The design starts with the primary winding inductance and the main output winding turns ratio. Once this is determined the remaining secondary windings are treated like a conventional transformer (there I said it yet again) but in this case it really does behave like a real transformer! Each output needs a separate diode and reservoir capacitor.

Suppose we have designed the main output winding and it needs, say, three turns to deliver 5V after the Schottky rectifier diode with a nominal 0.5V drop. Therefore the 'volts per turn' is 5.5V / 3 = 1.83. If we needed a 10V winding and also used a Schottky diode for this we would need 5.72 turns. All the other windings can be calculated the same way once the 'volts/turn' parameter of the main output winding has been established. It is prudent to keep the volts/turn in the region of 1 to 4 for minimising copper losses in the secondary windings. A good compromise is often to settle on 2V/turn if no other factors have a great effect.

With too many turns on the secondary, the duty cycle will be lower as the secondary turns have been over compensated. In the suite of programs I wrote for this purpose you can simply run the program and, after a few parameters have been established, the program allows you to pick the secondary turns for the main winding. Having fixed this, the rest of the secondary windings can be calculated.

Note: Once the main secondary volts/turn has been determined you must stick with this or the other outputs will not give the desired voltages. The control IC must use the winding that has the highest output power to regulate from. All the other secondary windings will 'follow' this main winding. Therefore it is important that the main winding has a relatively constant load. The other outputs have fairly good 'cross-regulation' under these conditions.

The output voltages of the other secondary windings depends on the main winding load, if this load varies by a large amount the others will 'follow' by increasing in voltage as the main winding load increases and vice versa. This is known as 'cross-regulation'. If this is not acceptable then we can use a low-drop-out linear regulator after each secondary winding-diode-capacitor combination to maintain a very constant output on all outputs. In order to do this we need to increase each output to take into account the dropout voltage of the series regulator used. In a PC power supply the output that is usually chosen to regulate from is the +5V winding as this has the greatest load and a relatively constant current output.

Peak secondary voltage

Despite what you would expect, the total peak secondary voltage can be much higher than the output voltage required. This is because the output across the secondary swings both positive and negative. The positive excursion is simply the output voltage plus the diode forward voltage, the output capacitor clamps the output voltage as the capacitor charges up.

The negative voltage is the ratio of the secondary to primary turns multiplied by the input primary voltage. In a high voltage flyback converter that develops, say 400V; the total peak secondary voltage will be much higher than the output voltage.

Assuming the input voltage is around 12V the total peak secondary voltage, excluding transient spikes, can be as high as 1200V, which make the choice of the rectifier diode critical. I have seen many high voltage flyback supplies where the designer is obviously unaware of this fact. Connecting a 'scope across the secondary showed that the diode was severely over stressed, with diode failure a likely result. It is as well to calculate the required PIV of the diode and then add at least a further 50% to the peak voltage to take care of short transient spikes, which occur during the switching.

The formula to calculate the total secondary voltage is shown in **Fig 9.9**:

Positive peak = $V_{out} + V_f$ (V_f = diode forward voltage)

Negative peak = $N \times V_{in(max)}$

where N is the turns ratio of the primary/secondary

Total secondary voltage (across diode) = Positive peak + negative peak

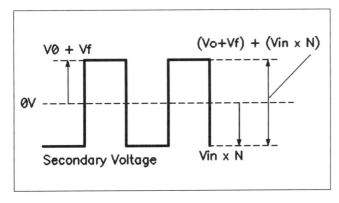

Fig 9.9: Secondary voltage excursions during the switching cycle

In a 400V flyback operating on 12V the secondary to primary turns ratio (N) will be of the order of 50. Therefore the minimum total secondary voltage which the diode has to cope with is (neglecting the diode forward voltage which is negligible in comparison):

$(400) + (50 \times 12) = 1000V$ minimum.

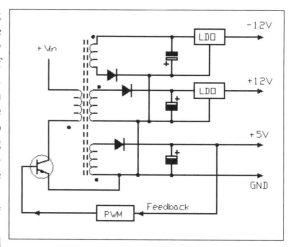

Fig 9.10: Multiple output flyback converter

A diode of 1kV would be over stressed due to the additional transient spikes commonly observed in these flyback switchers and therefore a prudent choice would be two 1kV diodes connected in series with voltage sharing resistors of about 560kΩ across each diode.

Note that damping capacitors are not required in parallel with the diodes and will lead to extra stress on the diodes if fitted.

In the suite of basic programs I wrote (see Appendix 2) the PIV of the diode is multiplied by a safety factor of 1.5 to account for spikes and other transients which can over stress the diode. A typical computer multiple output Flyback converter is illustrated in **Fig 9.10**.

The control IC regulates the +5V rail, as this is the winding with the greatest output power, and the remainder of the outputs use post regulation using Low-Drop-Out regulators. The secondaries for the two 12V supplies would be designed to give about 15V at nominal load current on the +5V rail. The efficiency of the supply suffers somewhat by using linear post-regulators, but the plus and minus 12V supplies are normally only about 1A so the final efficiency figure is still acceptable.

Worked example: Single output flyback converter

To illustrate some of the points, I will now detail the design steps for a single output Flyback Converter. I will use my Basic program (Flyback.bas) which is included in Appendix 2 to simplify the calculations as some of the steps are iterative and need several passes to get a working design. Later we will add a second output winding to illustrate the process used.

Let us start by specifying our requirements. I needed a DC-DC converter to power a 24V VHF transceiver from a nominal 12V vehicle supply. The maximum current drain was 2A. Therefore we can specify the input and output voltages and powers needed.

The 12V vehicle battery has upper and lower limits of 15V and 10V worst case and the output power is 48W. Assuming an efficiency of 75% gives an input power of 64W maximum. We also need to specify the output rectifier forward voltage, we will choose a Schottky diode for preference and this will have a forward voltage of $\approx 0.5V$. We also need to choose the switching frequency. I will choose 100kHz as I will be using a mosfet and a modern Current Mode IC - UC3843 - which works well at this frequency. The under-voltage lockout voltage of the UC3843 is around 8.4V so it will work down to below the 10V minimum voltage expected. (During engine cranking if the battery voltage drops below 8.4V the converter will be inhibited, so guaranteeing safety). I will choose a maximum duty cycle of 45% to start with because I may need later to change between DCM to CCM for stability reasons.

Plugging these into the program yields:

$I_{in\,(max)}$ = 6.4A (from the 64W at minimum supply voltage of 10V)

At the 10V input voltage the Duty Cycle is allowed to increase to 45% maximum. At higher input voltages the duty cycle will be lower, during engine cranking it will increase to more than 50% but the duty cycle has plenty of leeway to cater for this condition and the UVLO circuit will curtail operation if the input voltage drops below 8.4V.

The formula to calculate the primary peak current is:

$$I_{PK} = 2 \times \frac{I_{in\,(max)}}{D} \qquad \text{Where D = duty cycle, in this case 0.45}$$

Hence I_{PK} = 2 x 6.4 / 0.45 = 28.44A

or $I_{PK} \approx (5.5 \times PO) / V_{in(min)}$ gives an value of 26.4A, which agrees closely with the above.

The formula to calculate the RMS current in the switch is:

$$I_{rms} = I_{PK} \times \sqrt{D/3} \qquad \text{Since the waveform is a quasi triangular shape.}$$

Hence I_{rms} = 28.44 x $\sqrt{0.45/3}$ = 11A

The peak switch current is determined as $\approx 28.5A$ and the RMS switch current is determined as 11A. This now gives a figure to choose a suitable mosfet. I will choose the IRFZ44N (TO-220 package) as it is a low cost device and adequate for this application. The on-resistance of the IRFZ44N is about 22mΩ maximum which will yield a low dissipation and minimal heatsinking required.

The IRFZ44N is rated at 49A continuous drain current and 160A peak drain current with a drain voltage of 55V maximum, which is more than twice the maximum input voltage, so neither the peak current or supply voltage is going to trouble it. Also, the device will be very unstressed in this application and we do not need to include primary snubber networks, which degrade the efficiency.

The formula to calculate the required primary inductance is:

$$L_P = \frac{V_i^2}{2 \times P_o \times f} \times \eta$$

Where V_i is the 'effective voltage' across the primary, taking into account the on-resistance of the device and the voltage drop across the current sense resistor.

Note: The effective on-resistance of the device will be somewhat higher if we are intending to use a current mode control IC as we need to include the current sensing resistor in series with the ground of the switching device. This needs to be calculated to suit the control IC being used. The particular current mode control IC chosen is the UC3843, which has a current sense threshold of 1V. Hence the current sensing resistor needs to develop 1V when the primary current reaches I_{PK}.

$R = V / I$ gives: $1 / 25.6 = 0.039\Omega$. This needs to be input to the program when prompted as well as switch on-resistance of 0.022Ω, giving a total of 0.061Ω. For voltage mode control the switch on-resistance is simply the $R_{DS(ON)}$ of the chosen device.

From this we can calculate the effective primary voltage, V_i, when the input voltage is at minimum, 10V in this case.

$V_i = V_{IN(min)} - (R_{DSON} \times I_{rms})$

$R_{DSON} = 0.022 + 0.039 = 0.061$.

$10 - (0.069 \times 11) = 9.24V$

From this we can determine that the minimum primary inductance required is 7.1µH.

Next we need to specify the core A_L value. I will select a core with a value of $250nH/t^2$. (This represents a good choice as the gapped cores commonly available are often around this value).

To calculate the number of turns, N_P, we use the formula:

$N_P = \sqrt{L_P / A_L}$

where L_P is in µH and A_L is in µH

From this we calculate the minimum number of turns required for the primary. This yields a figure of 5.33 turns. As the core bobbin chosen can have either half turns or full turns I will increase this to 5.5 turns, as the inductance calculated is the minimum value required.

With 5.5 turns the primary inductance is calculated to be 7.56µH, which is more than the minimum required. ($L = N^2 \times A_L$).

Next the program uses the diode forward voltage added to the secondary voltage required to arrive at the number of secondary turns required. The formula for secondary turns is:

$N_S = N_P \times (V_O + V_D) \times (1 - D) / (V_{MIN} \times D)$

where: Np = number of primary turns
N_S = number of secondary turns
V_O = output voltage required
V_D = diode forward voltage
V_{MIN} = minimum supply input voltage.
D = maximum duty cycle

This gives a figure of 16.46 turns. I will again choose a half number of turns and select 16.5 turns.

Note: It is important not to increase the secondary turns much above the calculated value. A secondary winding with too high an inductance will not allow all the core energy to be discharged on every cycle.

With 16.5 turns the secondary inductance is 68µH. ($L = N^2 \times A_L$).

The turns ratio is therefore: $16.5 / 5.5 = 3$

The volts/turn constant is now established as 1.48V per turn, which is within the 1V to 4V/turn guideline.

The program next calculates the secondary peak voltage under low input and maximum input voltage conditions. This gives an estimate of the diode PIV required.

Note that the required secondary positive peak voltage for an application is the required output voltage plus the diode forward voltage drop. However, during the switch-on time the secondary voltage swings negative and is considerably more than this, and this voltage needs to be added to the nominal secondary voltage to find the PIV required for the diode. A conservative estimate of the required diode PIV is three times the output voltage calculated at minimum duty cycle (maximum input voltage).

Secondary peak voltage = $(V_O + V_D) + (N \times V_{in})$

where N = secondary to primary turns ratio

Therefore $V_{spk} = (24 + 0.5) + (3 \times 10) = 54.5V$ at low input voltage

High line input voltage yields a higher secondary peak voltage of:

$V_{PK} = (24 + 0.5) + (3 \times 15) \approx 70V$

The high line condition gives a figure of 70V. Adding a safety factor of 50% to the calculated value to cater for spikes gives a voltage of 105V PIV rating. This is too high for a Schottky diode where 100V diodes are about the maximum available and an Ultra-Fast diode would be an alternative, although the forward voltage will be higher - approximately 0.8V, hence the overall power dissipation in the diode and the overall converter efficiency will suffer somewhat. However, we will leave it like that for now. I would expect the efficiency to be higher than the 75% estimated.

A word of caution on diode PIV ratings

Amateurs are mostly familiar with the term 'peak-inverse-voltage' but few actually understand what the manufacturer is trying to warn you about. If you study the data sheet for a particular diode you will get the manufacturers test figure. Taking a common diode, such as a BYV96E rated at 1.5A, the specified repetitive inverse voltage is quoted as 1000V minimum. However, you need to look at the test parameters to see what this really means. Many amateurs believe that if you exceed the PIV rating by only a little bit the diode will fail - with magic smoke! Although exceeding the PIV by a large amount is definitely not recommended, small amounts of excessive PIV are not generally disastrous. Diodes more often fail because of excessive current, and hence high junction temperature, than inverse voltage.

The PIV test is performed with a sample of diodes from each production batch, possibly 10 in every 1000 diodes. These are randomly selected from a large lot. The diodes are subjected to varying reverse voltages and the leakage current measured with the diode at the maximum junction temperature, normally >150°C. The diode must pass the specified leakage current test with the nominal PIV applied under these conditions.

For the BYV96E the rated PIV is 1kV and the maximum leakage current specification is 1µA at 25°C and 150µA at 165°C. Asecond test is the avalanche voltage where 1.1 times the nominal PIV is applied and the reverse current must be less than 100µA at 25°C. From tests I have performed on similar diodes they can very often accept up to two times the specified PIV before the leakage current becomes excessive, greater than 10 times the specified figure.

All the manufacturer is interested in is that when the diode is used in a product where the inverse voltage is not more than the specified voltage the leakage current will be negligible. By batch testing it is able to confirm that the manufacturing process is stable and a reliable product is being made. Manufacturers are usually very conservative when it comes specifying semiconductors and the PIV should be taken as a guide. Brief overvoltage conditions of up to 30% are not normally disastrous as the device has so much leeway in the design, which is repeatedly tested.

Fig 9.11 shows the typical performance of the BYV96E at various junction temperatures.

I use the BYV96E in my CDI system manufactured for racing cars. In all the testing and

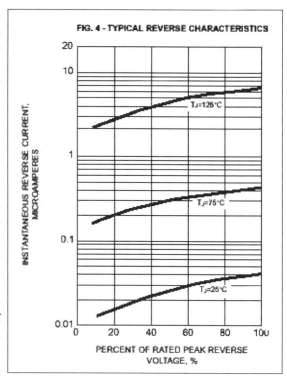

Fig 9.11: **Voltage rating of the BYV96E** [From General Semiconductors data sheet]

many hundreds of hours of use at elevated temperatures and very high RPM, I have not suffered a single diode failure.

The power dissipation in the switching transistor and diode are also calculated. The switch dissipation is the product of the average input current at low input and the on resistance of the transistor. The diode dissipation is the product of forward voltage times the output current.

It is important to appreciate the tradeoffs in the Flyback Converter design. Because of the high peak secondary voltages that can occur when the duty cycle is low, which happens at high input voltages, it is prudent to increase the duty cycle for the low input voltage case. It should also be borne in mind that abnormally low input voltages can occur in some systems, such as automotive applications during engine cranking, which makes choosing a maximum duty cycle something of a 'best guess' at times.

In high voltage supplies, such as a CDI supply delivering ≈400V, it is often necessary to use two or more ultra-fast rectifiers connected in series, with voltage sharing resistors of approximately 560kΩ across each diode, to achieve a high enough PIV rating for the diode stack. In the CDI supply I designed I used 2 x BYV96E diodes rated at 1000V because the total peak secondary voltage was measured to be in the region of 1400V. If only one diode had been used it would be likely to fail.

The switch dissipates 0.9W and the diode dissipates 1W, so little heatsinking is required for either.

The duty cycle at maximum input voltage is also calculated using the formula:

$$D = (V_O + V_D) / V_{PK}$$

This gives a figure of $(24 + 0.5) / 70 = 0.35$ [35%]

Finally the input current for the high line input (15V) case is calculated and this gives a figure of 4.3A.

Several passes would normally be needed to try various alternatives, such as different mosfets, diodes and core types. However for now we have a design which although not optimum is workable. With the program you can run through a complete design in less than five minutes to get a design you can breadboard to try out. In practice, the efficiency will be around 80% for most cases so we have been a little pessimistic with our assumption of only 75%. Only when our first prototype is constructed can we measure the actual efficiency and determine if any problems exist with any of the components.

Adding additional outputs

To add extra secondary windings is now simple, as the secondary volts/turn has been established. Suppose we also needed an output of 9V at 500mA. We can choose a 1A Ultra-Fast diode here as the current is quite low. This will have a forward voltage of around 0.7V, giving a required secondary voltage of 9.7V.

New secondary = 9.7 / 1.48 = 6.55 turns, so 6.5 turns should be acceptable. The diode PIV required is 42V minimum.

> The program allows as many additional output secondaries as you need. You need to bear in mind however that the original total power was all assumed to be supplied from one secondary. If the additional secondaries add more than 25% to the total this needs to be factored in at the start.

Selection of a suitable core

Selecting a suitable core is usually a matter of personal preference or the available height in the mechanics. For small production runs I prefer to use RM or ETD cores. These have a separate bobbin, which makes winding simple, and can either be obtained with several pins arranged in a circle for the RM cores or somewhat like a DIL configuration. The DIL type is known as 'Power-Pin' by Siemens, and allows either half turns or full turns. Remember that we need a gapped core.

Selection of the ferrite material requires the perusal of a manufacturers data book, I will use the Siemens data. My personal favourite is the N41 material as it is quite forgiving if small errors are made in the winding inductance and operates efficiently from 25 to 150kHz. The RM cores range from the smallest RM-4 up to RM-14.

The RM series of gapped cores offer AL values from 160nH/t up to 1000nH/t. Not all of these are available in every core size and material.

For a throughput power of 48W, which we calculated earlier, the RM-10 will provide plenty of leeway for a DCM flyback converter. In fact the RM-10 can easily handle up to 75W in a flyback converter at 100kHz. The RM-10 'Power Pin' bobbin has 12 pins, 6 on each side.

From the data provided we can ascertain the winding length per turn. The RM-10 bobbin has a nominal winding length of 42mm per turn. So our primary winding of 5.5 turns requires about 5.5 x 42mm, plus another 20mm or so for terminating onto the bobbin pins. This is a total of around 250mm.

The secondary requires 16.5 turns at 42mm per turn, plus the terminating length of approximately 20mm giving a total length of 715mm of wire.

Winding technique

For a low voltage transformer like this, because we have no lethal voltages to worry about, it makes little difference if we wind the primary first or second. My personal preference - whilst de bugging the initial version - is to wind the secondary onto the bobbin first and primary last. This makes it simple to change the number of primary turns without stripping the transformer down to the bare bobbin.

Before we can wind the first-off transformer we need to ascertain the gauge of wire to use.

Primary winding

The calculated primary peak current of ≈29A means we have to use a substantial wire gauge to keep copper losses within reason. However, a heavy gauge wire is a problem on small bobbins. It is particular difficult to handle and get a neat looking winding and without over-stressing the termination pins.

An alternative solution is to use several smaller gauge wires paralleled to get the required copper area and a low enough resistance. One advantage of this technique is that it is simpler to fill the winding width of the bobbin. It is important to use as much of the bobbin winding width as possible to ensure adequate flux coupling between the windings and the magnetic circuit.

Using the data on the RM-10 bobbin we can see that the bobbin width is approximately 12mm. We need to aim for a 'fill-ratio' of at least 80% so this allows a winding width of around 10mm minimum.

The type of wire we need for this sort of transformer has to be able to withstand fairly high temperatures. Ordinary enamelled copper wire is often not suitable due to the high operating temperatures, so special high temperature wires have been developed for these applications. The industrial name for these winding wires is 'Magnet Wire' and is available in many different types and insulating coatings.

Do not use self-fluxing types as these may melt under high temperature and cause shorted turns.

Magnet wires have a high temperature polyurethane varnish that needs to be scraped off with a sharp blade before they can be tinned.

One thing to remember is that the copper within the enamelled wire is a bit smaller in diameter than the OD of the wire due to the thick coating of the enamel used (because of the high breakdown voltages often required) and an allowance needs to be made for this factor.

The cross-sectional area of magnet wires is often expressed in either circular mils (American standard, where 1 mil =0.001 inch) or in mm^2 (European standard).

Circular mils per Amp (CMA) is a convenient way of specifying winding current capacity. CMA is the inverse of current density and is simply the ratio of cross-sectional area in circular mils to the RMS value of the primary current. In practice, a value of 200 to 500CMA is a good working point.

$$CMA = \frac{CM}{I_{rms}}$$

Before we can select a suitable wire gauge we also need to be aware of one other constraint, this is the 'skin effect'. As the operating frequency increases the majority of the current flowing does so on the outer portion of the copper and little flows within the centre core of the wire. This imposes a limitation on the maximum wire diameter that can be used.

At 100kHz the largest wire diameter acceptable is around 26AWG or 27SWG. Therefore we need a wire gauge with a smaller diameter than this. The bobbin winding width needs to accommodate multiple strands of wire laid side-by-side similar to a ribbon cable and wound onto the bobbin for the necessary number of turns.

For simplicity we will choose a wire gauge one size smaller - 28SWG which has a nominal diameter over the insulating enamel of 0.32mm. Therefore three wires in parallel will occupy approximately 1mm of bobbin width. A single strand of 28SWG wire can safely handle peak currents of $\approx$5A at 100kHz. Therefore we shall need to use a minimum of six parallel strands to cope with the 29A-peak current calculated. This gives a minimum winding width of 6 x 0.32 x 5.5t $\approx$ 10.5mm which is less than the width of 12mm and so we can make the primary a single layer.

Note that the wires should be laid in parallel like a ribbon cable and not twisted together.

The individual wires can be terminated onto the 'Power-Pin' bobbin with two or three wires on each pin. The pins will be connected to thick PCB tracks to form a common connection point.

Insulating tape should be applied over the individual windings to prevent possible shorting between windings. Special yellow polyester tape is made by the 3M™ company that is particularly good for this, however it is not readily available in small quantities. I have also used Magic-Tape™ and masking tape with good results. Normal Sellotape™. is not recommended. The coating on this special yellow tape acts like heat-shrink sleeving when heated up and so the temptation to wind it on too tight should be resisted or you will end up with a cracked bobbin. When the transformer is first operated the temperature causes the tape to shrink and tighten on the windings.

The outer of the bobbin is normally taped with a special glass-fibre adhesive tape to provide protection to the overall windings, several turns of masking tape cut to the bobbin width works just as well for prototype transformers.

Secondary winding

The secondary winding in this example is much simpler as the current levels are much lower. The peak secondary current is given by:

$$I_s = I_{PK} \times \frac{N_P}{N_S} = 29 \times \frac{5.5}{16.5} = 9.6A$$

This gives a peak secondary current which two strands of 28SWG wire can safely handle. Incidentally the 9.6A is the same peak current the rectifier diode has to pass and it therefore needs to be adequately rated.

Again we shall lay the two wires in parallel and wind on the required number of turns - 16.5. This gives an estimated winding width of 2 x 0.32 x 16.5 ≈11mm which can also be accommodated on the bobbin in a single layer.

Alternative winding techniques

When high peak currents are encountered, an alternative to using multiple stranded wire is to use copper tape of a substantial width, typically 2mm or more. If only a few turns are required then this can be made almost the entire width of the bobbin. This can be easily cut from a thin sheet of copper shim and then covered with high temperature electrical insulating tape. The ends are connected with a flexible high temperature insulated wire and brought out to the outside of the bobbin for termination. Another method uses copper braid or the sheath from coaxial cable that is stripped and rolled flat to make a high current conductor. When copper braid or sheath is used it is often covered with heatshrink sleeving, which is shrunk on. A word of caution, don't use solder-wick as this contains a flux which will exude under high temperature and cause corrosion.

Both of these alternative-winding methods are found where very high currents are needed. The copper shim and the copper woven sheath are particularly good at the high frequencies encountered in switch-mode transformers. The copper losses are some 10 to 20% lower than multi-parallel wire methods. For high current low voltage secondary windings, as often used for 5V main frame computer supplies, the copper tape is the preferred method.

Industry uses a more expensive type of winding wire that is not often available in the small quantities needed by the home constructor. This is known as Litz Wire and consists of many hundreds of individually insulated wires woven into a 'rope'. The advantages of Litz Wire is the excellent skin effect performance when the higher switching frequencies are used. Personally I have never had the opportunity to use Litz Wire in any of my designs.

Fig 9.12: RM-12 high voltage flyback transformer used in the author's Capacitive Discharge Ignition unit for racing automobiles. The board is made to accept an alternative transformer wound on an ETD-39 core for applications requiring higher output power

Fig 9.13: The size of the spark that the author's CDI unit develops, the spark gap is 12mm. The estimated peak voltage is around 60kV using a low inductance ignition coil. The simulated engine speed shown is approx. 12,000RPM for a four-cylinder engine. At full output the converter is transferring 150W

UC3843 in a current mode flyback converter

One of my particular favourite ICs for Flyback and Boost Converters is the UC3843. Originally designed by Unitrode Corporation (hence the UC prefix) it is now made by many semiconductor manufacturers. The UC3843 is one of four versions in a particular series.

The UC3842, which is virtually the same device, is intended for off-line switchers and has an under-voltage-lockout (UVL) set to approximately 16V which makes it unsuitable for 12V applications. The UC3843 has a lower UVL limit of approximately 8.4V that makes it usable on 12V vehicle supplies. (The premium grade devices are UC284x and feature tighter specifications for some parameters such as the reference voltage, but are not as easy to obtain in small quantities for the home constructor).

The UC384x series are available in either surface mount or conventional DIL configuration and have several temperature ranges. The premium device is guaranteed operable over the automotive temperature range of -40°C to +105°C. The SMD versions are available in either 8-pin or 14-pin packages. For home construction the DIL versions are the obvious choice for ease of bread-boarding and PCB layout.

The various package options and block diagram of the UC384x series is shown below. This information is for the Motorola version of the IC. Motorola sold the manufacturing rights to On-Semi around 2000, so you are more likely to find up to date information on their website (http://www.onsemi.com/home). Other manufacturers will utilise slightly different part numbering, eg Fairchild use the KA prefix for their version. Note in **Fig 9.14** that the premium temperature range devices are capable

ORDERING INFORMATION

Device	Operating Temperature Range	Package
UC384XBD		SO–14
UC384XBD1	$T_A = 0°$ to $+70°C$	SO–8
UC384XBN		Plastic
UC284XBD		SO–14
UC284XBD1	$T_A = -25°$ to $+85°C$	SO–8
UC284XBN		Plastic
UC384XBVD		SO–14
UC384XBVD1	$T_A = -40°$ to $+105°C$	SO–8
UC384XBVN		Plastic

X indicates either a 2 or 3 to define specific device part numbers.

Fig 9.14: UC384X device data

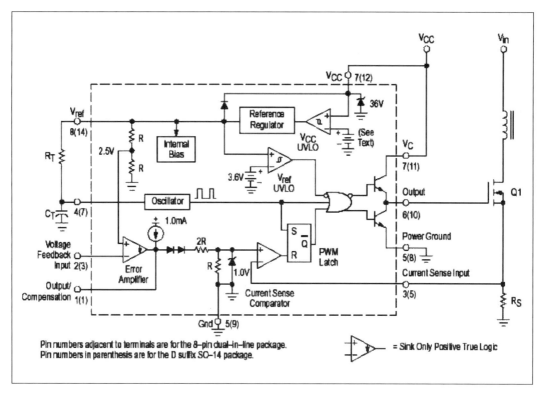

Pin numbers adjacent to terminals are for the 8-pin dual-in-line package.
Pin numbers in parenthesis are for the D suffix SO-14 package.

= Sink Only Positive True Logic

Fig 9.15: Block diagram of the UC384X series ICs. *Note:* **The transformer secondary winding, output rectifier and capacitor are not shown in the diagram. By the addition of an output diode from the inductor to a reservoir capacitor this could become a Boost Converter**

of operating at the new extended automotive temperature specification of -40°C to +105°C to suit the wide range found in 'under-the-hood' applications of North American automobiles.

The UC384x series (**Fig 9.15**) is designed to drive N channel mosfets directly and can operate at up to 500kHz.

The high current totem-pole output stage can drive high gate capacity mosfets and achieve rise and fall times of approximately 30ns with a gate current drive potential of more than 1A.

The oscillator frequency is set by two external components R_T and C_T and the IC can be synchronised to an external oscillator source if needed. The totempole output transistors are supplied directly from the V_{CC} pin in the 8-pin package and separately in the 14-pin package. If using the 8-pin package it is important not to exceed the maximum gate voltage of the external mosfet, in most cases the maximum gate voltage is approximately 15V and so a 12V supply is adequate.

The 14-pin package gives more freedom in choosing a supply voltage, which can be anywhere from above the UVL limit to a maximum of 30V. The IC contains a 36V Zener to clamp the supply should transients be present. Because of the 36V Zener, whose value is nominal and can be as low as 30V, it is prudent not to exceed about 28V as the supply voltage and to use a small series resistor to limit the IC current.

Note that a substantial electrolytic capacitor needs to be connected across the gate supply pin, as the peak gate current is to be supplied by this reservoir capacitor. A 47µF works well in most applications.

Setting the oscillator frequency

Capacitor C_T is charged via R_T from the 5V-reference supply to about 2.8V andthen discharged to 1.2V by an internal current sink. During the discharge of C_T the oscillator generates an internal blanking pulse that holds the centre input of the NOR gate high. This causes the output to be in a low state, thus producing a controlled amount of output dead time.

The oscillator frequency is set by the combination of R_T and C_T. However, whereas many different values of these two components can give the correct frequency, only one will give the correct period for the 'dead time'. For those applications, which are limited in maximum duty cycle due to the magnetics, this forms a good way of limiting the duty cycle to a safe percentage.

The graphs in **Figs 9.16 and 9.17** give the values for suitable values for the two components.

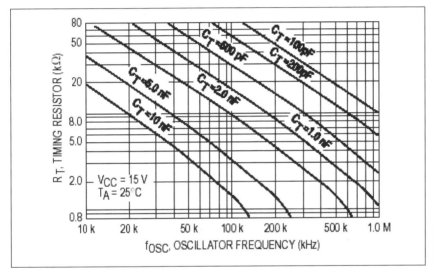

Fig 9.16: Oscillator frequency determining components

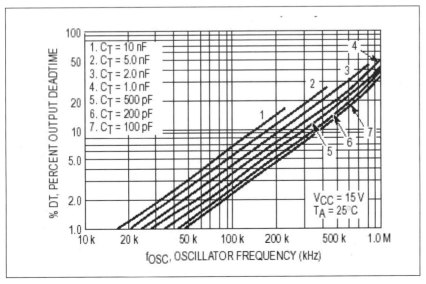

Fig 9.17: Graph to determine the oscillator dead-time

Synchronising to an external clock source

A circuit to synchronise the IC to an external oscillator is shown in Fig 9.18. In most applications this is not required and the converter can 'free run', but in power supplies operating inside a sensitive radio receiver the synchronising of the switching can help to prevent harmonics of the switching frequency from causing 'dead-channels'.

The external clock is usually derived from a high frequency crystal oscillator that often is the main system μProcessor clock. The clock is then divided down in a binary divider IC (a 74HC4024 works well) and used to drive the UC384x IC. This prevents the switching frequency from drifting with temperature and causing 'birdies' in the RF system.

A common choice of μProcessor clock is 6MHz and this when divided by 64 gives a switching frequency of 93.75kHz which is close enough to 100kHz not to cause a problem with the design.

Generally when trying to avoid 'dead-channels' in a radio receiver it is prudent to steer clear of exact multiples of 100kHz etc. The 93.75kHz will have harmonics at 187.5, 281.25, 375, 468.75kHz etc. The last one may be a problem if you are using a 470kHz IF, but far enough from 455kHz not to cause a problem. In any case some serious filtering will be needed between the PWM supply and the rest of the sensitive circuitry to ensure correct operation.

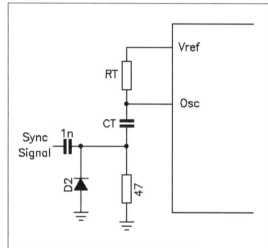

Fig 9.18: Synchronising to an external clock source

The frequency setting components R_T & C_T need to be selected to set the free running frequency to approximately 90% of the external oscillator. (In the above example using 93.75kHz clock the switching frequency would be set to approx. 85kHz using R_T and C_T). When the external clock is present the internal oscillator will be 'frequency locked' to the higher frequency and the switching frequency will increase to that of the external clock.

From my experience of using the UC384x series it is important to have sufficient amplitude from the external clock to give reliable locking. The low value resistor in the ground of the frequency setting components needs a low impedance drive source and needs to develop about 500mV across the 47Ω resistor to work correctly.

Paralleling several inverter gates usually provides sufficient drive. Too much external clock amplitude can also cause erratic locking - in this case the series capacitor can be reduced in value. The external clock is usually powered by one of the switching converter outputs and will therefore not be present at startup.

Power-up soft-start

Many ICs for PWM supplies feature a 'soft-start' facility where the supply output voltage under load comes up gradually to prevent over-shooting when the supply is first turned on. The UC384x series has a very good softstart feature that also operates when a short circuit (causing the output to drop to zero) is removed.

The Compensation pin is provided for the user to use as either soft-start or additional loop compensation. The soft-start circuit requires very few components and it is always a good idea to incorporate it in any PWM supply. The external components are shown here:

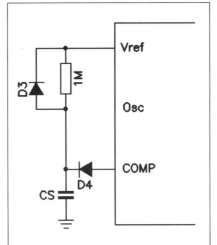

Fig 9.19: Soft-start circuit components. *Note:* The capacitor CS should be a low leakage type such as a polyester or tantalum

The capacitor connected to ground from the junction of the two silicon diodes (1N4148) is charged by the resistor from the VREF pin. The reference voltage is a very stable 5V and the time constant of the RC network should be chosen to allow the capacitor to charge up to two-thirds of the reference voltage in a time equivalent to approximately 1000 clock cycles. The diode in parallel with the 1MΩ resistor ensures the soft-start capacitor is discharged when the supply is turned off.

Problems when driving mosfets

In common with many control ICs the UC384x series needs a bit of help if the gate capacitance is high. Although it can source and sink over 1A of gate current the rapid changes in gate current brings about a problem with the Miller effect of large mosfets. This causes excessive ringing due to the parasitic inductance within the device leads.

To overcome this problem we need to slow down the gate current transients. Otherwise the Miller effect causes high transient voltages and currents to flow within the internal capacitance of the mosfet and this can be detrimental to the transistor.

It is necessary to limit the gate transient currents by inserting a low value resistor in series with the gate to slow down the rise and fall times. This resistor usually lies in the region of 10Ω. to 47Ω. This is shown in **Fig 9.20**. The resistor should be a low inductance type, typically a metal

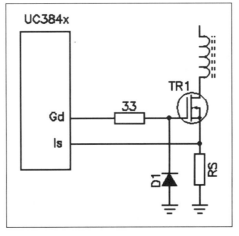

Fig 9.20: Driving a mosfet with a series gate resistor

UC3842B, 43B UC2842B, 43B

PIN FUNCTION DESCRIPTION

Pin 8–Pin	Pin 14–Pin	Function	Description
1	1	Compensation	This pin is the Error Amplifier output and is made available for loop compensation.
2	3	Voltage Feedback	This is the inverting input of the Error Amplifier. It is normally connected to the switching power supply output through a resistor divider.
3	5	Current Sense	A voltage proportional to inductor current is connected to this input. The PWM uses this information to terminate the output switch conduction.
4	7	R_T/C_T	The Oscillator frequency and maximum Output duty cycle are programmed by connecting resistor R_T to V_{ref} and capacitor C_T to ground. Operation to 500 kHz is possible.
5		Gnd	This pin is the combined control circuitry and power ground.
6	10	Output	This output directly drives the gate of a power MOSFET. Peak currents up to 1.0 A are sourced and sunk by this pin.
7	12	V_{CC}	This pin is the positive supply of the control IC.
8	14	V_{ref}	This is the reference output. It provides charging current for capacitor C_T through resistor R_T.
	8	Power Ground	This pin is a separate power ground return that is connected back to the power source. It is used to reduce the effects of switching transient noise on the control circuitry.
	11	V_C	The Output high state (V_{OH}) is set by the voltage applied to this pin. With a separate power source connection, it can reduce the effects of switching transient noise on the control circuitry.
	9	Gnd	This pin is the control circuitry ground return and is connected back to the power source ground.
	2,4,6,13	NC	No connection. These pins are not internally connected.

film or carbon film and adequately rated for power dissipation. Normally a half-watt resistor suffices for most applications. Keep all tracks and component leads as short and fat as possible.

The diode in parallel with the gate to ground is to prevent the gate being driven more than 1V negative. This diode can be a 1N4148 or a 1N5819 Schottky as the power is very low. The Miller effect between the drain and gate when switching high voltages generates a negative gate charge, which if not clamped can damage the device. The pinout of the UC384x series are detailed in **Fig 9.21**.

Operation of the UC384x series

The UC384x series of ICs operate as current mode controllers, where the output switch conduction is initiated by the oscillator and terminated when the peak inductor current reaches the threshold level established by the Error Amplifier Output/Compensation (Pin 1). Thus the error signal controls the peak inductor current on a cycle by cycle basis. The Current Sense Comparator PWM Latch configuration used ensures that only a single pulse appears at the Output during any given oscillator cycle. The inductor current is converted to a voltage by inserting the ground referenced sense resistor R_S in series with the source of the switch. This voltage is monitored by the Current Sense Input (Pin 3) and compared to a level derived from the Error Amplifier Output.

The peak inductor current under normal operating conditions is controlled by the voltage at Pin 1 where:

$$I_{PK} = \frac{V_{(Pin\ 1)} - 1.4V}{3 * R_S}$$

Under abnormal operating conditions when the power supply output is overloaded or if the output voltage sensing is lost, the Current Sense Comparator threshold is clamped to 1.0V internally. Therefore under these conditions the maximum peak current is:

$$I_{PK(max)} = \frac{1.0V}{R_S}$$

Eliminating leading edge current spike

A narrow spike on the leading edge of the current sense waveform can usually be seen and may cause the power supply to exhibit instability when the output is loaded lightly. This spike is due to the power transformer interwinding capacitance and output rectifier recovery time. The addition of an R-C filter on the Current Sense Input with a time constant that approximates to the spike dura-

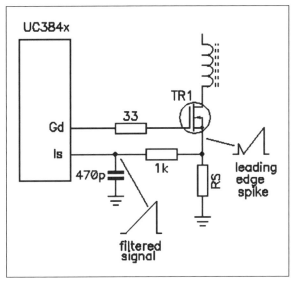

Fig 9.22: Current spike suppression circuit

tion will usually eliminate the instability. This is shown in **Fig 9.22**.

Typically a 1kΩ resistor with a ≈470pF capacitor will provide adequate filtering for a supply operating at around 100kHz.

Some tips on construction

Switch-mode power supplies require construction techniques very similar to VHF/UHF RF power amplifier circuits. Although the switching frequencies are normally not more than 500kHz the rapid rise and fall time of the square signals approach those of VHF circuits. Atypical mosfet and control IC will exhibit rise and fall times of the currents of around 10 to 50ns. These equate to RF signals of between 20 to 100MHz and, when the harmonics are taken into account, much higher. The importance of using wide, thick tracks on printed circuit board layouts to achieve low ohmic losses and low inductance cannot be stressed often enough. Although the average currents flowing can be quite small, the peak currents can be anything up to 100 times those of the average. High current peaks in long thin lossy tracks cause spurious voltages and oscillatory ringing to be generated which can couple into other parts of the circuit layout and these often upset the correct operation of the control IC.

A breadboard is often constructed to prove a design before committing to a printed circuit board. In many cases the breadboard does not perform as anticipated due to poor construction and assumptions about component lead length effects. Because the supply is operating at only a few hundred kilohertz the constructor is lulled into believing that a construction technique similar to a 160m receiver can be used. In most cases a design committed straight to a board layout is the best option, provided you have some experience in the 'hows and whys' of PWM construction.

In many of the supplies I have designed, the EMI aspects were often only met once a proper board layout was made and incorporated into the real mechanics.

My preference is to breadboard on a sheet of tin-plated steel sheet (cut from a biscuit tin), copper shim or single sided tinned board (about 300mm x 300mm) nailed with small panel-pins to a piece of chipboard or plywood to make it rigid. The metal is used as both the ground-plane and the method of heatsinking the smaller devices; larger devices usually have bolt-on heatsinks. The ICs and other components are grounded directly to the metal with leads as short as feasible, often in 'dead-bug' fashion with the DIL ICs upside down and the legs bent to connect to ground or other components. Because of the ease of soldering to the tin-plate or copper shim, all grounds are made either directly to the IC pins, transformer pins, other components or by short fat wires or Solderwick tape.

During testing, the EMI and RFI specifications in most cases will not be achieved due to the layout, because high currents radiate strong magnetic fields across from component to component. Only when a suitable low inductance printed circuit layout has been drawn and has been combined with the mechanical enclosure will the first-off pre-production units assembled meet the EMI specification - and even then it is sometimes necessary to make changes to comply with the emissions aspects. The breadboard simply confirms the 'soundness' of the basic design and it undergoes temperature testing at the required extremes for the application.

Motorola in one its application notes for the UC384x series has this to say about prototyping a new design:

DO NOT attempt to construct a PWM converter on wire-wrap or plug-in prototype boards.

High frequency circuit board layout techniques are imperative to prevent pulse-width jitter. This is usually caused by excessive noise pick-up imposed on the Current Sense or Voltage Feedback inputs. Noise immunity can be improved by lowering the circuit impedances at these points by fitting capacitors to ground.

The printed circuit layout should contain a ground plane with low current signal and high current switch and output grounds returning on separate paths back to the input filter capacitor. Ceramic bypass capacitors (0.1μF) connected directly to V_{CC}, V_C and V_{REF} pins may be required depending on the circuit layout. This provides a low impedance path for filtering the high frequency noise.

All high current loops should be kept as short as possible using heavy copper runs to minimise radiated EMI. The Error Amp compensation circuitry and the converter output voltage divider should be located close to the IC and as far as possible from the power switch and other noise generating components.

In most cases a double sided PCB layout will be mandatory, with one of the copper layers forming an almost continuous ground plane, broken only where clearance is needed to allow component leads to pass to the other side. Single sided boards are often not suitable for high power PWM supplies. In some of my professional designs I have had to resort to multi-layer fabrication (four layers) with the top copper being one ground and one of the internal layers used for a secondary ground, and to route tracks containing high voltages safely around low voltage points. This is an expensive option but often dictated by the stringent EMI specifications found in military and air-borne equipment.

Voltage regulation calculation

The output voltage needs to be divided down by a potential divider with suitable resistors and connected to the Feedback input. The feedback amplifier has a nominal internal reference of half of the 5V reference, or 2.5V. As long as the feedback voltage remains at 2.5V the supply will remain in regulation. The formula to select the resistors for the potential divider needs you first to specify a value for the bottom resistor, R2. In view of the noise immunity constraints this resistor value needs to be relatively low in value. A suitable choice would be between 2k2Ω and 8k2Ω.

$$V_O = 2.5 \text{ x} \left(1 + \frac{R1}{R2} \right)$$

Therefore if the bottom resistor, R2, were selected to be 4k7Ω and the required output were 13.8V then the value for the top resistor R1 would be 21244Ω. As this is not a standard value, another choice for R2 needs to be made. If we used a 22kΩ resistor for R1, as this is the closest value, the output voltage would be 14.2V, which is little high for our needs.

Try R2 = 3k3Ω, then R1 = 14916Ω. A 15kΩ resistor with a 3k3Ω for R2 will give a slightly higher voltage than desired of 13.86V, but this is close enough for our application.

Of course, if you have to have an exact output voltage you can split the value of R2 and insert a preset resistor to trim the output to the required value. Preset pots however are a temptation for people to 'twiddle', so fixed resistors should always be used if at all possible for a fixed output supply. It is very rare occurrence where a few tens of milli-volts out of specification cause a power supply to not suit the equipment attached.

Example: Off-line supply using the UC384x series

Motorola, in one of its application notes, gives the circuit of **Fig 9.23** to demonstrate the simplicity of the UC384x series. This supply is designed for 115VAC input and delivers 27 watts. The supply is intended to drive a small µProcessor board.

The voltage to operate the IC is obtained via two separate paths. On initial switch on, before the supply has stabilised, the IC is powered via the 56kΩ resistor from the rectified 115V AC. The initial starting current for the control IC is only about 0.5mA. The internal 36V Zener serves to clamp this to a safe level. Once the supply is running, a secondary winding supplies 12V to the supply pin of the IC, due to the values of 18kΩ & 4k7Ω feedback resistors. This

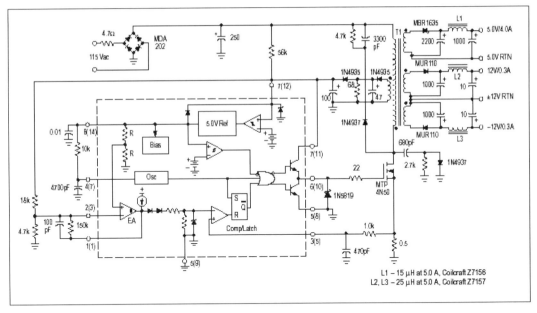

Fig 9.23: Example flyback converter design

will over-ride the current flowing in the mains derived input resistor and the dissipation in the 56kΩ resistor will drop to almost zero. The IC used therefore must have an under-voltage lockout lower than 12V and it is a UC3843 device - with 8.4V UVL threshold. The output voltage sensing is also derived from this same 12V bias/tertiary winding to provide the necessary high voltage safety isolation between primary and secondary.

The high voltage switching mosfet (MTP4N50, a 4A / 500V device) has two pairs of clamping or snubbing networks to protect it from over voltage spikes caused by the switching. Mosfet current sensing is performed by the 0.5Ω source resistor and filtered by the 1kΩ. and 470pF before being applied to the current sense input of the IC. Additional output filtering is used for the reduction of ripple voltage. Details of the performance are given in **Fig 9.24**.

Note that the +5V load regulation is not especially good, being 300mV over the output range. This is because the power supply is using 'remote sensing' from the 12V secondary feedback winding. However the equipment being powered is probably able to cope with this fluctuation.

Test		Conditions	Results
Line Regulation:	5.0 V	V_{in} = 95 to 130 Vac	Δ = 50 mV or ± 0.5%
	±12 V		Δ = 24 mV or ± 0.1%
Load Regulation:	5.0 V	V_{in} = 115 Vac, I_{out} = 1.0 A to 4.0 A	Δ = 300 mV or ± 3.0%
	±12 V	V_{in} = 115 Vac, I_{out} = 100 mA to 300 mA	Δ = 60 mV or ± 0.25%
Output Ripple:	5.0 V	V_{in} = 115 Vac	40 mV$_{pp}$
	±12 V		80 mV$_{pp}$
Efficiency		V_{in} = 115 Vac	70%

All outputs are at nominal load currents, unless otherwise noted

**Figure 9.24
Test parameters**

156

10

Isolated Forward Converter (Half Forward)

> **Tomorrow:** *"I never think of the future - it comes soon enough."* Albert Einstein

The Isolated Forward Converter is a derivative of the Buck Converter. It is similar to the Flyback Converter, as it is also a single switch isolated topology. However, the way the transformer acts is completely different. In the Forward Converter the inductance needs to be much higher than the Flyback to limit the peak current to manageable levels. Consequently the core is usually ungapped. Output voltage range is somewhat limited compared to the Flyback. In a Flyback many thousands of volts are possible, not so the Forward Converter because of the inductance required for the output filter choke. At voltages above approximately 100V the inductance required becomes very high and it is not usually practical to use a Forward Converter for this application. However, for low voltage, high current output supplies it is an excellent choice when the power output exceeds about 20W.

The forward converter transformer

In contrast to the Flyback, the Forward Converter has a true transformer action. This can be seen by noting the phase of the primary and secondary windings indicated by the dot notation in **Fig 10.1**. The energy is transferred during the switch on time directly through to the output, as in the Buck Converter. During the switch on time the primary current builds up flux in the transformer core and the secondary voltage developed forward biases the output diode D2.

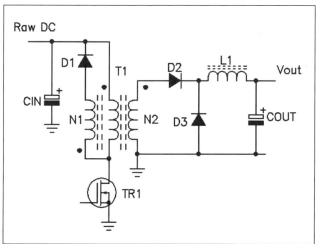

Fig 10.1: Basic forward converter

Output current flows in the series inductor L1 with an average current equal to IO and a peak-peak ripple current.

During the switch-off time the series diode D2 is reverse biased and the shunt diode D3 is forward biased and the current continues to flow in the output inductor in the same manner as the Buck Converter. The Forward Converter is a Buck Converter with the original series connected switch replaced with the series diode D2, which is supplied from the secondary winding.

The recirculation diode, (D3), output capacitor (Cout) and inductor (L1) are the same as the Buck Converter and the calculations to define them are exactly the same. The secondary voltage across N2 is the ratio of primary to secondary turns and can be greater or less than the input voltage by varying the primary to secondary turns ratio. The Forward Converter can therefore supply a lower or higher output voltage than the input voltage. The operation of the additional primary winding and the diode D1 are covered later.

The Forward Converter is always operated in Continuous Conduction Mode, since this produces low peak-peak input and output ripple currents. It also removes a destabilising pole in the control loop. As the CCM Flyback has a potential instability problem for duty cycles above 50% the Forward Converter operated in DCM has the same problem at all duty cycles.

The magnitude of the output ripple current and peak secondary current are determined by the output inductor, L1. By using a large inductance these currents can be reduced to low values making the choice of the output capacitor less stringent.

Since the transformer transfers energy directly there is negligible energy stored in the core compared to the Flyback, where all the energy is stored for each switching cycle. The only flux stored is the initial magnetising flux to enable the transformer to operate, and since it is very small a high primary inductance can be utilised, making the peak primary current relatively small. The Forward Converter theoretically has a peak primary current half that of a Flyback for the same throughput power.

The cores used for Forward Converters usually have a high permeability of about 2000 - 6000 and are normally ungapped ferrite types. Negligible energy storage means that the core volume required is smaller than the Flyback for the same throughput power. Also, the core losses are lower. However, because the transformer is operated asymmetrically, which means that power is only transferred during switch on-time, the utilisation is poor compared to other types and hence the core needs to be bigger than types which have symmetrical operation (push-pull operation).

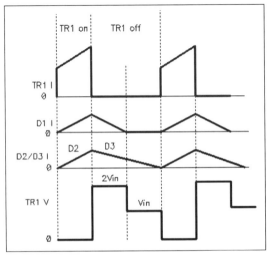

Fig 10.2: Current and voltage waveforms for a Forward Converter

Switching transistor requirements

The transistor has the same voltage rating as the Flyback requiring types able to withstand at least twice the input voltage. Because the primary peak current is approximately half of a Flyback of the same power, a lower power transistor can often be used. The lower primary current required translates to lower core losses and hence the same core can support about twice the throughput power of a Flyback at the same frequency. Consequently the Forward Converter is a popular choice for converters operating up to about 400W output where the Flyback would be limited due to excessive primary peak current.

Serious disadvantage of the forward converter

Because of the uni-polar switching action of the Forward Converter, there is a major problem in how to remove the core magnetisation energy by the end of each switching cycle. In the Flyback converter this is automatically performed by the secondary current 'sweeping out' the last remnants of core flux. In the Forward Converter no such path exists. If the residual flux is not discharged somehow the result will be a net DC flux build-up, which with successive switching cycles will increase until the core saturates. Remember the Forward Converter transformer does not have an air-gap and cannot tolerate very high flux levels and hence is liable to saturation.

This path is provided by an additional 'reset' winding or 'de-magnetising' (N_{mag}) winding wound in opposite polarity to the primary, note the dot notation in Fig 10.1. A clamp diode, D1, is added such that the magnetisation energy is returned to the input supply during the transistor off-time. Some engineers call this diode an 'efficiency diode'. The reset winding is usually bifilar wound with the primary to ensure tight coupling, and is normally made with the same number of turns as the primary, but can be a much smaller gauge of wire as the energy is small. The reset winding acts in exactly the same way as the secondary does in a Flyback, dumping excess flux energy back to the input supply. The diode D1 is connected to the input voltage side to reduce turn-on inter-winding capacity spikes to a minimum. (Some schematics show the diode and reset winding connected so as to discharge the energy to ground, this is wrong as the energy is wasted and it degrades the efficiency. Dumping the spare energy back into the input reservoir capacitor improves the overall efficiency, hence the name 'efficiency diode').

The time for the magnetising energy to fall to zero is the same as the switch on-time. Therefore the maximum duty cycle possible is 50%, (unlike the Boost and Flyback where duty cycles as high as 90% are possible) however due to

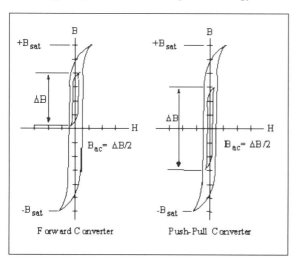

Forward Converter   Push-Pull Converter

Fig 10.3: Comparison of the BH loops of a single ended Forward Converter and a Push-Pull Converter

switching delays in the main switching transistor, this is usually reduced by designers to a more conservative value of 45% to ensure the core does not saturate. This limited duty cycle control range of 0 to 45% is one of the major drawbacks of the Forward Converter.

Due to the reset winding, in order to maintain volt-sec balance within the transformer, the input voltage is back reflected to the primary from the reset winding at transistor turn-off for the duration of the flow of the magnetisation reset current through the clamp diode D1. This means the transistor has to withstand 2 x V_{in} during switch-off. The voltage returns to V_{in} after the reset has finished, which means the transistor turn-off losses will be smaller. Often snubber networks are required to limit spikes to protect the switch transistor, particularly in off-line switch-mode supplies, which degrades the efficiency somewhat.

The diagram of the BH curves for the two types of converter (**Fig 10.3**) shows the unequal utilisation of the core, from which the single ended Forward Converter suffers. The core is operated in only one quadrant and for this the reason the magnetising flux causes the problem as the flux is always above a zero value.

By comparison, the push-pull converter (**Fig 10.4**) automatically removes any imbalance due to the operation being in two opposite quadrants. This removes any residual flux and performs an automatic core reset every switching cycle. In the push-pull converter there is no requirement to use a reset winding. Also note that a shunt recirculation diode is not required as the opposite secondary winding and rectifier diode performs this function. The control IC needs to be a type which provides two 'low-side outputs' 180° out of phase with a maximum duty cycle of ≈45% for each switch. A common choice is the SG1524.

An alternative to the push-pull converter often used in off-line forward converters is a type know as the two transistor forward converter (**Fig 10.6**). The advantage of this topology is the individual transistors only need to withstand V_{in} and not twice V_{in}. Here the primary is a single winding and the transistors are driven in phase. The top transistor is a 'high-side switch' similar to a Buck Converter switch and needs to have an isolated driver because the gate is at the input voltage. Special driver ICs are made for this application which can withstand voltages up to ≈500V. The operation is however still only in one quadrant.

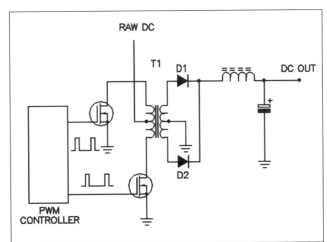

Fig 10.4: Push-pull forward converter

Fig 10.5: Push-pull Converter drive signals

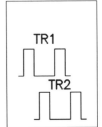

The two transistor Forward Converter requires a 'high-side' and 'low-side' driver IC. There are many ICs on the market offering isolation voltages of up to 600V for this application. One of the

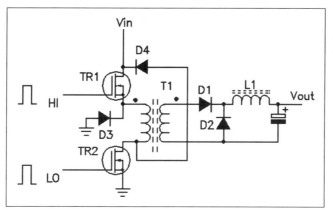

Fig 10.6: Two transistor forward converter configuration

many is the IR-2110 manufactured by International Rectifier. The circuit in **Fig 10.7** shows the IC in a typical application for an off-line supply.

The inputs HIN & LIN are connected to a controller IC, which provides nominal +5V, outputs with the required phase difference. In the case of the two-transistor Forward Converter, the inputs would be tied together and driven by a common PWM signal with a maximum duty cycle of ≈45%. The Vcc pin is normally connected to a supply of 12 to 15V and the capacitor connected from the source of the top switch provides a boost voltage to drive the top switch gate.

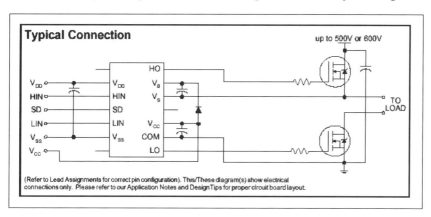

Fig 10.7: IR-2110 dual driver IC. *Used with permission of International Rectifier*

Output diode selection

The diodes in the output circuit both have to conduct the full magnitude of the output current. They are also subjected to abrupt changes in current, causing a reverse recovery spike, particularly in the recirculation diode. Because of this, high efficiency diodes with low capacity and high switching speeds such as Schottky or ultra-fast recovery epitaxial silicon types are required. Often the two diodes are combined into a common package with a centre tap, which is the common cathode.

For high current applications the diodes are often made in a TO-220 form which can be heatsinked to a

Fig 10.8: Philips BYV72 dual diode in TOP-3 package. The common cathode connects to the tab

convenient portion of the power supply enclosure or, in the case of a surface mount diode, soldered to a large area of copper foil.

Basics of the single ended forward converter

The design example that follows is rather complicated and causes many designers to get hung up with certain aspects of the design. However, when you understand how it works it is really quite simple! You simply have to keep two things in mind and the mystery disappears. The first relates to the effective voltage applied across the primary winding.

Effective Primary Voltage

Like the Buck Converter, the single ended Forward Converter uses the duty cycle to step down the input voltage, but in this case the voltage is applied to the primary. Therefore the effective voltage across the primary is:

$$V_{eff} = V_{in} \times D$$

where: V_{in} is the input voltage
D is the duty cycle

Therefore if the input voltage is 20V and D is 0.45 then the effective primary voltage is 9V.

Transformer Theory

The second thing to keep in mind is that the Forward Converter transformer acts like a 'real transformer' and the secondary voltage is simply the ratio of primary to secondary turns multiplied by the effective primary voltage. Therefore, if the secondary has the same number of turns as the primary the secondary voltages will the same as the effective primary voltage, 9V in our example.

This means that if we use a Schottky diode with a forward voltage of 0.5V then the secondary will be sized to deliver an output voltage of 8.5V DC after smoothing.

If these two facts are borne in mind the equations which follow in a worked example will make a lot more sense.

> To prove this is true, when the design is finished and the duty cycle at maximum input voltage has been calculated, work out the effective primary voltage and you will see the effective primary voltage is a constant no matter what the duty cycle. In this case you will see that it is 12V at all duty cycles and the primary to secondary turns will be 2:1.

Worked example of a forward converter

The design process listed on the next few pages was taken from an application note by Coremaster International Inc: AN-106 *Designing a Single-Ended, Forward Converter using a Coremaster E2000Q Core* by Colonel Wm T McLyman. I have eliminated some of the steps as they relate to ohmic losses in the windings and only cloud the issue.

For a typical design example, assume a single-ended converter circuit, as shown in Fig 10.1, with the following specification:

1.	Input voltage nominal	$V_{nom} = 28V$
2.	Input voltage minimum	$V_{min} = 24V$
3.	Input voltage maximum	$V_{max} = 32V$
4.	Output voltage	$V_o = 5V$
5.	Output current	$I_o = 2.5A$
6.	Frequency	$f = 100kHz$
7.	Temperature rise	$T_r = 20\ C$
8.	Efficiency	$\eta = 98\%$
9.	Regulation	$\alpha = 1\%$
10.	Diode voltage drop	$V_d = 1V$
11.	Design flux density	$\Delta B = 0.1T,\ B_{ac} = \Delta B/2$
12.	Max Duty cycle	$D_{max} = 0.5$
13.	Demag turns ratio	$N_{mag} / Np = 1$
14.	Demag power	$P_{mag} = 0.1 P_o$

Note: η is the assumed transfer efficiency of the transformer and not the overall circuit efficiency, this is taken into account in step 2 with a 'fudge factor' of 1.1

Select a wire so that the relationship between the AC resistance and the DC resistance is 1:1

$$\frac{R_{AC}}{R_{DC}} = 1$$

The skin depth, δ, in cm is $\dfrac{6.62}{\sqrt{f}}$ $\delta = \dfrac{6.62}{\sqrt{100kHz}} = 0.0209cm$

Then, the wire diameter is: $2\delta = 0.0418cm$

The bare wire area A_w is: $\dfrac{\pi \times D^2}{4} = 0.00137\ cm^2$

From the Wire Table, a 26 AWG wire has a bare wire area of $0.00128\ cm^2$. This will be the maximum wire diameter used in this design. If the design requires more wire area to meet the specification, then the design will use a multi-filar of 26 AWG. (*Note:* AWG stands for American Wire Gauge).

Step 1. Calculate the secondary output power

$P_o = I_o \times (V_o + V_d)$ $= 2.5 \times (5 + 1)$ $= 15W$

Step 2. Calculate the input power, P_{in}

$P_{in} = \dfrac{P_o \times 1.1}{\eta} = 16.8W$ (This assumes an efficiency of 90%)

Step 3. Calculate the electrical coefficient, K_e

$K_e = 0.145 \times f^2 \times \Delta B^2 \times 10^{-4} = 1450$

Step 4. Calculate the core geometry, K_g

$K_g = \dfrac{P_{in} \times D_{max}}{\alpha \times K_e} = 0.00579\ cm^5$

Step 5. Select from the data sheet a core with a figure for K_g greater than the calculated value. A suitable choice would be core number TEA0112Q in magnetic material E2000Q. The details for the core are shown below.

Magnetic path length, MPL	5.1cm
Core weight, W_{tfe}	9.5g
Copper weight, W_{tcu}	10.3g
Mean length turn, MLT	3.4cm
Iron area, A_c	$0.24cm^2$
Window area, W_a	$0.87cm^2$
Area product, A_p	$0.2078cm^4$
Core geometry, K_g	$0.005937cm^5$
Surface area, A_t	$24.9cm^2$

Step 6. Calculate the number of primary turns, N_p

$$N_p = \frac{V_{in(min)} \times D_{max} \times 10^4}{f \times A_c \times \Delta B}$$

$$N_p = \frac{24 \times 0.5 \times 104}{100kHz \times 0.24 \times 0.1} = 50 \text{ turns}$$

Note: The demag (reset) winding has the same number of turns as the primary.

Step 7. Calculate the current density, J, using a window utilisation, $K_u = 0.4$

$$J = \frac{2 \times P_{in} \times D_{max} \times 10^4}{f \times A_c \times \Delta B \times W_a \times K_u}$$

$$J = \frac{2 \times 16.8 \times 0.707 \times 10^4}{100kHz \times 0.24 \times 0.1 \times 0.87 \times 0.4} = 284 \text{ A/cm2}$$

Step 8. Calculate the primary RMS current, I_p

$$I_p = \frac{P_{in}}{V_{in} \times D_{max}}$$

$$Ip = \frac{16.8}{24 \times 0.707} = 0.99A$$

Step 9. Calculate the primary bare wire area, $A_{wp(B)}$

$$Awp(B) = \frac{Ip}{J} = 0.99 / 284 = 0.00348 \text{ cm}^2$$

Step 10. Calculate the number of primary strands, NS_p

$$NS_p = \frac{A_{wp(B)}}{\#26} = \frac{0.00348}{0.00128} = 2.7 \text{ (use 3 strands)}$$

Step 11. Calculate the secondary turns, N_s

$$N_s = \frac{N_p \times (V_o + V_d)}{D_{max} \times V_{in(min)}} \times \left(1 + \frac{\alpha}{100}\right)$$

$$Ns = \frac{50 \times (5 + 1)}{0.5 \times 24} \times \left(1 + \frac{1.0}{100}\right) = 25 \text{ turns}$$

Step 12. Calculate the secondary RMS current, I_s

$$Is = \frac{I_o}{\sqrt{2}} = \frac{2.5}{1.414} = 1.77A$$

Step 13. Calculate the secondary bare wire area, $A_{ws(B)}$

$$A_{ws(B)} = \frac{I_s}{J} = \frac{1.77}{284} = 0.00623 \text{ cm}^2$$

Step 14. Calculate the number of secondary strands, NS_s

$$NSs = \frac{A_{ws(B)}}{\#26} = \frac{0.00623}{0.00128} = 4.87 \qquad \text{use 5 strands}$$

This completes the calculations for the transformer, but we still need to calculate the output inductor value and the output capacitor. This follows the same process as for the Buck Converter. We need to choose a peak ripple current before we can begin the calculations. As with the Buck Converter the ripple current has a major impact on the overall performance.

Calculations for the output inductor

We will specify a ripple percentage of 20% to keep the output capacitor ripple current low. Remember that the inductor ripple current is the same current that flows in the output capacitor. Referring to Chapter 6 on the Buck Converter we can get the necessary formula:

$$L_{crit} = \frac{(V_{max} - V_o) \times V_o}{V_{max} \times \Delta I \times f}$$

where: V_{max} = maximum input voltage
V_o = nominal output voltage
ΔI = inductor ripple current (pk-pk Amps)
f = switching frequency (Hertz)

In the case of the Forward Converter, the factors which are the most important are the peak secondary voltage (V_{max}) and the duty cycle. We need to solve the equation to determine what the peak secondary voltage presented to the inductor is. This is relatively simple if you remember how the Forward Converter works.

The average rectified output voltage is the peak positive secondary voltage multiplied by the duty cycle. As we only know certain facts we have do a bit of extra calculating. However, we know for certain that at the minimum input voltage we fixed the duty cycle to be 50% maximum, because of the problems associated with demagnetising the core. Adding the diode forward drop to the secondary peak voltage gives us a figure for the secondary voltage under this condition. (This gives a number for the volts/turn of the secondary winding of 0.24V/turn).

We can therefore derive a formula to give the peak secondary voltage under these conditions.

$$Vs = \frac{Vo + Vd}{Dmax} = \frac{5 + 1}{0.5} = 12V$$

From this we can calculate the duty cycle when the input voltage is maximum.

$$D_{min} = \frac{V_{in(min)}}{V_{in(max)}} \times D_{max} = \frac{24}{32} \times 0.5 = 0.375 \ (37.5\%)$$

Now we derive the peak secondary voltage for the condition of input voltage at maximum because we need this to establish the inductor value.

The secondary voltage will be the ratio of $V_{in(min)}$ to $V_{in(max)}$ times the 12V already calculated.

$$V_{sec} = \frac{V_{in(max)}}{V_{in(min)}} \times V_s \quad or \quad = \frac{D_{max}}{D_{min}} \times V_s = 12 \times 1.333 = 16V$$

Having now calculated the peak secondary voltage at high input conditions we can calculate the minimum inductance required, L_{crit}.

$$L_{crit} = \frac{(V_{max} - V_o) \times V_o}{V_{max} \times \Delta I \times f} = \frac{(16 - 5) \times 5}{16 \times 0.5 \times 1 \times 10^5} = 56.25\mu H$$

It would prudent to increase this somewhat and a value of 68μH would be certain to be adequate. The minimum current rating required for the inductor is the sum of the output current and half the value of the ripple current.

The output current is 2.5A and the peak-peak ripple current is 0.5A so an inductor capable of 2.75A minimum is required. An inductor of at least 3A should be chosen. The wire gauge required would be approximately 18SWG if a single strand is used, or if two paralleled wires are used a gauge of 20SWG would suffice. The number of turns required can be calculated from the A_L value of the chosen core.

The maximum capacitor peak-peak ripple current is established as 0.5A and because the ESR has the dominant effect on the output ripple voltage, the value required can be calculated.

Using R = V / I where V is, say, 50mV the capacitor needs to have an ESR of less than:

$50 \times 10^{-3}/ 0.5 = 0.1\Omega$.

The minimum value of capacitor required can be derived from:

$$C = \frac{I_o}{8 \times f \times V_r}$$

where V_r is the ripple voltage required.

This is the minimum value that can satisfy the energy storage.

As we have decided to specify a 50mV ripple this sets the minimum capacitor value of 62.5µF. As it is unlikely we can find a capacitor of this value with an ESR of less than 0.1Ω, we need to increase the capacitor value until we achieve the required ESR.

Consulting the Nichicon catalogue for the PJ series: The 6.3V range starts at 100µF but the ESR at 25°C is 1.4Ω and 3.5Ω at -10°C. Looking at the ESR values, the lowest capacitor that can meet the ESR rating at low temperature is 3900µF/6.3V where the ESR is 0.093Ω at -10°C. In the 10V range the smallest value to meet this criteria is 2700µF, being 0.09Ω at -10°C and 0.036 at 25°C. However, we also need to consider the ripple current rating.

The 3900µF/6.3V has a maximum ripple current rating of 1910mA and the 2700µF/10V has a 1940mA rating. As we need a minimum of 500mA either of these would be satisfactory. However, both capacitors are quite tall being 31.5mm in height. If the height is a concern then several lower value capacitors of a lower height can be paralleled to get the equivalent ESR rating.

Looking at other suitable capacitors, we find that a 330µF/25V is 8mm diameter x 20mm high and has an ESR of 0.33Ω at -10°C and 0.13Ω at 25°C. If three of these capacitors are connected in parallel the required ESR will be met. The ripple current rating of the capacitor is 0.8A each so the total combined is 2.4A, which is more than required.

Alternatively a Sanyo-Os-Con would fit the application at a higher cost. A suitable value in the SA series would be a 68µF/10V, which has an ESR of 0.05Ω and a ripple current rating of 2A.

Diode PIV and current rating

Although the secondary voltage calculated is quite low it must not be forgotten that during the switch off time the secondary will fly negative by an amount up to twice the positive voltage excursion. This means that a conservative estimate of the diode PIV is around three times the peak secondary voltage. In our example a 50V diode would be the minimum required and an 80V or 100V diode would be a safer choice. The diode forward voltage chosen was 1V therefore an Ultra-Fast recovery dual diode would be suitable. Irrespective of whether an ultra-fast or Schottky is chosen the feedback loop will servo the output voltage by adjusting the duty cycle to obtain the correct voltage.

The diode forward current rating is the same as the maximum DC output current, therefore a diode with at least 2.5A rating should be used, in practice a 3A or higher diode would be suitable.

Choice of control IC

The optimum choice would be a current mode controller as this automatically performs current limiting in the event of a short circuit. The UC384x series would be ideal. The duty cycle needs to be set with the R_T and C_T components to limit the duty cycle to 45%. The current sense resistor will need to be chosen to suit the peak primary current plus approximately 25% to allow operation up to maximum rated output. The current sense input has a threshold of 1V. The peak primary current is given by:

$I_{pk} = \sqrt{3}/D$ x primary RMS current

where D is the maximum duty cycle, 0.5 in our example.

In our example the primary RMS current was calculated to be 0.99A, therefore the peak current is 2.4A. A suitable resistor needs to develop 1V when the current limit is required and therefore would be:

$$R = \frac{V_{sense}}{I_{limit}} = \frac{1.0}{(2.4 \times 1.25)} = 0.33\Omega$$

Designing with additional output windings

As with the Flyback Converter, adding additional outputs is quite straightforward. As we have determined the secondary volts/turn ratio it only remains to calculate the necessary number of turns for each output. Each additional output will require an output inductor and capacitor, which can be calculated knowing the output current and ripple current required. As in the Flyback, the extra output power needs to factored in from the start if the additional windings amount to more than ≈20% of the total throughput power.

For a Forward converter with many secondary windings the volume and board area occupied by the additional output inductors can present a problem. In many cases a number of similar current rating output inductors can be wound on a common core (**Fig 10.9**). This helps with the Cross-Regulation of these windings, as the common core tends to force each output voltage to stay within close tolerance of each other and the main winding. The peak flux density of the core needs to be high enough so that the core cannot approach saturation. Often one relatively expensive core, such as a moly-permalloy type, can reduce the size and cost over that of a design using many separate cores.

If the cross regulation figure is still too low then a better option, as with the Flyback with multiple outputs, is to increase the secondary voltage and then use low drop out three terminal regulators in series with each output rail.

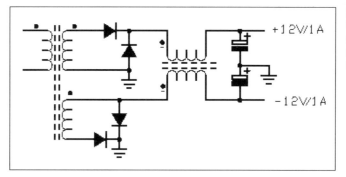

Fig 10.9: Common smoothing choke for a split-rail supply

Trouble shooting a forward converter

If the converter does not behave as expected we have to start delving into the circuit and see what the various measurements turn up. Start by running the converter on a fixed input voltage around the nominal input. Fix an output load of approximately 25% of maximum and, using an oscilloscope, look at the waveform across the secondary winding. You should see a square wave with a ramped top, probably with a leading edge spike of 50% more, with a positive amplitude of the peak secondary voltage and a negative voltage (swinging below ground) of approximately twice the first value. Vary the input voltage as you observe the duty cycle, does it get smaller as the input voltage increases? If this is correct then the converter has a problem somewhere else. If the ramped top of the square wave instead of showing a straight line shows a curve turning upwards the core is starting to run into saturation. This means the primary inductance is too low for the power rating, the core volume is too small or the output inductor is too low in value.

To get an accurate measurement, the best option is to connect the oscilloscope probe across the primary current sensing resistor between the mosfet source and ground. Ignoring any leading edge transient spike (as the primary turns on) the waveform should look that on the left of **Fig 10.10**. If the core is being driven into minor saturation the waveform will look like the right hand waveform with the curve beginning to turn upwards.

If the controller IC current sense input is tripped by the rapidly rising primary current when the core begins to saturate the switching pulse will be terminated and the regulator will drop out of regulation before the maximum current rating. Some IC current sense inputs need a leading edge spike suppresser to eliminate this problem. The board layout can also cause problems if

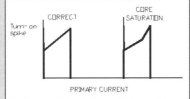

Fig 10.10: Primary Current waveforms

the primary current induces stray signals into the current sense pin of the controller IC due to spurious coupling.

The output inductor also has a huge effect on the overall performance. Often when the converter does not work correctly the transformer is considered the culprit, whereas in most cases it is because the output inductor is incorrectly scaled. If in doubt try increasing the inductor value by 50% and see the effect this has on the circuit. Also confirm you are using a gapped core for the inductor!

Sometimes extra measurements have to be made to pin down the problem. It can be necessary to make a "lash-up' Buck converter to use as a prototype converter to test the inductors in order to confirm they operate as expected.

Is the core big enough? With a marginal core volume, the risk of saturation exists and this can upset operation. Purchasing ready wound inductors usually eliminates one of the uncertainties, as they are normally conservatively rated by the manufacturer. Re-run your calculations again; have you made a silly mistake punching in the numbers?

Assuming you are trying to trouble-shoot a low voltage converter, you can use nature's senses, but don't try this with an off-line switcher because the voltages are lethal. A gentle 'feel' with your fingertip should be able to tell you if the core is excessively hot; likewise the output diodes or switching transistor. In many cases the cause is simple. For example is the phasing of the secondary correct? If you have this wrong, the converter will try to act like a Flyback and then the core needs to be gapped or it will saturate and get very hot.

The nose is also a good indicator of potential problems. Does anything smell hot?

Sometimes the culprit is not the prototype converter at all but the bench power supply feeding the converter. If you use a bench linear power supply this is often a source of incorrect operation. The peak current being demanded by the converter may be more than the bench supply can source without going into current limit and this will cause the converter to 'hiccup' because as the peak current is drawn the input voltage dips sharply at the critical moment. Most bench supplies need a bit of help to supply a switch-mode converter. Often connecting a very large electrolytic across the output of the bench supply will stop the problem (minimum of 10,000μF). Connect your 'scope across the input of the converter to confirm the voltage shows very little dip as the switch turns on. Are the input leads excessively long or thin?

If the converter is a multiple output one then try disconnecting all the additional secondary outputs and just use the main regulated secondary. If it now behaves correctly, it is either a diode related problem or a secondary winding which is either shorting or incorrectly polarised. To check polarity use the 'scope to confirm that the waveform shows the correct shape, polarity and voltage. Reconnect one secondary at a time until the problem reappears. Negative output voltages mean that the secondary winding phase needs to be reversed as well as the diode and capacitor polarity. It is easy to make a silly mistake when negative output voltages are used.

Conclusion

As you can see the procedure to design a Forward Converter is a lot more involved than a Flyback and, because of its complexity, it is something some designers prefer to stay away from if possible. In my experience the Forward Converter takes about twice as long to optimise as a Flyback because there are so many variables. However, if the requirement is for an output power of around 150 - 400W the Forward Converter is the best choice because the output ripple voltage will be much lower than a Flyback. Also the input and output capacitors need to handle much less ripple current and can be considerably smaller.

11

Other switch-mode converters in use

"Truth is what stands the test of experience." Albert Einstein

N ow that we have covered the four basic types and some of their variants, we can take a brief look at some of the others gaining popularity.

The SEPIC Converter

This converter finds many uses as it is a mix of the Buck and Boost but can supply a positive output voltage for a positive input voltage. In other words it is a non-inverting type of Buck-Boost converter. The name SEPIC stands for Single Ended Primary Inductance Converter. It features a single transistor low side switch as the Boost, Flyback and single ended Forward converters but uses a coupled inductor similar to a transformer. However, like the Flyback it does not operate as a transformer but two coupled inductors. The two inductors can be totally separate and not magnetically linked or wound on a common core, but the coupling between them is not totally by the magnetic flux but by an external capacitor.

The output voltage can be above or below the input voltage range, and because of this unique aspect it finds many uses in battery powered equipment. A common use of the SEPIC converter is to power portable equipment from rechargeable batteries where, for example, the input voltage varies from 6V to about 4V but the output voltage required is 5V. In other words it needs to work as a Buck converter when the battery voltage is above the output voltage and as a Boost converter when the battery voltage falls below the output voltage.

The major feature of the SEPIC (see **Fig 11.1**) over other similar converters is that it is possible to achieve zero ripple current in both the input and output capaci-

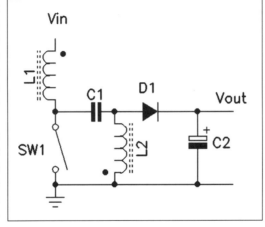

Fig 11.1: Basic SEPIC circuit

tors by the choice of the optimum coupled inductor value and coupling ratio, which greatly reduces the EMI filtering required.

The storage inductors need to have air-gapped cores as they are the same type as used in a Buck, Boost or Flyback converters. The total energy throughput is catered for by the coupling capacitor C1; this carries a high ripple current. Often a monolithic multi-layer capacitor is used as these types can sustain high ripple current with low ESR and are much smaller than aluminium types. The output diode also has a high ripple current flowing in it, similar to the Boost and Flyback converters. The SEPIC has a fail-safe mode, unlike the Boost. When the switching is disabled there is no direct connection between input and output because of the coupling capacitor.

Note the phasing of the windings if a coupled inductor is used. Often the coupled inductor is a 1:1 transformer wound with bifilar wire on an iron-powder core such as a toroid.

The duty cycle of the Sepic Converter is given by:

$$D = \frac{V_o + V_d}{(V_o + V_{in}) - (V_{SAT} + V_d)}$$

where: V_o is the output voltage
V_{in} is the input voltage
V_d is the diode forward voltage
V_{SAT} is the switch saturation voltage

The switch must be able withstand the required peak voltage given by:

$$V_{pk(sw)} = V_{in} + V_o + V_d$$

The peak switch current is:

$$I_{sw(peak)} = I_{L1(avg)} + I_o + \frac{\Delta I_{L1} + \Delta I_{L2}}{2}$$

where: $\Delta IL1$ is the ripple current in L1
$\Delta IL2$ is the ripple current in L2

Average current in the inductors are:

$$I_{L1(avg)} = \frac{I_o \times D}{1 - D} \qquad I_{L2(avg)} = I_o$$

The required minimum inductor values are:

$$L1 \geq \frac{V_{in} - V_{Sat}) \times (1 - D)}{2 \times I_o \times f} \qquad L2 \geq \frac{(V_{in} - V_{Sat}) \times D}{2 \times I_o \times f}$$

The inductors need to be rated for a minimum current of:

$$I_{L1(pk)} = \frac{D \times I_o}{1 - D} + \Delta I_{L1} / 2 \qquad I_{L2(pk)} = I_o + \Delta I_{L2} / 2$$

To calculate ΔI_{L1} & ΔI_{L2}

$$\Delta IL1 = \frac{(Vin - VSat) \times D}{L1 \times f} \qquad \Delta IL2 = \frac{(Vin - VSat) \times D}{L2 \times f}$$

HIGH CURRENT SELF-LEADED SMT INDUCTORS

Fig 11.2: Pulse Engineering data sheet for coupled inductors

- Materials meet UL94V-0 rating
- Frequency range of up to 1 MHz
- Can be used in series, parallel or as a 1:1 coupled inductor

Electrical Specifications @ 25°C — Operating Temperature -30°C to +130°C

Part Number	Hookup	Idc (amp)	L @ DC Ldc (µH)	ET (V-µsec)	Storage Capacity (µJoules)	L w/o DC Lø ±15% (µH)	DCR (MAX) (mΩ)	ET100 (V-µsec)
P0595	Series	9.5	18.10	18.0	816	38.00	16.8	7.22
P0596	Series	12.0	12.80	8.4	922	26.68	12.0	8.33
P0597	Series	13.5	9.80	12.0	893	20.40	8.8	9.84
P0598	Series	17.0	6.40	8.4	919	13.80	5.6	12.03
P0595	Parallel	19.0	4.52	9.0	816	9.50	4.2	14.43
P0599	Series	19.0	4.30	8.4	780	8.40	4.4	15.46
P0596	Parallel	24.0	3.20	4.2	922	7.17	3.0	16.65
P0597	Parallel	27.0	2.45	6.0	893	5.10	2.2	19.68
P0598	Parallel	34.0	1.60	4.2	919	3.45	1.4	24.05
P0599	Parallel	38.0	1.10	4.2	780	2.10	1.1	30.92

Mechanical

NOTES:
1. Temperature rise is 55°C in typical buck or boost circuits operating at 300 KHz with the rated Idc current and reference ET applied to the inductor.
2. Total loss in the inductor is 1.8 watts for 55°C temperature rise above ambient.
3. To estimate temperature rise in a given application, determine total losses (copper losses + core losses) and apply this formula: TempRise (C) = (Total Losses(mW))$^{.833}$ x 33.783
4. For copper losses, calculate: CopperLoss(mW) = Idc^2 x DCR
5. For core loss, using frequency (f: hertz) and flux density (B: gauss): CoreLoss(mW) = 1.0769E-09 x f$^{1.34}$ x B$^{2.11}$
6. For flux density (B), calculate ET (V-µsec) for the application, and multiply by the ET$_{100}$ factor from the table.
7. Add suffix "T" to part number for tape and reel package (i.e. P0595T).

Pulse P059X Date Code Country of Origin

SUGGESTED PAD LAYOUT

1.220 MAX / 30,99
1.100 / 27,94
4X .320 ± .020 / 8,13 ± 0,51
.600 / 15,24
1.000 / 25,40

1.097 / 27,86
.600 / 15,24
.400 / 10,16
.155 / 3,94

.500 MAX / 12,70
.006/0.15 / 4 SURFACES

Weight . . . . . . 18.7 grams
Tape & Reel 75/reel
Tube 20/tube

Dimensions: Inches / mm
Unless otherwise specified, all tolerances are ± .010 / 0.25

Schematic

1 ○——○ 4
2 ○——○ 3
1:1 ±1%

As with other switch-mode converters the value of inductor ripple current should be chosen carefully and the 40 per cent figure of I_O should be considered the absolute maximum. Increasing the value of L1 and L2 will reduce the ripple current flowing. If the two inductors are to be wound on a common core then once the values of L1 and L2 have been calculated a dual wound inductor equal to the higher of the two inductors will suffice. Several manufacturers make suitable coupled inductors, Pulse Engineering being one (see **Fig 11.2**).

Coupling Capacitor

The coupling capacitor needs to be a minimum value of:

$$Cs \geq L1 \times \frac{I_O^2}{(V_{in} - V_{SAT})^2}$$

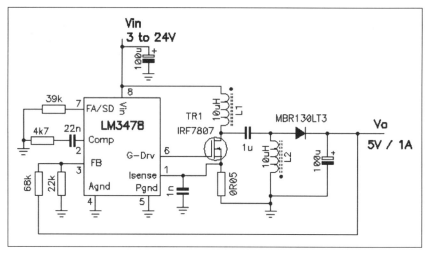

Fig 11.3: National Semiconductor application circuit

A Typical SEPIC Application Circuit

The application circuit shown in **Fig 11.3** uses a National Semiconductor LM3478, a current mode controller similar to the UC384x series. This uses an external logic level mosfet as the main switch. The peak switch current is sensed by the 50mΩ resistor in the source of the mosfet and processed in the same way as the UC384x devices. The nominal current sense input voltage is 325mV, which makes the resistor value very small and hence reduces power dissipation in the sensing resistor. In many designs a piece of printed circuit track can be used for the resistor.

The input voltage can be anywhere between 3V and 24V for a 5V / 1A output current. The SEPIC is often used in GSM cellular phones to allow more of the available energy from the rechargeable battery to be extracted than a simple Buck Converter ever could, hence giving more 'talk-time'.

The switching frequency can be adjusted between 100kHz and 1MHz by selecting a suitable resistor from the FA/SD pin to ground. This high switching frequency allows very low values of inductors and capacitors to be used. Typical efficiencies measured run in the lower 90% bracket. A circuit I built for an 3A-output converter measured 92% when operated at 500kHz.

Fig 11.4: Synchronous SEPIC

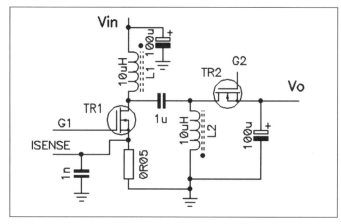

Synchronous SEPIC

A derivative of the SEPIC is the Synchronous SEPIC. This dispenses with the series diode and it is replaced by a second low on-resistance mosfet.

This scheme requires a dual driver integrated circuit with one output being a low side and one a high side with 180 degrees phase difference. A common IC such as the IR2110 is often used for this application.

Push-Pull Converter

The push-pull converter is usually used for an isolated Forward Converter to provide greater output power. The advantages of the push-pull converter is that the residual core flux is no longer a

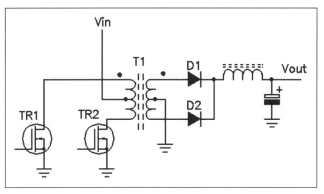

Fig 11.5: Push-pull forward converter

problem as the opposite switch when it conducts performs the core reset. Also no recirculation diodes are required. Power output from a push-pull Forward Converter can exceed 1kW.

The basic circuit of a push-pull converter is shown in **Fig 11.5**. The control IC needs to provide two low side drive signals of a maximum duty cycle of ≈45% with a precisely controlled amount of dead time between the outputs and 180° phase difference.

Advantages of the Push-Pull Forward Converter

The push-pull converter has a number of advantages over the single ended Forward Converter. If you remember when we discussed the Forward Converter, the core utilisation was poor because it only operated in one quadrant. The push-pull converter operates in two opposite quadrants and therefore the core is able to support higher power throughput. Theoretically, a push-pull converter can transfer twice the throughput power for a particular core size than a single ended converter. The need for a demagnetising winding is no longer required.

A further advantage is that the output ripple frequency is twice the single ended converter. The ripple frequency being twice the input means that a smaller inductor and capacitor value can be used. Also each diode only needs to handle half of the total output current, meaning smaller diodes can be used.

Switching Transistor Ratings

The voltage rating of the switching transistors need to be twice the input supply and snubber networks may need to be fitted to limit transient spikes to below the device breakdown voltage. For an off-line converter this will require devices rated at a minimum of 800V.

The current rating of the switching transistors is only half of the single ended converter, as each transistor only has to transfer half the total power. This often means that two smaller, lower cost devices can be used. In many designs SMD versions can be employed which saves considerable printed circuit board area.

Off Line Switch-mode Power Supplies

> **Curiosity:** *"The important thing is not to stop questioning."* Albert Einstein

O ff line switchmode converters provide a high efficiency, compact design without the weight penalties of a conventional iron-core mains transformer. Output powers can range from a few watts up to many kilowatts. As with the previous DC-DC converters the choice of circuit topology is also quite varied. For low power outputs the obvious choice is a form of Isolated Flyback Converter, which can provide up to approximately 250W. For higher output powers the Isolated Forward Converter is a better proposition. For even higher powers the Half-Bridge and Full-Bridge can provide output powers in excess of 1kW.

All off line converters use a similar input stage which consists of either a voltage doubler rectifier or a full wave bridge feeding a large reservoir capacitor, the voltage doubler is used for 115V mains and the bridge for 230V mains. This is usually preceded by filtering and spike suppression. Legislation in most countries now requires that the input filtering be not only adequate to prevent switching ripple from being injected back into the public mains supply, but also to provide safety isolation because of the high voltages in use.

The input filter and rectifier

A typical input circuit for a low power off line converter is shown in **Fig 12.1**. The input filtering is performed by a dual wound inductor (L1) and is known as a 'Common-Mode' choke. The mains current flowing in the two halves should

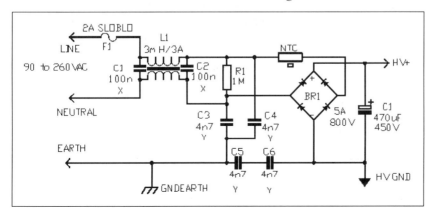

Fig 12.1: Off Line switcher input circuits

Warning!

Dangerous and lethal potentials are present in off line circuits!

Before proceeding any further, the reader is warned that caution must be used in the construction, testing and servicing of off line circuits. Extreme caution must be used in working with and making connections to these circuits.

Repeat: Off line circuits contain dangerous, AC line-connected high voltage potentials. Use extreme caution.

All testing performed on an off line circuit must be done with an isolation transformer connected between the off line circuit and the public mains supply. Users and constructors of off line circuits must observe this precaution when connecting test equipment to the circuit to avoid electrical shocks. This is especially important if the test equipment is also powered from the mains supply, eg an oscilloscope.

Repeat: An isolation transformer must be used whenever testing and servicing any off line circuit.

be equal in amplitude and of opposite polarity, but the high frequency switching spikes distort the line and neutral low frequency waveforms and produce an imbalance between the two. The Common-Mode choke acts as a Balun transformer and forces each side to carry the same current. This effectively suppresses the switching currents. With the addition of capacitors C1 and C2 the circuit becomes a balanced π filter (Pi filter).

Note that the supply has two separate grounds. The mains input protective earth is connected to the power supply metalwork; the high voltage rectified DC has a totally isolated ground from the mains input earth. The capacitors used for C1 to C6 are special high voltage types. C1 and C2 are X type, so called because they are designed to be connected across the mains supply. These two perform the bulk of the filtering in conjunction with L1, the common mode choke.

C3 to C4 are included to shunt high frequency switching spikes to ground and are Y types, notice how C3 and C4 are connected in series across the output of the choke and the centre point is connected to the mains earth. It is shaped like the letter Y hence the name for this type of capacitor. Both the X and Y types have very high AC voltage test ratings, are normally self-healing types and are tested to stringent regulations - you cannot use any capacitor for these applications.

Whilst we are discussing the input stages it would be as well to be aware of the potential hazards involved (see the shaded box).

It is also important when laying out any printed circuit board to allow adequate clearance between any tracks carrying high voltage and lower potentials, such as the ground portions.

Power factor correction (PFC)

I have already touched on this topic when we discussed the Boost Converter. Recent legislation in many countries now makes it almost essential to include

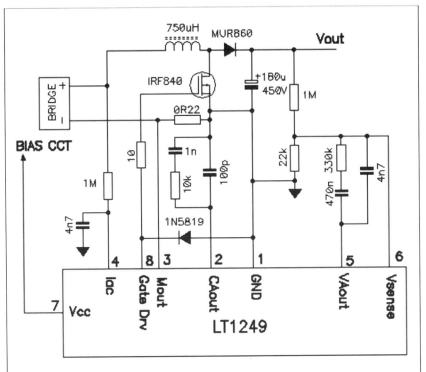

Fig 12.2: Typical application circuit of the LT1249 PFC stage. *Note*: The ground symbol shown is the high voltage isolated 'ground' and *not* the mains earth ground

PFC in large switchmode off line supplies. One such specification is IEC555-2, which most countries have already adopted or will, in the very near future.

The Boost Converter lends itself to a simple solution to the PFC problem and also provides a constant high voltage DC input to the main switching block. A bonus is that with the Boost input PFC stage the need to fit voltage selectors and voltage-doubling rectifiers has fallen away. By using a Boost input stage with a standard bridge rectifier the supply can operate from any input AC supply from about 90V AC to 270V AC, which is why the supplies are now called 'Universal Input'. It also saves one high voltage capacitor; this can take up a considerable volume in the conventional input stage when a voltage doubler is required.

A typical Boost input PFC stage is shown in **Fig 12.2**. This can support an off line supply of up to 1500W output and should cater for just about any kind of supply we are likely to construct. The control IC is the LT1249, made by Linear Technology Corporation. It is an 8 pin IC, available as a DIL or SMD package and it contains the necessary circuitry to control the high voltage switching mosfet and the inductor (**Fig 12.3**). The IC gets its operating supply from an overwind on the main boost inductor and this provides the safety isolation required.

The diodes are small signal types such as 1N4148 or 1N5819 Schottky because the current is low. The electrolytic capacitors are 35V rating. The secondary over-wind on the main boost inductor turns ratio needs to be sized to provide approximately 18V at the Vcc output. Normally a few turns are adequate to provide the required voltage. The insulation on the wire must be able to withstand at least 500V DC to prevent breakdown.

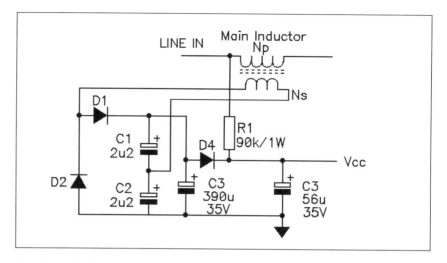

Fig 12.3: LT1249 supply circuit using the main inductor as the transformer primary

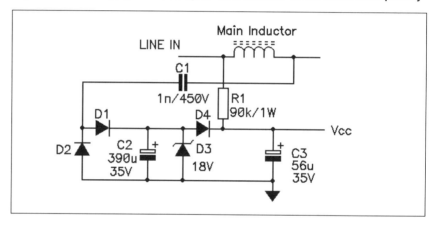

Fig 12.4: Alternative circuit to power the LT1249

The LT1249 supply circuits will not provide any voltage to the IC until the circuit starts switching, and will not start switching until the IC has a supply voltage. To get around this seemingly 'chicken or egg' problem the two supplies each feature a high value resistor to bleed a little current from the rectified mains to start the IC. This is the 90kΩ/1W resistor. When the IC starts switching it provides its own supply and the small current drawn from the high voltage input falls to virtually zero. The LT1249 needs a starting current of 250µA and a running current of approximately 9mA.

The LT1249 has an under-voltage lockout of 16V, so the IC supply needs to be above this figure for switching to commence. The maximum IC voltage is 27V and the manufacturer recommend a supply of 18V so that the IC gate drive does not exceed the common 15V limit of mosfets. (The gate drive supply is however internally clamped to a maximum of 16V to cater for the higher operating voltages). The gate drive circuitry in the LT1249 can supply up to 2A into a capacitive load of 10nF and has a rise and fall time of approximately 25ns with a gate capacity of 1nF, which suits the high voltage mosfets commonly

Fig 12.5: A typical personal computer switch mode supply

encountered. The mosfet used in the example circuit is an IRF840, which is a 500V device rated at 8A and the diode is a 600V device with an 8A rating.

100W off line flyback converter transformer

Now I will discuss the design of a transformer to supply an output current of approximately 7A at 13.8V.

Because we are dealing with lethal voltages the way in which the transformer is wound is critical.

The best option is to use margin-winding techniques. This is a method where the full width of the bobbin is not used, but at each end of the bobbin insulating tape is wound with a width of half the required creepage distance. This creepage distance is about 5mm, so the bobbin width is reduced by half this amount at each end, or a total of 5mm overall. The 2.5mm-wide tape is wound onto the bobbin at each end until it is as high as the primary winding is anticipated to be. The exact height will depend on how many layers are required for the primary winding. This depends on three factors, the number of primary turns, the gauge of wire used and the number of turns you can wind on each layer between the 'margins'. When the primary has been wound, several layers of high voltage insulating polyester tape are wound on top to provide an adequate safety barrier for the secondary and other windings required.

An alternative to using tape to provide the margins is to use a specially made split bobbin former. There are several types manufactured with a dividing partition between the two halves of the bobbin. This allows the primary and secondary to be adequately isolated.

The number of primary turns is defined by the primary inductance required and the A_L value for the core used. We have a wide selection of gapped cores to

Fig 12.6: Two section bobbin for off line switch mode supplies

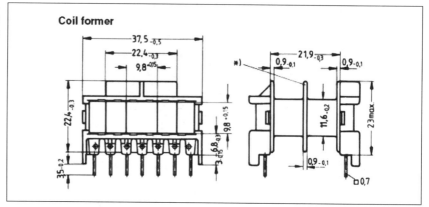

Fig 12.6: Two section bobbin for off line switch mode supplies

choose from, except that RM cores are not as suitable for off line applications as the other types. We will choose an ETD core because it has a DIL bobbin, is low cost and is adequately insulated for the anticipated voltages we will encounter. For the throughput power required an ETD-39 size core would be adequate.

As we seem to have a number of variables, each of which each interrelates. We need some means of getting a starting point.

You will recall in the chapter dealing with Flyback Converters that I mentioned that the primary to secondary turns ratio was not the same as a conventional transformer. Hence, we can select a suitable number of turns for the secondary based on the Volts/turn and then use this to calculate the required number of turns for the primary using the critical inductance criteria. If we choose to set the Volts/turn to be equal to somewhere between one and four this generally works satisfactorily for most applications.

Let us choose 3V/turn. As the diode forward voltage has also to be taken into account in this equation we will select this to be 0.5V, as a Schottky diode will be used. Therefore the secondary voltage required is 13.8 + 0.5 = 14.3V and at 3V/turn this means we need 4.76 turns. As we choose to use a bobbin which can accommodate half turns as well as full turns we will increase the secondary turns to five.

If the number of turns chosen for the secondary are more than required this is not a serious problem because the converter will adjust the input pulse width to provide the correct output voltage. Taken to extremes this means that the on-time will decrease to approaching zero as the secondary turns increase. It is preferable to choose a higher number of turns than fewer, as in this case the duty cycle at low line input will increase to possibly dangerous levels.

Minimum DC voltage

Now we need to consider the minimum input voltage after rectification that will be applied to the transformer primary winding. Assuming we are operating from 230V AC mains this sets the lower AC voltage at around 206V minimum. But the actual input voltage applied to the primary is not simply 206 x 1.414; we have to take into account the voltage when the input capacitor voltage drops into the trough due to the ripple voltage. For a switchmode supply operating off a 50Hz mains supply and running at 100kHz there will be 2000 switching events occurring each mains cycle, and approximately 500 of these cycles occur when the input capacitor voltage is in the trough. For this we need to consider the input reservoir capacitor value, too high or low an input capacitor value also has other consequences which I will cover later.

The formula to derive the minimum DC voltage is shown below:

$$V_{min} = \sqrt{(2 \times V^2_{ACmin})} - \left[\frac{2 \times P_o \times \left(\dfrac{1}{2 \times F} - t_c \right)}{\eta \times C_{in}} \right]$$

where: P_o is the output power in watts
        η is the assumed efficiency
        F   is the AC mains frequency
        V_{ACmin} is the mains lowest voltage
        C_{in} is the input capacitor value
        t_c is an estimation of the conduction time for the input rectifier

Assuming an efficiency of 80%, capacitor value of 330μF, low mains of 206VAC, a diode conduction time of 6ms, and an output power of 100W we arrive at the answer of 286V DC.

The maximum DC voltage is the product of the high mains AC voltage of 260V times 1.414 = 367V.

Effective primary voltage

Because we are using a high voltage mosfet as the switch, it has a much greater R_{dson} than devices used at lower voltages. The device we choose needs to have a drain-source rating of at least two times the maximum input DC voltage, therefore we need an 800V device. Low cost mosfets of this rating that can handle the anticipated drain current will have on-resistances of approximately 3 to 5Ω. Because of this, part of the applied input voltage is 'lost' across the mosfet and needs to be subtracted from the input voltage to arrive at the 'effective primary voltage'. The voltage drop across the mosfet can be calculated from the average input current. Assuming an efficiency of 80% we can work out what the input power will be under low-line conditions, which is where the highest current will flow in the mosfet.

$P_{in} = P_o / \eta$

We have assumed an output power of 100W at 13.8V which is a current of approximately 7.25A, but we need to consider the short circuit current limit conditions. Increasing the current by 25% to arrive at our maximum output power yields a result of 9A and Po = 125W.

Therefore P_{in} = 156.25W under short circuit conditions. This is the power we need to calculate the primary effective voltage, as it is the worst case the converter will be expected to work under.

Therefore primary effective voltage = 286 - ($I_p \times R_{DSon}$)

where $I_p = (P_{inmax} / V_{inmin})$

    I_p = 156.25W / 286V   =   0.55A

Therefore effective voltage = 286 - (0.55A x 5Ω) = 283V

From this we can calculate the mosfet dissipation. Since an average current of 0.55A flows in the drain-source region with a resistance of 5Ω we can ascertain the power dissipated.

P= I² x R where I = 0.55, R = 5 therefore P = 1.5125W as a first stab at the problem. Taking into consideration the conductance losses, which can be as high as the resistive losses for a high voltage off line switcher, we arrive at a first estimate of approximately 3W. Therefore the device needs little heatsinking.

Minimum input capacitor value

Apart from the obvious problem of too much ripple voltage, if the input capacitor is too small, a further problem also needs consideration. This is concerned with short periods when the mains voltage disappears. This occurs all too often in some electricity supply systems - ask me how I know! Where the electricity sub-station has auto-tap-changing transformers the mains supply can disappear for a short period whilst the taps are being changed. This is usually very short but can add up to several 'dropped cycles'. If the input capacitor has too small a value the capacitor cannot supply sufficient energy to keep the supply running for more than a cycle or two when this occurs and hence the supply stops working whilst this occurs. In computers this is a serious problem and can lead to loss of vital data and in extreme cases permanent corruption of the hard-disk data. The condition where the mains voltage drops below normal for a short time, but doesn't totally disappear, is known as a 'brown-out'. Dropping cycles is often called a 'black-out'.

With an oversized input capacitor the energy stored in the capacitor can allow the supply to carry on working to specification for several missing cycles. A common specification is to allow five to ten consecutive dropped cycles without the supply falling out of regulation.

Most off line switchmode designers prefer to err on the safe side and double the capacitor value calculated. This should not be taken too far as the negative result is that the input rectifier peak diode current also goes up when the capacitor is oversized. A safe maximum is about 250% of the calculated value.

$$C_{bulk} = \frac{I_{in(av)}}{8 \times F \times V_{ripple}} \quad \text{gives the value in Farads}$$

where: F is the mains ripple frequency (100Hz for a 50Hz mains supply)
V_{ripple} is the allowed peak to peak ripple on the rectified mains.
$I_{in(av)}$ is the average input current.

Hence, if we use a 50Hz mains supply with an average input current of 1A and desire a maximum of 20V p-p ripple we need an input bulk capacitor of:

$$C_{bulk} = \frac{1}{8 \times 100 \times 20} = 62.5\mu F$$

This value will only be able to cater for one dropped cycle, hence if we need to cater for more dropped cycles then the value needs to be increased. In most applications five dropped cycles will probably suffice. For this case the value would need increasing to approximately 312.5μF. The nearest standard value is 330μF and would suffice for our needs.

Primary inductance required

The primary needs to have a minimum inductance in order to transfer sufficient energy on each switching cycle. This we can calculate using the formula below:

$$Lp = \left[\frac{(V_{eff} \times D_{max})^2}{2 \times P_o \times f} \right]$$

where: Veff   is the effective primary voltage
Dmax   is the maximum duty cycle allowed
Po   is the maximum power output
f   is the switching frequency

We will set D_{max} to 45% and we will choose the frequency to be 100kHz.

The minimum primary inductance therefore works out to be 648μH. We can increase this a little, as it is the minimum value required. Let us increase it by 10% to 715μH.

We now need to choose an A_L value for the core we are intending to use. I will pick a value of 250nH/t².

With this core type we can calculate the number of primary turns required and then having selected a suitable wire gauge we can establish how many layers will be required to achieve this inductance value. With the chosen A_L we need 53.47 turns and since we can have either half or full turns we will choose 53.5 turns. Half turns are an advantage as they place the two ends of the winding on opposite sides of the bobbin, which is often convenient from a board layout point of view.

We have already calculated the average current flowing in the primary as being about 0.6A under worst case conditions and therefore a suitable wire gauge would be approximately 28SWG (0.375mm) as this can safely handle 4A.

Now consider the other windings required. The control IC needs an isolated DC supply to power it and the main secondary winding has to supply considerable current.

Bias winding

The control IC supply is provided by a small number of turns wound with a very small wire gauge as the current required is very low. For convenience we will use the same wire gauge as used for the primary, although this is an overkill. As we have already established what the secondary turns need to be we can simply scale from this to arrive at a suitable number of turns.

Suppose the control IC required a 15 volt supply, as it needs to drive the mosfet gate. With the 13.8V secondary we chose five turns and this works out to (13.8 + 0.5) / 5 = 2.86V/turn. Since we need a 15V supply and will use a silicon diode such as a 1N4148 as the current is very low, we know that the bias winding requires to develop 15 + 0.7V and therefore needs 5.48 turns. Five and a half turns will be acceptable.

Secondary winding

The secondary needs to supply an average current of approximately 9A maximum and have five turns. Because of the higher current we need to parallel several wires to handle the current. A good choice would be three strands of 22SWG wound as a flat ribbon.

So the final winding schedule looks like this:

Primary winding:	53.5 turns	28SWG
Insulation Layers		
Bias winding:	5.5 turns	28SWG
Insulation Layer		
Secondary winding:	5 turns	3 x 22SWG paralleled
Insulation Layer		

Feedback voltage sensing and safety isolation

Because of the dangerous voltage existing on the primary side of the circuit we cannot simply connect our voltage divider resistors from the low voltage output back to the control IC. To do so would negate all the trouble we have taken to make a transformer with high voltage isolation. There are several ways around this problem.

One common method is to use an Opto-isolator IC to provide the high voltage isolation between the primary and secondary. Another method, although not as good, is to use the voltage developed across the bias winding to get an indication of the output voltage. As the bias winding and the primary winding are on the same side of the transformer (the high voltage side of the circuit) and the secondary is isolated but tightly coupled to both, this is a valid way out of the problem. However, the output voltage regulation will not be as good as the Opto-isolator method, but probably acceptable for our needs.

Another method is to use a separate sensing winding, similar to the bias winding, ground referenced to the input side. This only need supply a low voltage, say 5V, and have a half-wave rectifier such as 1N4148 and a small smoothing capacitor and a load resistor to draw a few mA of current. The feedback resistors need calculating for this sense voltage to suit the control IC being used. A potentiometer can be used to set the final voltage.

In **Fig 12.7** several things need to be noted. Firstly, all the primary side circuitry uses a common isolated ground. The output winding is connected to the

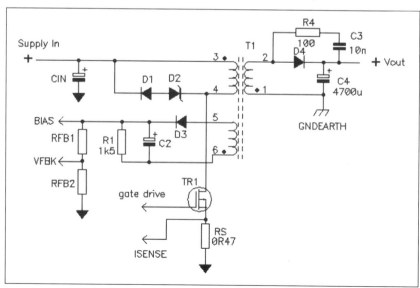

Fig 12.7: Primary side sensing using the bias supply

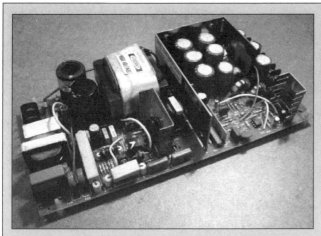

Fig 12.8: A typical multiple output off line flyback supply for a main frame computer. The supply shown provides a 5V supply at 20A, +12V & -12V at 1A and a +24V supply at 1A

A friend of mine bought a quantity of supplies similar to these from a scrap merchant for next to nothing. They had been scrapped from a large main frame computer and he pressed them into service for his shack supply. The supplies were rated 5V at 100A. The 5V output terminals were isolated so it was a simple matter to connect these supplies in series on the output and the input mains connected in parallel. Setting each supply to about 4.5V gave a nice 13.5V supply at 100A.

mains ground only. This maintains a safety barrier between the primary and secondary. Also because the control IC is connected to the high voltage ground it is effectively connected to the mains and great care needs to be exercised when fault finding.

A snubber network is connected across the primary. This consists of a high voltage tranzorb and a diode connected in series. The tranzorb needs to be rated at less than the breakdown voltage of the mosfet, in practice a 500V rating will be adequate. The snubber network serves to clamp transients to below the mosfet rated drain-source limit. Without the snubber the mosfet could fail as the potential voltage when it turns off is twice the DC input voltage plus any spikes. The power rating of the tranzorb needs to be adequate to dissipate the anticipated power. Failure to use a big enough device will cause disastrous results.

A similar RC snubber network is connected across the output rectifier diode for the same reason.

Mosfet current sensing is performed with a low value resistor in the source return. This is connected back to the controller IC current sense input to set the peak primary current, as the preferred control IC would be a Current Mode type such as a UC3842.

Start up bias supply

As with the other types of off line supply the control IC gets its operating supply from an over wind on the main transformer. Until the controller IC starts the mosfet switching, there will be no bias supply. Until there is a bias supply the controller IC cannot start switching, so we have the same 'chicken or egg' problem we saw with the PFC input stage. A simple solution is to bleed a little of the rectified mains DC via a high value resistor to feed the bias supply. If the controller IC is a UC384x series the start up current is very low, around 250µA, the resistor only needs to supply 1mA or so worst case. In most cases a value between 56kΩ and 100kΩ with a 1 watt rating will suffice. It is prudent to connect a parallel Zener across the bias supply to cater for unexpected voltage transients. If the 14-pin version of the UC384x series is used, this contains an internal 36V nominal Zener clamp. A good choice would be a 18V/1W Zener, as this is above the nominal 15V bias supply it will not affect the regulation via the feedback divider.

13

Introduction to High Voltage Supplies

> *"Why wait any longer for the.world to begin. You can have your cake and eat it too."* Bob Dylan

Most amateurs today have used only modern low voltage equipment and will have not much appreciation of the high voltage supplies used in earlier days. However, in high power RF linear amplifiers the use of valves is still common. For more than about 200W RF output, a valve is the only game in town. The voltages used are extremely dangerous and lethal for the unaware. But with care in design and construction the supply can be as safe as a low voltage type and simpler to make than low voltage, high current regulated or switchmode supplies.

Safety aspects

The VHF/UHF DX Book (ed Ian White, G3SEK, pub DIR Publications), there is a section devoted to this subject by John Nelson, GW4FRX, who has considerable experience on this topic. In a sidebar in the first couple of pages, there is this sobering warning about the hazards of working on HV power supplies.

"Amateur radio, working DX and building amplifiers are all enormous fun - but has its own hazards. If you connect yourself across a 2000V supply, the very best you can hope for is a serious heart attack with severe burns thrown in for good measure".

High Voltage Safety

KEEP ONE HAND BEHIND YOUR BACK - when working on any high voltage equipment.

NEVER WEAR HEADPHONES - or anything else connected to ground whilst working on a high voltage supply.

DON'T ADJUST TEST PROBES ON A LIVE HV SUPPLY - switch off, clip on the probes, step back, pause for thought, and then switch on.

DON'T WORK WITH HV IF YOU ARE TIRED OR IN A HURRY. When you have worked all evening finishing the HV supply, leave the testing for tomorrow. And don't decide to do it when you get back home from the pub!

DON'T FORGET THAT LOWER VOLTAGES ARE DANGEROUS TOO - the screen-grid and control-grid supplies will kill you if you let them. The AC mains supply can also see you off prematurely if you are careless.

It's your life and you only have one.

Connection between HV supply and amplifier

One aspect that constructors often fall down on is the way the power supply is connected to the amplifier. If the RF amplifier box also contains the power supply, this topic does not enter into the equation. However, supplies for high power linear amplifiers are big and bulky and the choice is often made to have a separate RF amplifier and a power supply in its own box. This saves space on the operating desk as the RF amplifier can be made much smaller and the power supply can be situated some distance away under the desk, keeping your feet warm on cold winter evenings! Making the power supply a separate item is especially convenient whilst constructing or fault finding an amplifier. Having to lug a heavy box around on the workbench is tedious.

Having always taken cognisance of 'Nelson's Rule' (John Nelson, GW4FRX) which states "if you can lift the power supply, the transformer is too small", I have always used a separate power supply. This is also convenient if you have two separate amplifiers for 2m and 70cm requiring the same voltages, making one power supply for the two RF decks saves a bundle of work and cash! Of course, you have to swap the connectors over from one RF deck to the other but that only takes a few minutes and as my shack is a little cramped these days it saves a lot of space.

In such a design, the choice is often to put the main on/off switch on the RF amplifier deck. This is convenient from an operating point of view but means that we need extra wires in a multi-way cable and plugs and sockets to cater for all the extra circuitry.

The current drawn by a big RF amplifier power supply from the mains can be high, in some cases a wall outlet may be overloaded. In my new shack I ran a separate 30A 230V AC feed from the distribution board in the house with its own earth leakage circuit breaker, to cater for the anticipated current load of all the high power amplifiers. My wife got fed up with me tripping the earth leakage in the house when something went wrong!

Fig 13.1: The author's power supply for a K2RIW 70cm amplifier. The front panel contains the main cooling fan, main fuse holder, circuit breaker and an indicator lamp. The top cover is removed in this picture

Incidentally, in South Africa we haven't yet adopted the 13A fused flat-pin plug as the UK. We still use a round pin 3-pin plug, which is rated at 16A; this is the same as the old 15A used in the UK in older days. In my opinion the 16A plug is a better proposition than the 13A plug.

The only safe way to switch mains is with a double-pole switch that simultaneously disconnects the line and neutral. In this case the mains supply from the wall outlet will need to enter the power supply box, pass via a two-pole circuit breaker (or a two-pole switch) then exit it to go to the RF amplifier box main on/off switch. It then returns to the power supply box to feed the transformer(s) primary, this requires a minimum of 4 wires each one being quite a substantial gauge of wire.

Now consider the problems with this arrangement. The multi-way connectors and cable need to be adequately rated to carry this current. We would need a connector with a minimum voltage rating of 400V DC and a current rating of about 20A for each pin. A connector of this rating can be obtained, but they are expensive. Common connectors, such as "D" type connectors, can be readily obtained which have voltage ratings up to 500V DC and a current rating of up to 5A per pin. These are much cheaper and can, with sufficient ingenuity, perform the task. I will show how I do it later.

What about the high voltage? The anode voltage may be anything from 500V to 5kV depending on the RF output valve being used. For 400W+ class of amplifiers, it will be more than 1500V DC and very often much more. About 6kV is the highest I have seen in the various publications.

How are we going to connect from the power supply box to the RF amplifier? I have seen many ways of doing this, some professional and very safe and others that I don't even want to talk about! You can forget about using the multi-way connector used for the other supply rails, a connector that can handle these sorts of voltages would be astronomically expensive.

The preferred way is use a type of coaxial connector that accepts a type of shielded cable, similar to coax. In fact, you can use certain types of RF coaxial cable for up to about 3kV. There are high voltage versions of the BNC (HNC) connectors made by several manufacturers for this application and some exotic types (PET100) which turn up at swap meets (rallies) from time to time. The current required is usually not more than 1A and a BNC type high voltage connector can safely carry 2A or more.

My old 2 metre EME amplifier, which was originally built by Joe Ludlow, GW3ZTH (when he worked for the same company as I did in Durban, SA), uses a pair of PTFE insulated Amphenol plug/sockets of the PL-259/SO-239 generation and RG-213 coax. This is now over 20 years old and has safely carried the 3.3kV between the power supply and RF deck without any trouble.

Now answer this question: Where is the ground connection between the power supply and the RF amplifier deck ? If you cannot come up with an answer in less than a few milliseconds, you could be in for a disaster.

It absolutely vital to have a solid and totally reliable connection between the power supply, the RF amplifier, and the whole set of metalwork must be solidly connected to the public mains supply earth terminal.

Failure to observe this could be the last thing you ever do in this life.

Suppose you lose the amplifier HV ground return while operating. If you are lucky, all that will happen will be a spectacular firework display with lots of magic smoke. However, the chassis and metalwork could silently float up to several kV, just waiting for you to touch it. Or maybe the HV return finds a devious route back to the power supply, such as the antenna or rotator cable, and you would be none the wiser until you parted an innocent looking connector with a plug in each hand - RIP!

Despite the fact that you have made up a multi-way cable to connect the RF amplifier to the power supply, with several pins dedicated to ground, this is useless if you then have a separate HV unscreened cable plugged between the two units.

It is essential to have a dedicated ground strap bolted between the chassis of the two units, one you would stake your life on - because that is exactly what you are doing!

Supply voltages required

This depends on the RF output valve you are intending to use and the power output expected. The manufacturer of the valve will usually give recommended operating conditions that can be taken as reliable. Depending on the type of valve chosen there may be a need for more than anode and filament (heater) supplies. If the valve is a grounded grid triode such as 3-500Z, only two supplies are essential; these are the anode supply and the filament supply. In most cases the filament supply will be a simple AC supply provided by a low voltage winding on the main transformer. For other triodes a negative control-grid supply may be required. The current drawn by the filament of a large valve can be high, the 3-500Z requires a 5V supply at 14.5A and the option is usually chosen to have a separate filament transformer located close to the valve to reduce voltage drop in the filament leads. For amplifiers using two 3-500Z valves, we need a 29A-filament transformer.

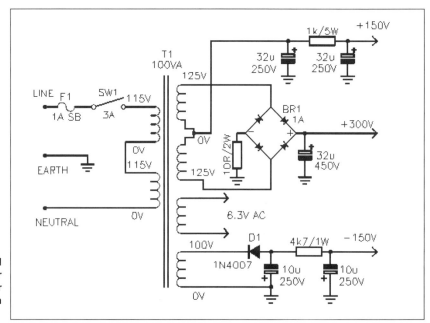

Fig 13.2: Typical arrangement for supplying the lower voltages for a high power amplifier

For tetrodes the screen grid and control-grid need regulated supplies. All the valve types will require some other DC low voltage supplies to operate relays, possibly 12V or 24V depending on the relay types you intend to use.

Let us take a common VHF valve, the 4CX250B, and list the voltages and currents required. (Current ratings quoted are for a single valve; for a dual-valve amplifier double the figures given).

A single 4CX250B on 144MHz can produce ≈300W PEP reliably with low intermodulation, but only if the power supply is designed correctly.

- The manufacturers recommended maximum anode voltage rating is 2kV at maximum anode current. The anode voltage off load can safely be as high as 2.5kV. The maximum continuous anode current is approximately. 400mA. Therefore, allowing a little extra anode current for tuning up, the supply needs to be able to source about 500 to 600mA at an anode voltage of between 1800V to 2.2kV

- The screen-grid supply needs to be stabilised and supply approximately +300V to +350V at a current of 30mA, and able to sink the same sort of negative screen current. (A peculiarity of the 4CX250 family).

- The control-grid supply needs to supply a voltage adjustable between -30V and -150V with a capability to sink approximately 10mA of grid current.

- The filament needs a supply voltage of 6V at 3A max; this can be AC or DC.

Of the four supplies above, the only one that needs any comment is the anode supply. You will note that I have specified the maximum anode voltage at 2.2kV whereas the manufacturers recommended maximum is 2kV. This is because the manufacturer quotes the voltage to give maximum valve life for continuous commercial service (CCS rating), ie 24hr/day at full output.

As experience has grown with this type of valve, the use of a higher anode voltage offers a little higher output power and gain with little effect on its longevity when used with the ICAS rating (intermittent commercial and amateur service) in other words the envelope can be pushed quite a bit without serious consequences.

In fact, in my 2m EME amplifier I run the 2 x 4CX250Bs much harder, with nearly 3kV on-load, but I expect to change valves more frequently as they are being 'caned' to squeeze the last possible drop of power out of them. However, I have had only one valve failure in over 15 years of operating, and that was caused by a lizard crawling into the anode compartment whilst the amplifier was off, 4CX250's are incredibly tough beasts!

Filament supply

Most valve manufacturers recommend that no anode or screen voltage be applied until the filament has reached operating temperature. This means we have to arrange some sort of time delay between switching on the filament transformer and the anode high voltage transformer. This time delay can be performed by a simple timer circuit.

Transformer requirements

The builder has a choice as to whether to only use one mains transformer for the various supply voltages, or two or more transformers. The choice is often down to what you can find or have in your "storeroom". There are certain advantages in using separate transformers for the high and lower voltage supply rails. By using a large high voltage transformer that only supplies the anode voltage the remainder of the supplies can be handled by a smaller multi-winding transformer and this makes commissioning the power supply safer. My preference when building the K2RIW dual-valve amplifier for 432 MHz was to use three transformers. The high voltage transformer has only one secondary winding which supplies the anode voltage. (I will leave the screen-grid supply description until later as I use an unusual way of obtaining this).

The second transformer contained windings for the control-grid supply, and low voltage windings for 12V and 24V relay supplies. The third transformer is contained within the RF deck and supplies the 6V at 6A required by the filaments. The reason for this was the way I performed the on-off switching of the power supply and the problem with volts drop in the multi-way cable between the power supply and RF deck. The filament supply with 6A flowing meant a heavy pair of wires, which I chose not to accommodate.

On-off switching

The main on-off switch on my 432MHz amplifier (see **Fig 13.3**) is contained on the RF deck. This is a small 5A dual-pole toggle switch that fitted in with the cosmetics of the rest of the controls. This switch supplies the primary of the small transformer, about 50VA rating. The small transformer when enabled provides the control grid regulator and the control circuitry with several low voltage rails; it also powers the power supply cooling fan. The main on-off switch also switches 230V AC to the filament transformer and the cooling fan on the RF deck.

The control circuitry contains a timer that controls the high voltage transformer primary. The high voltage transformer primary current is quite high and needs a substantial switch or relay. When the main on-off switch is thrown the control circuitry starts a timer running which delays the start up of the high voltage. The timer runs for about 60 seconds and then turns on the high voltage

Fig 13.3: The author's K2RIW 70cm amplifier. The three small switches to the left of the front panel are the reset push button, the amplifier mode switch (FM/SSB) and the main on-off switch. The three indicators are 'Ready', 'Mains ON' and 'Trip'. The temporary paper labels have since fallen off some of the controls. I will get around to labelling these permanently sometime! The meter switch is to the left of the meter

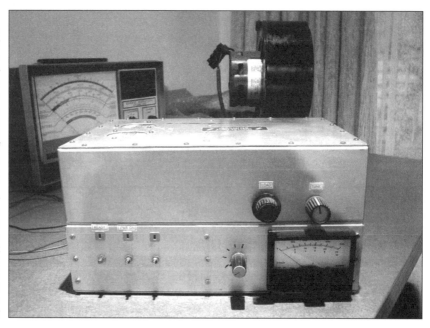

Fig 13.4: Rear of the K2RIW amplifier. The high voltage enters the anode compartment via the high voltage BNC connector. All other supplies are carried by the 25 way D connector. The grid bias pre-set is under the cooling fan. The RCA connector below the D type supplies a sequenced 24V supply to the mast head preamp and the second RCA connector is the main PTT input from the 70cm transceiver

transformer. I went to all this trouble because of the filament warm-up time required for the 4CX250B valves. The valve manufacturer recommends that no anode voltage or screen grid voltage be provided until the valve filaments have reached operating temperature.

The 24V relay that controls the primary of the high voltage transformer has big contacts which are well able to cope with the heavy current. I could have used separate big toggle switches on the power supply to switch the high voltage transformer, as I did with the old 2m EME amplifier power supply, but this is inconvenient as the power supply lives under the operating bench. Also when arriving in the shack at 3am in the middle of winter for an EME sked I am not the most awake person and I didn't fancy the consequences of not being able to throw the necessary switches in the correct sequence! Now all I need to do is throw one small switch and the power supply being more competent than me goes through the 'boot-up' sequence whilst I try to find the scrap of paper I wrote the callsign and other details on.

In-rush current limiting

Simply throwing a mains switch connected directly to a big transformer can cause some interesting results! Have you noticed the "Thwung" noise when you do this? This puts a massive strain on the high voltage components - the transformer, diodes and smoothing capacitors. The smoothing capacitors are at zero volts when the supply is switched off. When the switch is operated, the secondary voltage immediately rises to its full value and the in-rush current that the diodes, smoothing capacitors and the transformer primary and secondary have to cope with can be thousands of amps, especially if you are unlucky and catch the mains as it hits the peak of the sinewave. This often causes something to expire (usually the diodes and/or the capacitors) with a loud bang - and lots of magic smoke!

By correctly sequencing the power supply 'boot-up' I can be assured that every time I throw the on-off switch nothing more spectacular than the cooling fans in the amplifier and power supply starting disturbs my shack.

The control circuitry, as it has been switched on by the main on-off switch, is wide-awake and ready for action. After the 60s filament delay timer runs down, the control circuitry tells the 24V relay on the Soft Start board (**Fig 13.5**) to switch the mains through to the high voltage transformer. In series with the primary winding is a 12Ω high wattage, heat sensitive resistor. This resistor limits the initial primary surge current to something safe (≈20A). When the high voltage rectified output has risen above a point of two-thirds of the final voltage the current limiting resistor is shorted out with another 24V relay of the same type as the primary one. The time for this to happen is less than half a second and the 'Ready' indicator on the front panel of the RF amplifier is then lit telling me it is now OK to transmit. The control circuitry also has some spare relay contacts to prevent the transceiver PTT activating the amplifier before the supply is correctly established.

The heat sensitive resistor has a soft-soldered springy link, which if the resistor gets too hot causes the solder to melt and opens to disconnect the primary supply. These resistors are used in television sets as a 'last-gasp' protection. You will see later why I chose this route.

The real bonus of this is that I needed just two extra small wires at mains potential between the power supply box and the RF deck which the 'D' type connector was easily able to handle. The multi-core cable I used was rated at 2A per wire; the 'D' type connector is rated at 5A per pin. The heavy wiring from the mains input dual pole circuit breaker to the high voltage transformer is all contained in the power supply box, making for low volts drop.

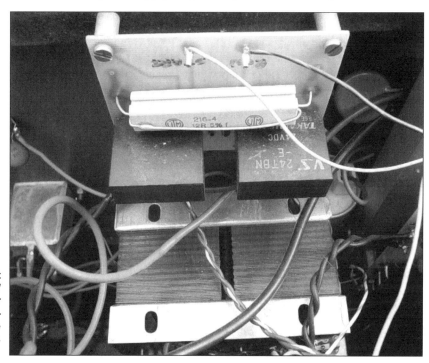

Fig 13.5: Soft-start board in the K2RIW amplifier power supply. The auxiliary low voltage transformer is below

Mains transformer specification

The high voltage transformer needs to supply a secondary voltage suitable for feeding a bridge rectifier/capacitor input filter that will supply the anode. We have already decided that we need a HT voltage of between 1.8kV to 2.2kV at a current of 500mA maximum (this is for a single 4CX250). This is a rating of 1100VA. However, as we saw in the chapter dealing with mains transformers, we can derate this somewhat as we aren't going to be running 'key-down' for very long periods. SSB and CW ratings are approximately 30% of full carrier so we can safely get by with a transformer rating of about half the calculated, or about 500VA for a single 4CX250. Included in the power supply box is a substantial cooling fan, which means we can derate the transformer even more.

Assuming a bridge rectifier feeding a capacitor-input reservoir, we need a peak secondary current of approximately 800mA because of the rectification efficiency of 62%. The regulation of the transformer doesn't have to be spectacular; a regulation of 10% would give a variation of the rectified DC of about 200V. The regulation can be allowed to be worse than this and a figure of 15 to 20% should be satisfactory. The secondary voltage rating needs to be:

$$V_{DC} / 1.414 = 1555V \ AC$$

A transformer with a secondary of 1400V to 1600V AC should be fine. Of course, if you happen to stumble across a centre-tapped secondary of 1500-0-1500 at 500mA this will also do fine in a bi-phase full wave rectifier. However, the likelihood of finding one of those beasts is getting rare these days and isn't such a good a choice as the bridge configuration as you will see a little later.

> The regulation chosen needs to be carefully considered as this has a direct bearing on the capacitor working voltage. If the regulation were 10% the off-load secondary voltage would be 110% of the full load rating. If the secondary was rated at 1500V AC at the estimated 800mA the full load output voltage would be 2121V DC and the off load rectified voltage will be at least 2333V DC. Allowing the regulation to drop to 20% would yield an off load voltage of 2545V for the same full load voltage, and we haven't considered the high mains condition yet!

Diode rating

As we have opted for a bridge rectifier we will need quite a few diodes to get the required PIV. The PIV required is at least twice the highest output voltage (the off-load condition), therefore we will select a diode with at least a 1000V PIV and a current rating of at least twice the rectified current, or about 1.5A. The nearest available type is the 1N4007 but these are only rated at 1A average current and a poor choice today, so I prefer to go up one size and use the 1N5408 which is a 1250V device rated at 3A RMS with a surge rating of 120A. We will play safe and use at least four diodes in each leg of the bridge; therefore we need 16 diodes. When diodes are connected in series to gain the higher PIV, we need to ensure they share the applied voltage. This is done by connecting a high value resistor across each diode; a value of 270kΩ to 680kΩ with a half-watt rating is a good choice. Our bridge will have an equivalent PIV of 8 x 1250V, which is very good for reliability.

Diode block stacks

There are made up diode stacks on the market containing several high voltage diodes with the sharing resistors, all encapsulated in an epoxy block. For a bridge set up we would need four of these, however, and the cost of these is far more than buying the individual components and providing a suitable insulated mounting. They are also rated at much higher voltages than we would normally need, starting at around 8kV, so I would only use these if I came across a job lot at a swap-meet (rally) at the right price.

Diode damping capacitors

Some published designs in the past have recommended the addition of capacitors across each diode to damp out transients as well as the sharing resistors. These capacitors were usually ≈1nF disk ceramics with a voltage rating of at least the diode rating. Therefore we would need to fit 1kV minimum rated capacitors. I used to use a safety capacitor that was designed as the TV antenna isolator with a rating of 470pF at 3kV, but these are now hard to find. However, many diode manufacturers now warn about the dangers of fitting these capacitors as they can cause diode failure. I no longer fit them.

Smoothing capacitor

The smoothing capacitor needs to have a working voltage of at least 25% more than the expected off-load voltage, to cater for abnormally high mains. You might think this is unlikely, but after many years of contesting from mountain tops I can assure you that this does exist when portable generators are used. These typically can be 25% up on the nominal AC voltage when the load is suddenly removed and they become lightly loaded. If your smoothing capacitor cannot tolerate this sort of over-voltage condition you will have an exciting time when the smoothing capacitor bank lets go!

In the old days the preferred capacitor was a single large block paper type, but these today are expensive and rare. If you manage to find one at a swap meet be very cautious. Some of these old capacitors have been lying around for many years and will certainly have a high leakage current unless they have been regularly reformed. They also contain a carcinogenic electrolyte that is highly toxic. If it shows signs of weeping, steer well clear! I have in my shack two very fine examples of these animals. A friend of mine and I between us bought a scrap medical defibrillator at an amateur swap meet. It contained two enormous paper capacitors each rated at 3.75kV at 32µF (see **Fig 13.6**). These were very high-grade medical equipment specification and must have cost a small fortune when new. These capacitors were charged up to around 3500V and discharged across a patient's chest to 'kick-start' the heart when a cardiac arrest occurred. Today I use the capacitor as a paperweight!

For most of us, the only solution is a string of high voltage electrolytic capacitors connected in series to get the required working voltage. What sort of value do we aim for? This largely depends on the voltage regulation we require, the chief culprit in the regulation equation is the transformer. Having a capacitor value greater than the regulation required is a waste of money, and causes problems with the peak diode current. Increasing the capacitor value excessively will stress the diodes and the secondary winding because of the higher peak currents flowing.

Fig 13.6: Two block paper high voltage capacitors. The round one is the medical defibrillator capacitor rated at a test voltage of 15kV. The rectangular one is 16µF at 7.5kV. The date code on this one is 1974, definitely suspect without reforming! The oscilloscope in the background gives some indication of the size

Suppose we could accept a ripple voltage of, say, 50V at full load current, this is about 2.5%. We can use the standard formula to calculate the capacitor value.

$$C \approx \frac{I_{(avg)}}{8 \times f_r \times V_r}$$

where: $I_{(avg)}$ is the average secondary current

f_r is the ripple frequency, normally 2 x the mains frequency

V_r is the allowable ripple voltage - peak to peak in volts

With our transformer secondary current of 800mA and 50Hz mains supply this works out to:

$$C \approx \frac{0.8}{8 \times 100 \times 50} = 20µF$$

Depending on the working voltage of the capacitors available, we then need to multiply the required capacitor value by the number of capacitors needed to get the required safe working voltage.

Suppose we need a capacitor value of 30µF and the capacitors readily available are rated at 450V. We need a voltage rating of at least 10% more than the expected maximum high voltage. This would require a total voltage rating of:

$V_{DC(max)} \times 1.1$

where: $V_{DC(max)}$ is the off load secondary AC voltage x 1.414

In my K2RIW amplifier I used a secondary voltage of 1500V AC at 800mA with a regulation of 15%.

$V_{DC(max)}$ is 1500 x 1.414 x 1.15 = 2439V, to cater for the abnormal off-load condition expected, and a full load anode voltage of ≈2100V, on a good day!

Therefore we would need a capacitor safe working voltage of ≈2450V, requiring a minimum of 5.44 capacitors and hence we choose to use 6 capacitors. The capacitors would need to be at least 180µF so we opt for the next higher standard value, which is 220µF. The capacitor bank will have a nominal voltage rating of 6 x 450 = 2700V, and an equivalent capacitance of 36.66µF.

450V capacitors normally have a surge rating of 525V so our capacitor bank can safely withstand 6 x 525 = 3150V for a few seconds. The ripple current rating of a typical 450V / 220µF capacitor is 1A, which is adequate, as we need a maximum ripple rating of 800mA for our supply.

Working out the nominal off-load voltage across each capacitor gives an answer of 406V which is well below the maximum rating of 450V.

My final choice of transformer was dictated by the 'flaky' mains I suffer here in rural South Africa and the trade-off of using a down-sized core to lower the cost. Your requirements will dictate the final choice, so do the sums to be sure your choice is correct!

In the K2RIW power supply I chose Rubycon capacitors intended for off-line switching supplies. This was because they were readily available and lower cost than other types, and adequately rated for ripple current and temperature.

Voltage sharing and bleeder resistors

Fig 13.7: The high voltage board in the K2RIW amplifier power supply removed for clarity. The electrolytic capacitors, bridge diodes, sharing resistors, current sensing and limiting resistors and voltage sensing resistors are mounted on the board. (The large wire wound resistor at the top is the dropper resistor for the screen stabiliser)

The capacitors need sharing resistors to equalise the voltage across each capacitor. These need to have a high value to reduce the power wasted but not so high that the sharing isn't correctly performed. These sharing resistors if correctly dimensioned can also perform the function of the 'bleeder' resistor, to ensure the output voltage falls to zero when the supply is turned off. Failure to 'bleeddown' the capacitor bank is a recipe for disaster because if you try to work on the power supply and the bank has some residual voltage the chances of getting a lethal shock are very high.

Assume that the power supply has two equal value capacitors in series to obtain a working voltage of twice each capacitor. The tolerance of electrolytic capacitors is such that the actual value can be within 80% and 150% of the marked value, so the voltage split will not be equal, even with two capacitors from the same batch.

Taking a 100µF capacitor as an example. One can be as low as 80µF and one as high as 150µF and the ratio of the voltage across the capacitors will be the inverse of the actual capacitance, meaning the 80µF capacitor will have almost twice the voltage of the 150µF. Therefore if no attempt is made to equalise the voltage the lower value capacitor will have the majority of the applied voltage, which will stress the capacitor and cause it to fail.

My preference is to use 47kΩ / 5W wirewound resistors for voltage sharing. This value is quite a bit lower than most books specify but the extra current drawn helps to hold the off-load voltage down to safer levels and provides a rapid bleed down when switching off. These will get fairly warm and need to be mounted away from any part of the supply liable to be affected by heat. I normally mount the bridge diodes, smoothing capacitors and the sharing resistors on

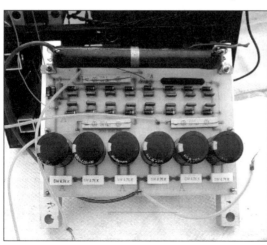

a printed circuit board (**Fig 13.7**). As my supplies are usually fan-cooled, I arrange the PC board to be in the main fan draught. The dissipation in my sharing resistors was calculated to be approximately 22W which is well below the nominal 30W dissipation the resistors are rated at. By utilising the draught from the cooling fan the dissipation can safely be assumed to be at least 50% more. However, here is a trick I learnt a long time ago.

Centre-tapped secondary

When I design a high voltage supply that uses several electrolytic capacitors connected in series, I always specify a centre-tapped secondary even though I will be using a bridge rectifier and I always use an even number of capacitors. The reason is this:

In a centre-tapped secondary feeding a bridge rectifier the centre point of the winding sits at exactly half the output voltage. If the centre point is connected to the mid-point in the capacitor bank (see **Fig 13.8**), the secondary forces the voltage at that point to be exactly half. The current that you can draw from the centre tap is about 20% of the total output current before the voltage sharing becomes affected. This arrangement means that higher value sharing resistors can be used with less heat. But there is one other bonus, which I haven't mentioned. I use the centre point as the source for the screen-grid stabiliser.

This voltage will only be present when the HT is present so if the anode voltage fails the screen-grid voltage also disappears, saving costly damage to the

Fig 13.8: My high voltage supply, showing the use of a centre-tapped transformer

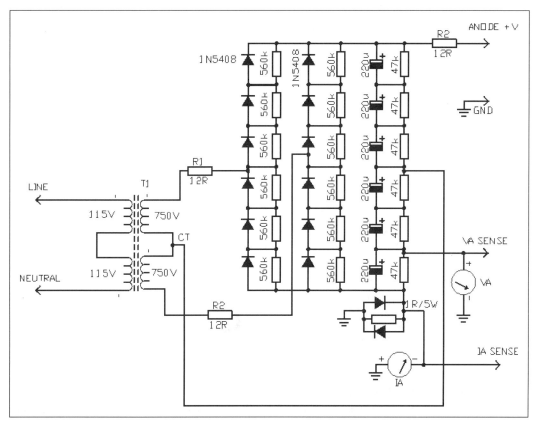

fragile screen grid in the 4CX250. The large wire wound resistor shown in the previous picture is connected to the centre tap of the capacitor bank and the transformer centre tap.

You may wonder how the HT can disappear. Well, in all the years I have been building high voltage supplies I have seen some weird things happen which defy logic, often with vast emissions of magic smoke!

You will remember that I use a heat sensitive resistor in series with the primary of the HT transformer for Soft-Start. Consider what happens if for some reason the HT does not get above the two-third trip point of the control circuit when the HT transformer is first switched on. This could be because a valve has decided to give out and go short circuit between the anode and cathode, or a spider has crawled into the RF amplifier and started making a nest, or a lizard has taken up residence in the power supply because it was nice and warm, yes all of these happened to me!

This is a dead short across the anode supply and if we did not have a 'last-gasp' device in case the main fuse or circuit breaker did not disconnect the mains, an expensive transformer could burn out. In a case like this, the second relay will not be switched to short out the in-rush-limiting resistor. After a few seconds the resistor heats up enough for the low temperature solder to melt and the primary supply is disconnected.

> You will notice in Fig 13.8 that I have included a high wattage resistor in series with each leg of the secondary feeding the bridge rectifier and another in series with the HT output. These resistors are also used as current limiting for additional soft-start and are also the heat sensitive types mentioned earlier and are designed to go open circuit if something fails. The HT output resistor is to take some of the sting out of a high voltage flashover and limit the current to something manageable, ≈150A.

Fail-safe built into high voltage supplies is a must in my book! You may think I am being a little obsessive, but having missed more than one exotic contact because the power supply 'conked out' when I most needed it has made me that way! I also hate having to do things over because I took a short cut when I first built the supply.

I will give details later of some of the other protection built into my high voltage supplies. I can safely drop a screwdriver across the anodes and ground with no spectacular flashes and bangs, it quietly shuts down, simply because I have everything covered in the protection circuitry.

Screen-grid stabiliser

The screen grid uses a shunt stabiliser drawing current via a dropper resistor from the centre-tap of the high voltage transformer. This resistor has a high dissipation and is also positioned in the fan cooling draught. The voltage drop across the resistor is approximately 750V and the shunt stabiliser draws a constant 60mA (for two 4CX250s). The dropper resistor can be made up from several wire-wound resistors, connected in series. In my K2RIW power supply I was able to find a suitable 100W wire-wound resistor which is mounted with spring clips and positioned in the fan-cooling stream. The total dissipation required is approximately 45W. The stabiliser uses three high voltage transistors connected in parallel and they are heatsinked to a substantial bracket, also fan cooled.

The peculiar screen-grid antics of the 4CX250 range of valves means that with low drive the screen current is usually very negative. With a conventional series stabiliser, because the screen grid of the valve is trying to 'push' current back into the screen power supply from the anode potential, this causes the screen voltage to rise above the set point. If this is allowed to continue, eventually the voltage rises enough to cause the fragile screen decoupling capacitor built into the valve airflow socket to fail. This causes a 'monstrous bang'; the result is usually one or both valves, and airflow sockets are destroyed. Very expensive! To protect the fragile screen grid and airflow socket it is also a good idea to connect a 400V MOV across the valve pin and ground as an added safety clamp. However, with a correctly designed shunt stabiliser this should never be called upon to operate.

The 4CX250 series needs a screen supply that is very 'stiff' and able to 'sink' as well as 'source' current. The shunt stabiliser is the best option. In earlier designs most people used a string of high voltage Zeners to clamp the screen voltage. Although this works to some extent, the dynamic regulation under SSB is poor (due to the relatively high impedance of high voltage Zeners) and the screen voltage therefore has an audio frequency ripple voltage caused by the intermittent current flowing. This severely degrades the intermodulation performance and causes the signal to spread across several tens of kilohertz, which the other local operators don't like! To achieve full performance that the 4CX250 valve is capable of requires a screen stabiliser that can hold the voltage within ±20mV, not a simple task.

Don't even think about using series connected gas stabilisers valves such as OA2s. These cannot sink enough current to hold the screen grid within the required range and have very poor dynamic impedance. If the voltage across the stabiliser tubes falls low enough for the internal gas to stop conducting the voltage needs to rise to a much higher level before the tube re-strikes and then the voltage is stabilised again. (The striking voltage is usually about 110V and the running voltage about 85V). Often when gas stabiliser valves are used, the need arises to fit a large electrolytic capacitor across the stabiliser valve to lower the impedance. This makes the circuit into a relaxation oscillator that produces an audio frequency 'buzz-saw' signal on the RF output; not exactly what we are trying to achieve!

Control grid stabiliser

As with the screen grid supply, the control grid also needs a bit more thought than most people suspect. In all my years experimenting with different valves I have become aware of some which need more care than others. Many of the older amplifier designs simply use an unregulated negative supply, and a potential divider formed from resistors and a preset pot to set the grid voltage. If the resistors used have a very low value this works, but the dissipation in them becomes excessive. Because the negative supply is not stabilised the idle current drifts around as the mains voltage varies, not a very satisfactory situation!

It is interesting to hook a 'scope to the control grid supply of a triode or tetrode and observe what happens when RF drive is applied. If the valve is operated in Class AB1 the resulting grid current is very low and little disturbance of the grid voltage is seen. But change the conditions to AB2 or Class C and the grid voltage gets much greater (negative) as the RF drive is increased due to the control grid acting as a rectifier diode. In fact with valves such as the QQVO-6/40 and the 4CX250 series the grid voltage increases so much that the valve gets driven into the grid cut-off region and the output power actually starts to fall above a certain drive level! This is definitely what we don't want if the linearity has to be maintained. A poor control grid regulation is as bad as a poor screen grid regulation and both contribute to severe intermodulation products and adjacent channel splatter.

As with the screen grid, the control grid also needs to be supplied from a low impedance or 'stiff' supply.

With the QQVO-6/40 control and screen grid circuits I published some years ago in *Radio ZS*, many amateurs reported gain and output power increases as much as 100% over the original designs. This was also with a considerable reduction in intermodulation distortion and lower running temperatures in the valve for the same output power. The intermodulation distortion that the amplifier introduces to the final signal should be negligible if the control and screen grid regulators are correctly designed and the valve is operated within its linear range. A 'Linear Amplifier' should be just that - *linear*.

Again a shunt stabiliser is the best choice and later you will see the circuit I developed for this.

Metering voltage and current

I have seen many home-built high voltage power supplies, (and some commercial ones!) where the constructor has obviously not even considered what can go wrong. A classic example is the anode current metering. I suppose if you simply connect a milli-ammeter in series with the HV positive it will read correctly. But the internal bits of the meter are sitting at the full HV and only the plastic case is between you and the lethal potential. Many meters do not have sufficient insulation for this when mounted on a grounded metal panel and will break down, with a spectacular flash and bang!

Another problem is that if you are unfortunate to get a minor flashover in the valve, which is quite common with valves being pushed to the limit and you will experience at least one especially when first commissioning a new amplifier. A flashover is a dead short across the HV supply for a fraction of a second. Usually the valve or power supply isn't damaged if it is a very short flashover. But the meter needle will accelerate to around one trillion times supersonic speed until it hits the end stop. This normally destroys the fragile movement and the result is a dead meter.

The only safe and sensible way to meter the anode current is do it at a low potential. A safe and reliable way is to measure the return current in the negative lead of the HV supply. Here the voltage is close to zero and the meter shunt used means that only about 1V maximum exist between the meter terminals and ground. For this you need a meter shunt that will not under any circumstances

Fig 13.9: The home made meter scale on my K2RIW amplifier. The top scale indicates anode current, 500mA FSD. The middle scale is the screen grid current (25mA) and the HT voltage (2.5kV) the bottom scale indicates grid current (10mA) and relative RF o/p (1kW FSD). The scale was plotted twice full size and reduced photographically, then printed on Polish Paper, a special photographic film, and then glued onto the meter plate. The meter is a standard 1mA movement

go open circuit no matter what the flashover current peaks at. In other words, you need a resistor that can withstand high peak surge currents. I usually use a 1Ω, 5W wire-wound resistor. This is convenient, when 0.5A flows the voltage developed is 0.5V, which can be used to drive a standard 1mA meter with suitable divider resistors. Across the shunt resistor is a pair of anti-parallel diodes (1N5408) to clamp the voltage to 0.7V maximum. This protects the meter when a flashover occurs and should the shunt resistor go open circuit.

Metering the HV is also quite simple. As we will have a string of sharing resistors across the capacitor bank we could use the voltage developed across the bottom capacitor as an indication of the total voltage. This can then be reduced with a suitable multiplier resistor to drive a standard milliammeter.

An alternative is to use the voltage divider for the under-voltage detector circuit. In my previous amplifier I managed to find some very nice 5W metal-film resistors of 2MΩ which could withstand 1500V. I used three of these in series and the bottom resistor was a 10kΩ, 1W fixed resistor, with a 4V7 Zener in parallel. The current in this potential divider is about 500μA, which has very low power dissipation in the 2MΩ resistors. The voltage across the 10kΩ, 1W resistor is fed to an op-amp used as a voltage follower. The output of the op-amp then splits two ways, one feeds another op-amp configured as a comparator used as the under voltage detector, and the second output drives the front panel voltmeter via an adjusting preset resistor. The meter is scaled to read 2.5V full scale, which corresponds to 2.5kV (see **Fig 13.9**). The low voltage signals for the anode current and voltage pass via the multi-way cable to the RF amplifier and then via the meter selector switch to the meter. All very safe and reliable.

The K2RIW amplifier power supply used a television focus resistor for the voltage sensing. These are very high voltage resistors (25kV) with a nominal value of 6.6MΩ. This is the long black object near the large wire wound resistor on the high voltage board.

Control and protection circuitry

I have already mentioned some of the functions of the control circuitry. The circuit board that contains the various functions also contains the control relays for antenna relay and other functions such as powering the masthead preamp and the low voltage rectifiers. If desired, the amplifier can be switched out of circuit and the transceiver run 'bare-foot', there are several relays that control the RF switching route.

In order to fully protect an amplifier and power supply, I prefer to have some built-in redundancy. The under-voltage circuit has already been described. An op-amp is used for the anode current metering and over-current trip. If the anode current exceeds a set level, the power supply will be tripped and latched into a standby mode until reset. A flashover or valve failure will normally cause the circuit to trip the power supply.

If any circuit causes the power supply to trip, a reset button is used to restore the supply. If the fault still exists the trip will again operate. Sometimes a minor flashover will cause the supply to trip whilst I am tuning up. When the reset button is pushed, the supply goes through its boot-up sequence with the 60s timer running down, just as if it had been switched on for the first time.

I also have a vane switch in the amplifier deck to monitor the main blower for the 4CX250s. If the fan stops, the supply is tripped by another circuit. Blowers can stop without you noticing, especially when you are operating with headphones on.

I once many years ago 'lunched' a pair of 4CX250s in a 2m contest on a mountain top when someone accidentally tripped on the lead from the power supply to the main blower. In the midst of a contact with the wind howling outside and wearing headphones I didn't hear the fan noise drop. After a few minutes that familiar smell of something cooking was the only thing to alert me, and by then it was too late.

On another occasion whilst operating from the highest mountain in Lesotho (7P8), near the Katze Dam at over 3000m ASL, the fan on the 2m amplifier would keep stopping every 30 minutes or so. The air was so rarefied that the blower motor would overheat and the internal over-temperature sensor in the blower would trip. It took about 10 minutes for it to cool enough to reset despite the air temperature of -20°C, a real pain as we were trying to work W5UN on EME for this very rare country and his last country required for DXCC on 2m!

Primary transient protection

Finally, a word or two about suppressing mains spikes and transients. Although the mains input filtered connector contains some filtering I prefer not to rely entirely on this. Across the primary of the HT transformer is connected a 400V MOV. This device serves to clamp any mains-borne nasties that could destroy the rectifier diodes. As well as this I normally fit a high voltage capacitor to back up the MOV. A 0.1µF / 630V DC rating X type suppression capacitor is OK for this task.

Component parts of the ZS5JF power supply

The printed circuit boards I developed for my K2RIW amplifier cover almost all the features you will ever need for the typical 4CX250 amplifier. The set consists of four boards.

Startup Board

This board contains two relays rated at 16A, and the soft-start resistor plus relay coil clamping diodes. The relays have 24V coils.

High Voltage Board

It contains the bridge rectifier components, smoothing capacitors and sharing resistors. Also incorporated are the heat sensitive resistors and the anode voltage metering and current sensing resistors. The smoothing capacitors are 6 x 220µF / 450V Rubycon USP series (intended for off-line switchmode supplies) with snap-in mounting pins.

Control Board

This contains the low voltage supplies, the relays to switch the various functions of the amplifier, the filament timer, over current trip, under voltage detector and the various protection circuits and metering scaling circuits.

Bias Board

This board has the screen grid and control grid regulators. The series dropper from the transformer secondary centre tap is mounted separately due to the high dissipation.

These boards are all single sided fibreglass with a thickness of 1.6mm and are mounted on metal tubular spacers with the mounting holes connected to the power supply chassis for grounding. In addition I normally fit a separate grounding wire to a solder tag fastened to the chassis with star washers to ensure a solid ground return.

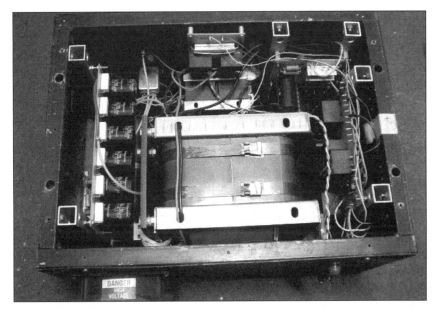

Fig 13.10: Top view of the complete power supply. The high voltage board gets plenty of cooling air from the fan

If you wish to copy any of these boards, it is as well to appreciate the clearances required for high voltage. If the board is to be left uncoated, ie no high voltage EHT varnish, an adequate clearance needs to be allowed between any track carrying high voltage and a lower potential, eg ground. If the humidity levels are low then an uncoated board is sometimes OK. But where I live, on top of a 2,600ft mountain, we are often above the cloud base and the relative humidity can become close to 100%. High voltage and moisture do not mix well! I would recommend that at least the EHT rectifier board be coated with a high voltage varnish or conformable coating to exclude moisture. There are several aerosol canisters manufactured for use in television sets to seal high voltage components. These are a quick air drying clear varnish sealer that provides adequate protection up to many tens of kilovolts. It can also be found in automotive parts supply shops for waterproofing ignition components.

Mechanical construction

The mechanical construction used in the K2RIW power supply is one the other local amateurs and I have evolved over a long time and was originally thought up by Eric McMillan, ZS5JM. It consists of 20mm square metal tubes welded up into a substantial chassis. On the six sides the individual panels are made from either aluminium or steel sheet of about 1mm thickness. Having only to work with flat pieces makes life simpler. The panels are fastened onto the chassis side rails with M3 screws that have holes tapped into the chassis rails. Cooling slots are formed in the panels to allow air to circulate and the 100mm cooling fan pulls the warm air out of the box. Using this form of construction makes assembling and wiring the supply simple and easy to work on should servicing become necessary. The mounting for the large HT transformer is made from two additional cross pieces of the same tubing used for the chassis. This has the necessary holes for the mounting feet of the transformer and the transformer is held down with 6mm bolts.

Fig 13.11: Carrying handles fastened to the top panel make life easy when lugging the supply around. The screen shunt stabiliser transistors are mounted on a metal bracket and heatsinked to a convenient chassis rail

High voltage wiring

The portions of the power supply that carry high voltage need special attention; I have already mentioned the PC board precautions. The other parts carrying high voltage are the wiring from the transformer secondary, the centre tap and the output to the high voltage connector. You can buy special high voltage wire that has a heavy insulation but this is expensive and difficult to find in small quantities. Being descended from Scottish ancestors I balk at the cost of this type of wire. A suitable alternative, which costs almost nothing, is the centre core of RG58 coaxial cable. This can be stripped out with

Fig 13.12: View of bottom of power supply with the bottom cover and high voltage board removed. The high voltage transformer is bolted to two cross tubes. The smaller transformer is for the low voltage supplies

care from the braided outer and has more than adequate insulation for up to 5kV. Do not discard the braid and outer insulation of the RG58 however as this is perfect for the grounding strap between the RF deck and the power supply - "waste not, want not" as the saying goes!

Input circuit breaker or fusing

You have a choice of using either fuses or a circuit breaker to isolate the mains from the power supply in the event of a fault occurring. My preference is for a magnetic circuit breaker as these are instantly resettable, whereas fuses need

Fig 13.13: Close up of top of power supply. The board at the top is the control board and the board at the left is the grid and screen stabiliser. The low voltage transformer and the soft-start board are also visible

Fig 13.14: View of the rear of the power supply. The high voltage BNC connector, mains input connector and the 25 way D type connector are shown

replacing and require you to have spares on hand. I utilised a toggle switch operated circuit breaker, with a rating of 15 amps, on the front panel of the power supply. As the supply has comprehensive fail-safe circuitry built in the use of fuses is a bit redundant and a circuit breaker performs a much better function.

Mains input connector

The choice is largely personal but I prefer to use a three pin "kettle-plug" connector (IEC30 / BS4491) as is commonly used on computers. This connects to a filtered mains receptacle (IEC30) that is rated at 16A and provides additional input filtering.

Power supply boards - schematics

Soft-start PCB

The soft-start board (**Fig 13.15**) connects between the mains incoming live and the transformer primary.

The relays are 24V SPCO types with 16A contacts - Takamisawa 24TBN-E. The START pin supplies the relay power when the 60s timer has run down. The RUN pin is grounded by a transistor when the high voltage has risen above the two-thirds point. These relays are controlled by the Control board. The 12Ω resistor is a heat sensitive type - Vitrohm 216-4. (In my power supply I chose to use 24V relays because it fitted in with the antenna relay coil voltage. I also have a 12V supply available for other relays and the masthead preamp supply).

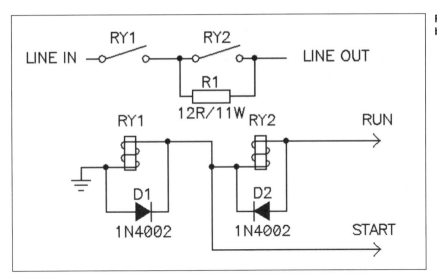

Fig 13.15: Soft-start board circuit

Bias and screen grid board

The bias and screen grid board contains two shunt regulators. The screen regulator is supplied by the HT transformer centre tap via a high wattage resistor. This can be either a $10k\Omega$, 50W single resistor or can be made up from several $3.3k\Omega$ or $3.9k\Omega$, 15W resistors connected in series. (The authors power supply used an external $10k\Omega$, 100W resistor as it was to hand). The circuit shown in **Fig 13.16** assumes the input voltage is about 400V fed from a secondary winding and a bridge rectifier. The value of R1 will depend on the input voltage and it should be rated adequately. The Zener D3 is required if the input supply voltage is greater than 450V to protect the mosfet during switch on, as the IRF840 is a 500V device. A 10nF capacitor is connected between the drain and ground to clamp transients. A 450V MOV is also a good idea. The IRF840 mosfets are connected in parallel (only one is shown in the schematic) and need mounting on a suitable heatsink with an insulating washers and bushes. My power supply has three mosfets externally mounted on a metal bracket. Dissipation in the mosfets is the screen voltage multiplied by the maximum shunt current.

For a single 4CX250 the maximum shunt current will be approximately 40mA, and 80mA for a two-valve supply. The maximum dissipation will occur during standby or receive and if the screen voltage were 350V the power dissipated for a single valve regulator would be 350 x 0.04 = 14W. An IRF840 is rated at 125W dissipation on an infinite heatsink, in practice 50W is a better figure to work with. As the IRF840 mosfets are cheap it makes sense to use at least two in parallel for best reliability.

Note the type of operational amplifier used. This is a very low noise device and it is necessary because any noise generated within the IC would be amplified by the large closed loop gain of about 60. The Signetics NE5534AN is a DIL package with the same pin out as the common 741 but having a noise performance of 100 times better.

The output of the screen regulator contains a $10k\Omega/5W$ current limiting resistor for when CW or FM (or during initial tune up) are used. This causes the voltage to drop when RF drive is applied and provide a lower output power when

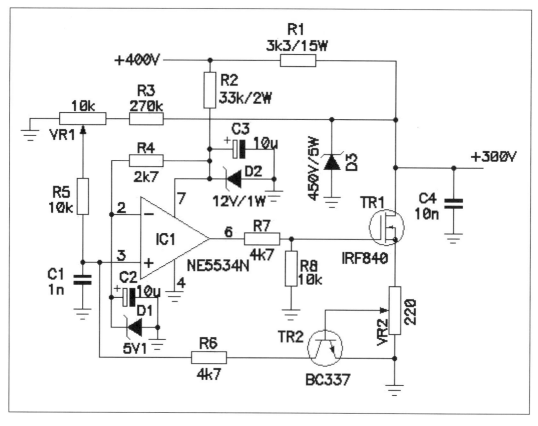

Fig 13.16: 300V Screen grid shunt stabiliser

these modes are used. For SSB, were the best linearity is required, the limiting resistor is bypassed by a switch contact. The resistor and switch are contained in the RF deck. Also in the RF deck is the low value resistor for screen grid current monitoring.

The Control board contains additional switching for the control and screen grid, and the current metering resistor. During receive, the screen grid is switched off and grounded to prevent shot noise in the valve. The BC337 transistor senses the total current drawn and backs off the regulator voltage if this is excessive. The 450V Zener and 10nF capacitor are to absorb transient spikes should a flashover occur and protect the shunt mosfets. The stabiliser reference is supplied by the 5V1 Zener giving almost zero temperature coefficient. This needs to be well decoupled to eliminate the Zener diode noise from modulating the high voltage supply.

The grid regulator (**Fig 13.17**) is supplied by a 100V AC winding on the low voltage control transformer and contains a bridge rectifier using 1N4007 diodes and a 100µF/250V smoothing capacitor. The adjustment pot is mounted on the RF deck so there are three wires that exit the board and are routed in the multiway cable between the power supply and the RF deck. The grid cut-off is performed by a relay contact on the Control board. When the amplifier is on receive this contact is open and the control grid is pulled up to approximately 150V. Grid current metering is provided by the 47Ω resistor in series with the output, giving negligible grid voltage shift with RF drive.

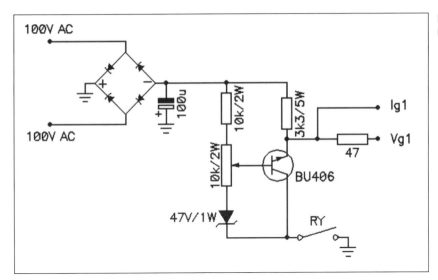

Fig 13.17: Grid bias regulator

High voltage board

The high voltage board contains the bridge rectifier, smoothing capacitors, the voltage and current metering components as well as the surge limiting resistors. The anode current is metered between the power supply ground and the negative return, the 1Ω / 5W resistor with the 1N5408 protection diodes provide the meter shunt. The diagram is Fig 13.8 shown earlier in this chapter.

Control board

The Control Board contains a lot of circuitry and needs to be described in some detail in order for the reader to understand it fully.

The functions it performs are:

- Provides 12V and 24 volt supplies to both itself and to other parts of the amplifier.
- Performs the soft-start on switch-on or after a trip condition.
- Monitors the anode current and voltage and provides a calibrated signal for the metering.
- Detects fault conditions and trips the amplifier.
- Controls the output of the screen and grid stabiliser feeding the RF amplifier.
- Controls the RF switching of the amplifier and external masthead preamp.

An interconnection diagram of the Control Board is shown below and this shows how it interfaces to the rest of the power supply and amplifier units. The various parts of the circuit are too big to fit onto a single sheet and so I have split these up into logical blocks in the later schematics. The pin numbers correspond with the Control Board. All the relays on the control Board operate off the unstabilised 24V supply.

The auxiliary transformer, T1, powering the Control Board has four secondary windings. The primary is switched by the main on-off switch in the RF amplifier. The secondary windings are: 6 volts AC, 9 volts AC, 18 volts AC and 100 volts AC. This last winding is routed to the Bias Board for the grid-stabiliser.

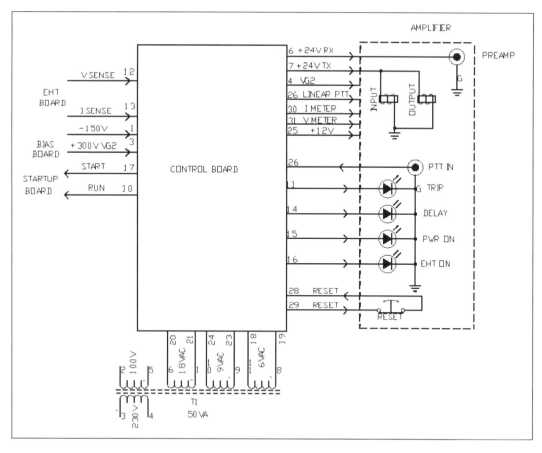

Fig 13.18: Control Board interconnections

The 6V AC winding is used to generate a negative supply for some of the op-amps, this is necessary as the anode current sensing resistor provides a voltage which is negative with respect to ground and these op-amps need to run off a split rail supply. The 9V and 18V windings generate 12V and 24V DC unregulated supplies respectively for the rest of the circuitry.

The 25 way D type connector carries the connections between the Control Board and the RF amplifier.

Timer and trip latch circuits

The filament delay timer and the trip latching trip circuits are shown in **Fig 13.19**. Note, as is the convention in relay circuits the relay contacts are shown in the non-energised state. All the relays have 24V coils but could just as easily be 12V types.

A bridge rectifier supplied by the 18V AC winding on the auxiliary mains transformer, T1, provides the 24V unregulated supply. The rectifier is made from 1N4002 diodes and this feeds a 1000μF/40V reservoir capacitor. This supplies the Control Board via the Reset pushbutton on the amplifier front panel. The Reset button is a normally closed switch.

In series with the reset button is a set of relay contacts, RY2A, which is part of the latching trip circuit. RY2A feeds RY1B and RY1A, which are the contacts controlled by the delay timer. The 'PWR ON' and 'DELAY' LEDs will be lit.

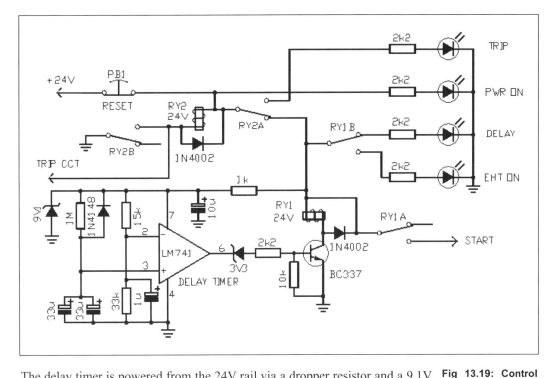

The delay timer is powered from the 24V rail via a dropper resistor and a 9.1V Zener.

Fig 13.19: Control Board delay timer and trip latching circuits.

The delay timer is configured around an op-amp, in this case an LM741, and the inverting input is biased to two-thirds of the supply rail with two resistors. The time delay is provided by a 1MΩ resistor and two 33µF tantalum capacitor. When the capacitors have charged up to the trip point of the op-amp it switches on the BC337 which pulls in RY1. When this happens the 'DELAY' LED will go out, the 'EHT ON' LED will be lit and the Soft-Start board is supplied with 24V via RY1A. This switches on the primary of the high voltage transformer and the high voltage should climb to near full voltage. When this happens the under-voltage circuitry operates a NPN transistor which grounds the second relay on the Soft-Start board to give full mains voltage to the high voltage transformer primary. This circuitry is covered later.

When the circuit is tripped or the RF amplifier is shut down by the main on-off switch the timer capacitors are discharged by the 1N4148 diode across the 1MΩ resistor.

In the event of a fault occurring the trip circuitry will operate and switch on the NPN transistor, which is connected to RY2 and it will be turned on. When this occurs, the second pair of contacts, RY2B causes the relay to latch on until the Reset button is pressed. When RY2 operates, the first set of contacts, RY2A, cause the 'TRIP' LED to be lit, the 'EHT ON' LED to go out and the supply is removed from the timer delay circuitry and the Soft-Start board, causing the high voltage transformer to be switched off. To clear the fault the Reset button has to be pressed and this disconnects the 24V from all the control circuitry, RY2 drops out and the power supply starts as if it had just been switched on for the first time.

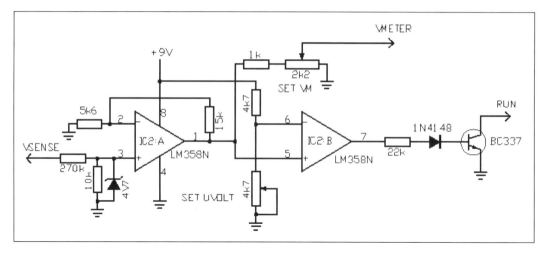

Fig 13.20: Under-voltage and volt-meter drive circuits.

Under-voltage circuit

The anode voltage under-voltage circuit is shown in **Fig 13.20**.

The VSENSE input is provided by the high voltage board and this is amplified by an op-amp (IC2a) to raise the level. The output of the first half of the dual op-amp is fed to the metering adjustment and to the under-voltage comparator (IC2b). The potential divider with an adjusting pot sets the trip point. When the anode voltage has risen to a level set by this threshold the op-amp switches on the NPN transistor which pulls in the RUN relay on the Soft-Start board.

During operation, if an abnormally low anode voltage condition occurs the comparator will switch off the RUN relay on the Soft-Start board and after a few seconds the heat sensitive resistor will go open circuit.

Over-current detector

The over-current detector and anode current metering is shown in **Fig 13.21**.

Fig 13.21: Over-current and current metering circuit

The ISENSE input from the high voltage board is a voltage that swings from zero to approximately -0.5V at 500mA. Because of this, the signal requires inverting to make it a positive voltage before processing. The first half of the

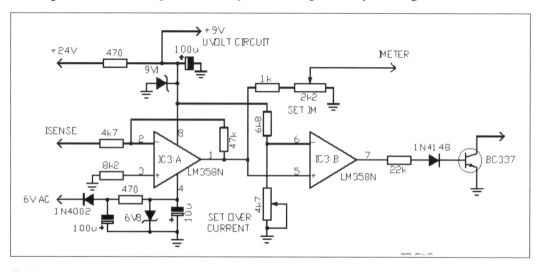

dual op-amp (IC3a) is configured as an inverting gain stage and this then feeds the metering circuit and the over-current comparator (IC3b). This op-amp requires a split supply (negative and positive supply) rail. The op-amp negative supply is provided by a half-wave rectifier from the 6VAC winding on the auxiliary mains transformer and regulated with a 6.8V Zener. The positive 9V supply is provided by another Zener from the 24V supply and is also fed to the under-voltage circuitry.

If the anode current rises above the trip point, the NPN transistor pulls in relay RY2 which latches and the amplifier is shut down until reset by the Reset push-button.

Switching and metering circuits

The final diagrams detail how the switching and metering is performed. (For convenience it is best to place the meter shunts and adjustment potentiometers for the control grid in the RF amplifier, this reduces the number of wires needed in the multi way cable).

The PTT from the transceiver is connected to the RF amplifier and passes via a switch that allows the amplifier to be switched out of circuit. The relays RY4 and RY5 control the switching.

When the RF amplifier is switched out of circuit the relay RY5 is inoperable and hence the control grid and screen grid are not enabled, but RY4 still functions to switch the supplies to the antenna relays and the masthead preamp. The use of 12V or 24V for these is a user's choice.

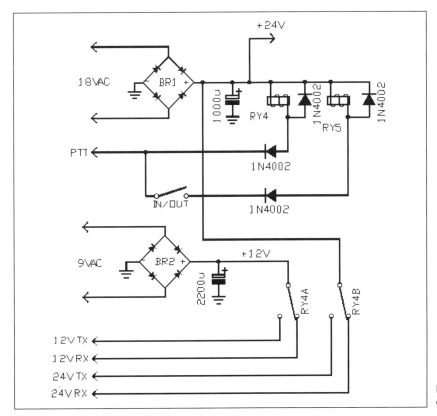

Fig 13.22: Switching circuits

Fig 13.23: Switching and metering circuits

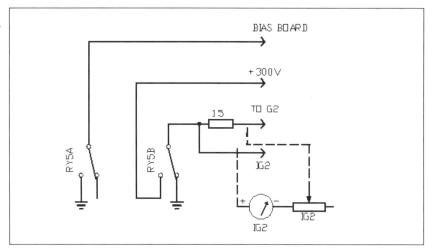

It would have been possible to run the whole Control Board from a 12V supply, but because 24V antenna relays are usually available at swap meets at low cost it was decided to use 24V instead. If the reader wishes to use only 12V then the other relays in the system need to be changed to types with 12V coils.

Fig 13.24: Mains wiring between PSU and amplifier

Finally, **Fig 13.24** shows how the various transformers are supplied with mains voltage.

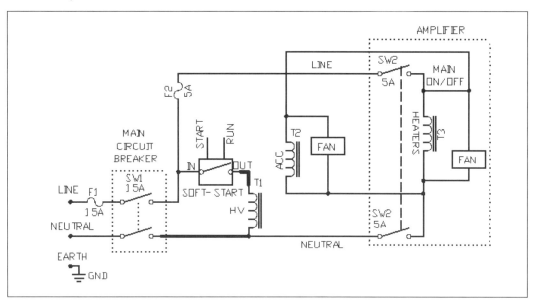

14

Battery Backup Supplies

> *"Don't worry about your difficulties in mathematics. I can assure you mine are greater."* Albert Einstein

I mentioned early in this book that often a good way of providing a fixed 12V supply was to use a storage battery and dedicated charger to provide a continuous output voltage in case of mains failure. I have been using these types of supply for a very long time and have two commercially manufactured ones in my shack (**Fig 14.1**). These serve double duty as my regular 12V bench supplies for experimenting.

These supplies use 7AH sealed lead acid batteries and a trickle charger and remain plugged into the mains at all times. My 6m and 70cm transceivers are those annoying types that feature memory storage which is lost if the supply is removed. So using a battery backup supply was a necessity!

Fig 14.1: Two sealed lead-acid battery supplies. The one on the left uses a single 7AH cell the other uses two 7AH cells

A local company manufactures the supplies for a friend of mine who supplies the two-way radio trade and who also happens to be a radio ham, John ZS5JG. You might spot that my callsign and the 'other John' as he is known locally are sequential, this is because we both did the RSA Morse test at the same time. In RSA the regulatory authority will on request issue the callsign that uses your initials, if it has not already been taken, in the case of the 'other John' he was unlucky! In my case I inherited the callsign of the late Jim Foster, G2JF who was also ZS5JF, on recommendation by his daughter and son in law, ZS5NO. The "other John's" surname begins with C and the RSA authority declined to issue ZS5JC on religious grounds!

The two supplies have either a single 7AH gel-cell or two 7AH cells connected in parallel. The charging circuit is simple and uses a LM317 IC to provide a current limited constant voltage charging supply.

However, the design of a charging circuit is not as straightforward as it seems!

Discharge characteristics

The rated capacity is only obtainable for relatively low rates of discharge. The table presented in **Fig 14.2** is taken from the Powersonic Corporation data sheet on their range of gel-cells. Other manufacturers have similar details.

Here we can see the general trend is that if the discharge current is high the apparent available capacity is much less than the rated capacity. For example, a 7AH battery discharged at 1C (7A) will not give 1 hour as expected but only a little over half an hour with an apparent capacity of only 3.85AH.

Sealed lead-acid battery charging parameters

Sealed lead-acid batteries (Gel-Cells) are not the same as motor vehicle batteries although they use a similar technology. Because the battery is sealed it cannot tolerate overcharging or excessive charging voltage. The maximum charging current is limited to a fairly low level to prevent excessive gassing which would raise the cell internal pressures to dangerous levels and cause the formation of hydrogen and oxygen, which is a highly inflammable mixture, and will cause the internal sealing valves to vent electrolyte.

The applied charging voltage is also critical. Like a car battery the sealed lead-acid battery is very sensitive to over voltage conditions and if the applied voltage is too high the cells will be damaged in a short time. Conversely if the applied charging voltage is too low the cells will not reach the fully charged state. The cut-off voltage for the charger needs to be carefully set to the battery manufacturer's recommendation for reliable service.

Rated Capacity	@ 0.05C rate (20 Hr. Rate) Current Amps.	Capacity Amp. Hrs	@0.1C rate (9 Hr. Rate) Current Amps.	Capacity Amp. hrs.	@0.2C rate (4 Hr. Rate) Current Amps.	Capacity Amp.Hrs	@0.5C rate (1.3 Hr. Rate) Current Amps.	Capacity Amp. Hrs.	@1C rate (33 Min. Rate) Current Amps.	Capacity Amp. hrs.	@2C rate (12 Min. Rate) Current Amps.	Capacity Amp.Hrs	@3C rate (7.2 Min. Rate) Current Amps.	Capacity Amp. Hrs.
0.5AH	0.025	0.50	0.05	0.45	0.10	0.40	0.25	0.325	0.50	0.28	1.00	0.20	1.50	0.18
0.8AH	0.04	0.80	0.08	0.72	0.16	0.64	0.40	0.52	0.80	0.44	1.60	0.32	2.40	0.29
1.0AH	0.05	1.00	0.10	0.90	0.20	0.80	0.50	0.65	1.00	0.56	2.00	0.40	3.00	0.36
1.3AH	0.065	1.30	0.13	1.17	0.26	1.04	0.65	0.845	1.30	0.715	2.60	0.52	3.90	0.47
2.3AH	0.115	2.30	0.23	2.07	0.46	1.84	1.15	1.495	2.30	1.288	4.60	0.92	6.90	0.83
3.0AH	0.15	3.00	0.30	2.70	0.60	2.40	1.50	1.95	3.00	1.65	6.00	1.20	9.00	1.08
3.2AH	0.16	3.20	0.32	2.88	0.64	2.56	1.60	2.08	3.20	1.76	6.40	1.28	9.60	1.15
4.5AH	0.22	4.40	0.45	4.05	0.90	3.60	2.25	2.92	4.5	2.47	9.00	1.80	13.50	1.62
5.0AH	0.25	5.00	0.50	4.50	1.00	4.00	2.50	3.25	5.00	2.80	10.00	2.00	15.00	1.80
6.5AH	0.325	6.50	0.65	5.85	1.30	5.20	3.25	4.23	6.50	3.64	13.00	2.60	19.50	2.34
7.0AH	0.35	7.00	0.70	6.30	1.40	5.60	3.50	4.55	7.00	3.85	14.00	2.80	21.00	2.52
8.0AH	0.40	8.00	0.80	7.20	1.60	6.40	4.00	5.20	8.00	4.48	16.00	3.20	24.00	2.88
9.0AH	0.45	9.00	0.90	8.10	1.80	7.20	4.50	5.85	9.00	5.04	18.00	3.60	27.00	3.24
10.0AH	0.50	10.00	1.00	9.00	2.00	8.00	5.00	6.50	10.00	5.60	20.00	4.00	30.00	3.60
12.0AH	0.60	12.00	1.20	10.80	2.40	9.60	6.00	7.80	12.00	6.72	24.00	4.80	36.00	4.32
18.0AH	0.90	18.00	1.80	16.20	3.06	14.40	9.00	11.70	18.00	9.90	36.00	7.20	54.00	6.48
20.0AH	1.00	20.00	2.00	18.00	4.00	16.00	10.00	13.00	20.00	11.20	40.00	8.00	60.00	7.20
26.0AH	1.30	26.00	2.60	23.40	5.20	20.80	13.00	16.90	26.00	14.30	52.00	10.40	78.00	9.36
28.0AH	1.40	28.00	2.80	25.20	5.40	21.60	14.00	18.20	28.00	15.40	54.00	10.88	84.00	10.08
33.0AH	1.65	33.00	3.30	29.70	6.60	26.40	16.50	21.45	33.00	18.15	66.00	13.20	99.00	11.88
40.0AH	2.00	40.00	4.00	36.00	8.00	32.00	20.00	26.00	40.00	22.40	80.00	16.00	120.00	14.40
55.0AH	2.75	55.00	5.50	49.50	11.00	44.00	27.50	35.75	55.00	30.25	110.00	22.00	165.00	19.80
60.0AH	3.00	60.00	6.00	54.00	12.00	48.00	30.00	39.00	60.00	33.60	120.00	24.00	180.00	21.60
75.0AH	3.75	75.00	7.50	67.50	15.00	60.00	37.50	48.75	75.00	41.25	150.00	30.00	225.00	27.00
80.0AH	4.00	80.00	8.00	72.00	16.00	64.00	40.00	52.00	80.00	44.80	160.00	32.00	240.00	28.80
100.0 AH	5.00	100.00	10.00	90.00	20.00	80.00	50.00	65.00	100.00	55.00	200.00	40.00	300.00	36.00

Fig 14.2: Table reproduced from data sheet supplied by Powersonic Corporation, San Diego, CA

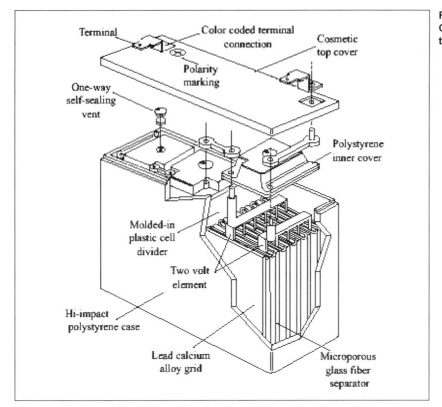

Fig 14.3: Construction of a typical Gel-Cell

The technology used for some sealed lead-acid 'gel-cells' is similar to that used by caravan storage batteries. These are known as 'Deep-Discharge' or 'cyclic' batteries and can be charged and left for a long time before being discharged at a low drain current.

The charging current is limited to about 1A per 7AH and the float charge cut-off voltage needs to be set accurately to approximately 2.45V/cell, which for a 12V battery is a maximum of 14.7V.

The difference between the two technologies is quite subtle. A normal car battery will be killed in a short time if it is continuously trickle charged without a controlled cut-off voltage. A sealed lead-acid on the other hand can safely survive prolonged periods of trickle charging. These batteries are often used in emergency lighting applications and are permanently trickle charged at a low rate to combat the inherent small self-discharge current.

A normal vehicle battery on the other hand uses an alternator to replenish the drained charge and usually charges at a cut-off voltage of around 14.4V. Whereas there doesn't seem to be much difference between the car battery charged by an alternator and the sealed lead-acid 'gel-cell' the main difference is the charging current.

In a car battery charged from an alternator the need to limit the charging current is not as critical. When the engine is cranked to start it the current drain is very high and as soon as the engine is running the alternator 'thumps' the charging current back into the battery in a very short time. Often the alternator will charge the battery back up in a few seconds with currents as high as 80A. This would damage the sensitive 'gel-cell' and cause buckling of the plates and excessive gassing. Car batteries thrive on the charging abuse the alternator provides, the sealed 'gel-cell' behaves differently and will soon expire if treated to the same charging regimen.

Assume the starter motor draws an average current of 300A for a period of 2 seconds to start the engine. To replenish the charge taken to start the engine the battery requires the following:

- 80A for 9 seconds, or
- 25A for 30 seconds, or
- 1A for 12 minutes.

> One of my other hobbies is motor racing and I help to prepare several cars used for racing. One of these is a single-seater Can-Am sports car made by Carroll Shelby in the USA. This uses a 14AH gel-cell battery, to keep the vehicle weight down, and is charged by a normal vehicle alternator. Because the gel-cell has a limited charging current capability it exhibits a high resistance when the charging current is too high. On several occasions the battery has literally exploded due to excessive charging current and caused extensive damage to the rest of the vehicle's electrical components due to excessive voltage. It was necessary to fit a high power 'Zener-clamp' across the main battery to prevent further damage.

Sealed lead-acid batteries are used for many applications. Some of these are golf-carts, invalid carriages, emergency lighting, floodlighting, burglar alarms, uninterruptible power supplies (UPS) and many more. Each application requires a slightly different charging regimen. There is no one circuit that satisfies all of these, especially if long life is essential.

A further problem with lead-acid batteries is that the charging and float voltage needs to be made variable with temperature. The gel-cell has a typical voltage variation of -4mV/cell per °C. A voltage chosen for, say +25°C, will cause undercharging at 0°C and severe over-charging at +50°C.

The charging current is often rated as a percentage of the nominal capacity. The symbol for the capacity is C. So if a battery is charged at 10% of the nominal capacity it is known as 'C over 10' or C/10. For a 7AH battery this is a current of 700mA.

The time to recharge the battery from being fully discharged is usually about 12 to 14 hours. At the start of the charging period the current needs to be restrict-

> In some automotive applications the battery charging voltage and current is controlled by a computer. In the Chrysler/Dodge series of automobiles charging was controlled by the engine management computer. In early models this was the SBEC computer (Single Board Engine Computer) and this was situated directly behind the battery. The SBEC computer had an air temperature sensor to indirectly measure the battery case temperature. The charging was performed by a Pulse Width Modulated circuit that controlled the on-time of the alternator field winding. When the temperature is low the battery needs more voltage and hence current to attain full capacity. When the battery is at a high temperature the voltage and current can be reduced.

ed to C/10 to C/8 maximum and then the current will naturally taper off to a low level as the battery voltage rises to the fully charged point. Therefore if the cut-off voltage is set to 14.1V the charger needs to behave as a current-limited constant-voltage supply delivering ≈700mA for a 7AH battery. Using a common IC such as the LM317 the charging circuit is quite straightforward.

For the supply with two 7AH batteries connected in parallel the charging current will be ≈1.4A. As the LM317 is rated at 1.5A maximum output this fits in nicely with the requirements and was why this IC was chosen.

Choosing the correct cut-off voltage is a little tricky. One requirement is to ensure an acceptable charge capacity; the other is to prevent overcharging. If the cut-off voltage of the charger is set to 13.8V the gel-cell battery will reach only about 70% of its potential capacity, however, 70% of the nominal capacity when the mains fails is better than nothing! As the battery temperature has a profound effect on the required charging voltage this presents a problem, if maximum battery life is a requirement. What we really need is a more intelligent charger than a simple fixed voltage type such as a LM317 set for current limited output.

A more sophisticated charging method

An IC especially made for charging gel-cells is the UC2906, originally made by Unitrode Corporation. This features a temperature compensated voltage reference that accurately matches the requirements of a gel-cell. It also features several safety features and multiple level charging rates to ensure the gel-cell reaches its full potential charge. Texas Instruments, who bought Unitrode Corporation, now manufacture this IC. The block diagram of the UC2906 in a typical charging circuit is shown in **Fig 14.4**. D1 is fitted to prevent the battery discharging into the IC and the pass transistor should the input supply fail. The

Fig 14.4: UC2906 block diagram

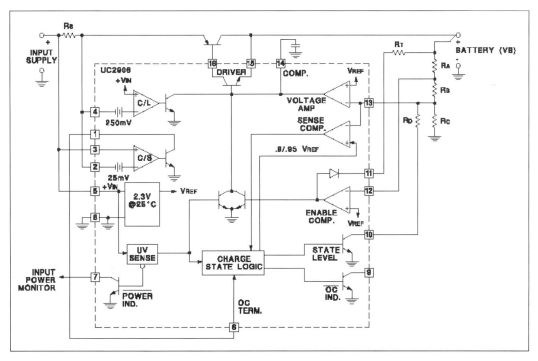

voltage sensing resistors across the output are high values and cause very little discharge current when the mains fails, typically less than 1mA.

The bulk charging current is set by the current sense resistor on the input of the charger. This controls the charging current delivered by the external PNP pass transistor. The feedback resistors determine the charging voltage.

Operation of the UC2906

When a battery is first connected, the voltage sensing portion measures the battery voltage. If this is below 10V the charger first applies a trickle charge to try and raise the voltage into a region suitable for bulk charging. If the voltage fails to rise to the required level, possibly because the battery has a faulty cell, the charger will remain in the trickle region indefinitely, so protecting the battery. Assuming that the battery voltage reaches this plateau the charger then applies a current limited charging current (bulk charge mode) determined by the current sense resistor value.

When the bulk charge has raised the battery voltage towards the cut-off voltage the charging current will taper off to a low level. When the current has dropped to 10% of the initial bulk charge current the IC then applies a lower trickle charge current to maintain a float charge state. If now a load is applied to the battery and the voltage drops below the cut-off voltage, the internal circuitry senses that the voltage is too low and applies a further bulk charge current, the voltage is restored and the float state resumes. By using this technique the battery is maintained at close to 100% capacity at all times.

The internal temperature compensated voltage reference accurately tracks the ambient temperature and adjusts the charging voltage to suit the charging mode currently in use. It is advantageous to thermally couple the IC package and the battery case so that the IC accurately measures the battery temperature. Usually placing the circuit board for the charger close to the battery is sufficient. The mains transformer should be located away from the circuit board so that any heat generated does not cause a false temperature reading.

Further details of the UC2906 can be found on the TI website, *www.TI.com*

A mast-head mounted battery supply

My original EME array used a home brewed elevator that used a beefy 12V windscreen wiper motor driving a large reduction gearbox. The current drawn by this was quite high and would need two substantial gauge wires about 20m long to run from the shack to the top of the tower. This caused a bit of head scratching until I hit on the idea of putting a 14AH gel-cell battery in a waterproof box at the top of the tower and running a charging cable from the shack. The battery box contained a thermistor to measure the local ambient temperature, as it can get quite warm in South Africa due to the solar energy and I was concerned about the battery being overcharged at high temperatures.

This whole scheme worked out very well and the elevator control box in the shack contained the charging circuitry as well as the controls to select the appropriate relay driver (mounted in the tower top battery box) to make the array either go up or down. I fitted a couple of waterproof push buttons on the battery box so that I could operate the elevator whilst up the tower.

Later when I was donated a solar panel this was mounted near the top of the tower and used to charge the battery. (See later section for details of this charger circuit).

A high current battery shack supply

For applications that require a higher current than a gel-cell can safely deliver, an alternative scheme is to use another battery float-charge system. In a float-charge system the bulk of the equipment current is supplied by the charging circuitry and the battery simply fills in the extra current required over and above that which the charger can supply. This is exactly what our 12-V HF transceiver requires as the majority of time is spent receiving with limited periods of transmitting. Often a heavy-duty lead-acid car battery can fulfil this role. It is important that the final charging voltage is kept below the battery gassing voltage or the electrolyte will be depleted due to excessive gassing. For a standard car battery the best choice is approximately 13.8 to 14.0V. A battery with a capacity of around 60AH will be adequate. This should be mounted in a well-ventilated area, preferably outside the shack, and protected from the elements in a box.

The charger circuit can be quite crude as long as the cut-off voltage can be accurately set. The requirement is to be able to supply a fairly heavy current with the battery attached in parallel as a sort of 'capacitor' to filter out any ripple voltage and to supply the extra current required when transmitting. A cheap solution to this problem is the Bucket-Regulator. This contains very few components,

When I was a young apprentice in the British Post Office, I was attached for about six months to a team who maintained the batteries in the telephone exchanges. These varied in capacity from about 500AH for a small exchange up to more than 1MAH for large exchanges. They employ a float charge system with the bulk of the exchange current being supplied by a large charging unit. The biggest one I saw was in an inter-continental main switching exchange near Edinburgh. This had a float-charger rated at 10,000A.

Exchange batteries are 48V and usually supplied in pairs, one being used to run the exchange whilst the standby battery was being conditioned. They were designed to last for at least 15 years and would easily meet this if they were correctly maintained. The criterion was for the battery to be able to run the exchange for a minimum of 8 hours in the event of a mains failure.

With proper maintenance, ie switching over between the main and standby batteries every seven days and conditioning the battery not in service, the life of an exchange battery could often reach 20 years or more. One manual exchange I worked on had been in use since the early part of WW2 and still had the original battery, some 25 years later when we were sent in to demolish it.

Some of the technicians in charge of an exchange were delinquent in their duties and then we would be sent in to perform a full performance rectification program. This involved several charge/discharge runs to build up capacity to the rated value. All this took about a week. Sadly we knew we would back again in a few months time to do the whole thing again as the technician wasn't really interested in such things as batteries!

Fig 14.5: Bucket-Regulator charger for lead-acid batteries

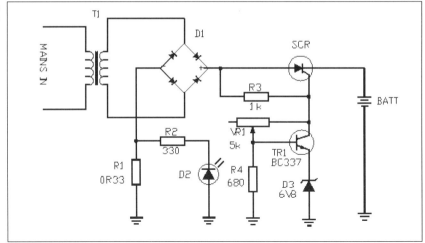

runs at a high efficiency and provides adequate current and voltage setting capabilities. The circuit of a typical Bucket-Regulator is shown in **Fig 14.5**. A hefty mains transformer supplies the current, and a bridge rectifier and a SCR to control the current supplied to the battery.

Principle of operation

Note: There is no reservoir capacitor fitted across the bridge rectifier output. The Bucket-Regulator uses unsmoothed (pulsating) DC to supply the SCR.

At switch on, the battery voltage is low and the positive half wave pulses from the bridge rectifier will drive the gate voltage of the SCR, via R3, positive with respect to the cathode until it is clamped by a Zener to the required battery voltage. This causes the SCR to conduct only whilst the gate voltage is greater than the cathode. The transformer secondary rating, diode voltage drop and the current sensing and limiting resistor R1 determine the current flowing into the battery. For every half cycle when the SCR is conducting the return of the bridge current flowing via R1 causes the LED to be lit. (Note that the LED is connected to the opposite polarity as the current flows from the ground back to the bridge).

As the battery reaches the fully charged state the voltage difference between the gate and cathode will decrease towards zero so causing the SCR to turn off. The output voltage will remain fairly constant unless an external load causes it to fall slightly. When this occurs the SCR will again turn on for successive half cycles until the battery voltage has risen to the cut-off point. Thereafter the LED will only blink every few seconds as a further small amount of current is passed to replace energy lost due to either internal discharge mechanisms in the battery or an external load drawing some current. It is this 'topping up' of the battery that gives the Bucket Regulator its name. If the current being demanded is high the SCR will be turned on for every positive pulse and supply the maximum current to the load/battery combination. Any current demand in excess of that able to be supplied by the charger will be drawn from the battery.

The gate voltage of the SCR could be regulated by a standard value zener, however as we require a better controlled voltage an 'adjustable Zener' has been included which is formed by TR1 and associated components.

> By substituting a large electrolytic capacitor for the battery this makes a nice low cost high current supply which can be used to power audio amplifiers and other equipment not requiring the same sort of regulation as a conventional linear power supply. I first used this circuit many years ago to make a high current battery charger for an invalid carriage that used two 12V batteries connected in parallel.

The bridge rectifier, transformer and SCR need to be adequately rated for the anticipated current and amply heatsinked. With the value of R1 shown, the maximum current is approximately 6A when charging a standard 12V car battery. The transformer secondary only needs to supply a little more voltage than the fully charged battery voltage. For a 12V battery a 12V secondary would be adequate with a rating of about 75VA.

In fact this makes an excellent battery charger for vehicles and can be safely left connected indefinitely. A transformer salvaged from an old battery charger is the best option, as it will have inherent current limiting built in due to the flux-limited core used in this type of transformer. The 6V8 Zener can be a 500mW rating and all the other resistors can be half-watt except R1 which needs to be at least 15W, this can be made from three paralleled 1Ω / 5W wire wound resistors.

To set up the charger first connect a large electrolytic capacitor ($\approx$3300μF) in place of the battery with a load resistor (100Ω / 2W) in parallel and adjust the Zener preset VR1 to obtain the required output voltage. When this has been done connect the battery across the output and remove the electrolytic and load resistor.

Because the SCR acts like a reverse biased diode, when the mains input is removed the charger does not discharge the battery. A suitably rated fuse needs to be connected between the battery and the transceiver. Be aware, however, that the Bucket-Regulator is not short circuit proof and care should be taken to insert fuses in appropriate points in the wiring where an accidental short could occur. At the least a fuse of suitable rating should be inserted in the Line side of the mains and also a fuse between the bridge rectifier and the SCR to protect the charger.

Some words of caution on using car batteries

Although car batteries are generally safe this assumes that the user respects the potential dangers involved.

A typical car battery can generate an awful lot of current under a short circuit condition. I have seen spanners accidentally dropped across the battery terminals of motor vehicles that have then welded themselves in place. The short circuit current has been large enough to make the spanner glow yellow and then white hot, at this point the spanner vaporised with a loud bang. When a lead-acid battery is heavily discharged a lot of gassing takes place. If the spanner melts it will generate a spark, the hydrogen and oxygen gassed off by the discharge can make the battery literally explode and this causes severe damage to anything in close proximity apart from spraying boiling hot sulphuric acid in all directions! Similarly when working on a vehicle it is prudent to remove any rings or watches that might accidentally cause a short between the battery positive and ground.

Consider the typical vehicle application where the battery supplies the starter motor. Current drains as high as 1000A or more are common. Even a small vehicle will require something like 300A to crank the engine. During this starting phase the battery voltage rarely drops to below 9V, if the battery is in good condition, therefore the internal resistance of the battery is very low and can give short circuit currents of many thousand amps for a short time.

Also, when being charged or discharged the chemical process generates hydrogen and oxygen, which is a highly explosive mixture! Because of this, battery manufacturers have over the recent years developed an alternative technique to package the battery. This involves a totally sealed case, the so-called 'Maintenance-Free' battery. Because the case is sealed, any gassing which occurs does not result in the electrolyte being vented and so the loss of water has been reduced to practically zero.

One of the subtle factors about this is that the materials used for the battery plates have been changed to include additional materials, such as calcium, and these batteries require a different charging cut-off voltage. For example: The later General Motors vehicles, which employ AC-Delco batteries as original equipment, have a different alternator cut-off voltage to the previous battery types.

> If you replace a sealed maintenance free battery in a GM vehicle, such as an AC-Delco, with a non-sealed lead-antimony or lead-antimony/calcium low maintenance battery, you will need to check the electrolyte levels more often. This is because GM sets their voltage regulators at higher charging voltage, 14.6 to 14.8 volts, to recharge the sealed maintenance free lead-calcium/calcium batteries.

The four stages of lead-acid battery charging are shown in **Fig 14.6**. The penultimate stage (equalisation phase) shows that the battery voltage will increase to as high as 15.6V before the float charge state reduces this to around 13.6V.

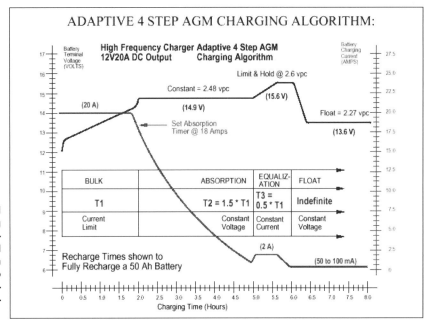

Fig 14.6: Lead-acid battery charging profile. This diagram was supplied by the Deltran Corporation who manufacture lead-acid battery charging systems

Fig 14.7: Output voltage of the author's solar panel driving a 6W lamp   **Fig 14.8: A 40W solar panel.**

Solar powered battery back up supplies

A solar panel and a lead-acid battery make an excellent source of low voltage power. Most solar panels are very inefficient but as the Sun's energy is for free this is of little consequence.

A typical medium size solar panel will generate about 40W of DC. I was given a panel originally used on a remote repeater site that had no mains power. The panel generates an open circuit voltage of approximately 18 to 20V and can supply a current of 1.75A when fully illuminated. Solar powered repeaters in South Africa are quite common, as the cost of supplying mains power to a remote hilltop is very costly. One installation I saw had 60 x 200W panels charging a 28V / 6800AH battery bank to power a long-range microwave radio link.

The output current and voltage varies with the amount of solar irradiation and hence the charging circuit for a lead-acid battery needs to be carefully designed. A simple series regulator is often not adequate as it can allow the battery to discharge into the charging circuits during night-time. A shunt-regulated charger is a much better proposition, particularly for gel-cells.

A suitable circuit for a solar powered shunt regulated battery charger is shown in **Fig 14.9**. The reverse polarity diode D2 is to prevent the battery discharging during periods of low solar illumination and should preferably be a low forward voltage drop type such as a Schottky. The solar panel, SP1, is connected across the charger circuit and powers the regulator when sufficient output voltage is available. VR1 sets the cut-off voltage. To set up the cut-off voltage substitute a 100Ω / 2W resistor in place of the battery and adjust VR1 to obtain the correct voltage with the solar panel fully illuminated.

The battery and charge regulator are best mounted at ground level and the two wires from the solar panel brought into the charger enclosure. The voltage drops in the leads help to limit the charging current.

Fig 14.9: Solar powered battery charger circuit

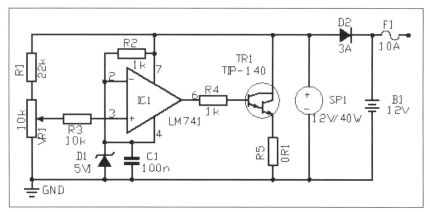

Fig 14.9: Solar powered battery charger circuit

All the resistors can be half-watt except the 0.1Ω in the Darlington emitter, which needs to be rated for the full charger shunt current. A 5W or 11W wire-wound resistor would be suitable. Diode D2 can be a 1N5400 or a Schottky type. The op-amp can be almost any type; the diagram shows a LM-741 being used.

TR1 needs mounting on a suitable heatsink, as it will dissipate a large amount of power when the battery is fully charged and the panel is fully illuminated. If the solar panel is a 40W type then all of this is dissipated in the charger shunt regulator.

Nickel-cadmium battery charger

Rechargeable batteries are used in many items of equipment, from handheld radios to items found around the home such as cordless drills and other tools. Often the battery charger supplied with these items is of very poor quality and may lead to reduced battery life because of over charging. As rechargeable batteries are quite expensive to buy it makes sense to use the best charger available to maximise the life.

The circuit detailed in **Figs 14.10 and 14.11** is a deluxe charger that not only limits the charging current to the correct value but also incorporates a timer to switch off the charger after the nominal charging time has expired. This prevents damage if a cell in the battery pack has developed a reverse polarity mode, which is caused by deep discharge or a long period of inactivity.

The charger can handle batteries from the popular AA cell up to D size cells of 4AH. By selecting the component values the charger can be customised to suit the battery pack to be charged. With sufficient ingenuity it would be possible to make a Universal Charger by switching various components into circuit to suit the battery type.

The manufacturer's normal recommended charging current for normal Ni-Cd and Ni-Mh cells is between C/10 and C/5 depending on the cell type, where C is the capacity in Ampere-Hours (AH). Fast Charge cells normally use C/5 and other types use C/10. A normal charge level AA cell is nominally 500mAH and so will require a constant current charge of 50mA. A D size cell is nominally 4AH and so the correct constant current charging rate is 400mA. The time to recharge a standard charge level battery is normally 14 hours at C/10 assuming the battery is discharged to the 1V/cell level.

In many cases the battery may not be totally discharged and we have no easy way of telling the amount of charge remaining in the cells. There is no harm in charging a partially discharged cell. People who do not understand how the cell chemistry works have written a lot of rubbish over the years. A cell has a finite number of charge/discharge cycles before it no longer attains its full capacity. Most manufacturers put a capacity limit of 80% of the nominal on the end of useful life parameter.

A typical Ni-Cd cell can sustain about 2,000 charge and discharge cycles down to 1V/cell before the capacity falls to 80%. However, if you only discharge the cell to 50% of its rated capacity and then recharge it you will achieve about twice the normal charge/discharge cycles before the cell falls to the 80% capacity level.

It is the chemical usage that causes this. There is only so much electrolyte contained in the cell and when it is partially depleted the capacity starts to fall off. Extrapolating the capacity curve against charge/discharge cycles shows that for a 25% discharge and then recharging gives about four times the normal number of cycles.

The constant current charger uses a LM-317 voltage regulator. This device can be set to 1.2V to over 30V with just two resistors and is capable of supplying up to 1.5A. The output current is limited to the required value by a low value resistor (R2) in series with the output. The charging circuit is shown in Fig 14.10. When the charger is first switched on the current drawn by the battery pack is limited due to the series resistor. The LM-317 delivers a constant voltage and as the battery charges the voltage appearing across the battery rises towards the fully charged condition. The recommended fully charged voltage of a Ni-Cd cell is approximately 1.45V/cell.

The LM-317 is adjusted by VR1 to the required output voltage. The input voltage to the LM-317 needs to be at least 3V greater than the output voltage. The exact cut out voltage will depend on the cell type and manufacturer. The number of cells in the battery will determine this. Different manufacturers have different recommended cut out voltages depending on the application. The spread

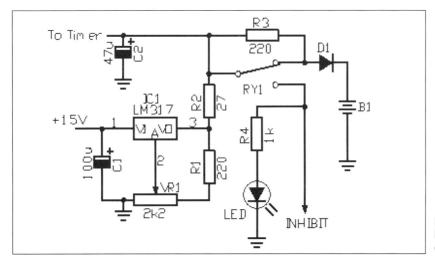

Fig 14.10: Current limited battery charger

is typically between about 1.4V/cell up to as high as 1.55V/cell. For example, a nominal 9V battery for a handheld radio consists of seven cells and the nominal voltage is 8.4V, but the fully charged voltage will be about 7 x 1.45V = 10.15V. It would be advisable to check with the manufacturer what the safe maximum voltage is before adjusting the cut out voltage.

When the battery is first connected the relay contact is closed shorting out R3 and the charging current causing a voltage drop across R2 will hold down the voltage. As the battery reaches the fully charged condition the terminal voltage will rise to the 1.45V/cell condition. When this occurs, the voltage difference across R2 will fall to almost zero and only a very small trickle charge current will flow into the battery. Provided the cut off voltage is correctly set by VR1 the battery can be left connected indefinitely. The value of R2 determines the maximum charging current and should be selected accordingly. The value of R3 should be roughly nine times the value of R2.

This charging method is not the usual constant current mode normally used for Ni-Cd cells. In a true constant current charger, the current when fully charged is the same as the initial charging current when the battery is discharged. The problem with constant current charging is that the cell terminal voltages can reach unsafe levels and consequent liberation of gas that can lead to premature failure. If the internal gas pressure rises too high the safety vent opens and electrolyte is lost. If this is performed on a regular basis then the cell will have a very short life.

Some of the techniques used in the past are to monitor the cell temperature and to terminate the charge when the cell exceeds a certain temperature, hopefully before the gassing point. This is only successful for a limited type of Ni-Cd cell. The best method would be to monitor the internal gas pressure and terminate the charge when it starts to rise because of gassing. Some large industrial Ni-Cd cells have this feature but the smaller cells cannot be fitted with the pressure pipe and sensor required.

Another method is to try and measure the very small change in the cell voltage when the gassing begins. Typically we need to be able to measure about a 2mV difference in the cell voltage as it begins to gas. This can work with some Ni-Cd cells but isn't always accurate enough. Hence, the safer option is the method used in this charger and this is known in the industry as 'Taper Charging' as it is a mixture of constant current and constant voltage. Of all the charging methods it is the only one that is 100% safe, although the charging time can be longer than other types.

D1 prevents the battery discharging back into the circuit should the input supply fail. As this has a bearing on the available terminal voltage it would be optimum to use a low voltage drop diode such as a 1N5819 Schottky. However, because we can compensate for the additional voltage drop with VR1 a normal silicon diode is adequate. For most applications a 1N4002 will suffice. The LM-317 will require bolting to a suitable heatsink with an insulating washer between the tab and any grounded metalwork.

The control of RY1 is by the timer circuit in **Fig 14.11**. When 14 hours has elapsed the relay RY1 will be energised so inserting the additional resistor R3 in series to limit the trickle charge current. This is a useful safety feature because the cell may not have reached its fully charged voltage because of an internal partial short. Irrespective of whether the cell has reached the fully charged voltage or not the charger will enter the trickle charge routine after 14 hours.

In many battery packs one or more cells may flip polarity during discharge because they have a lower capacity than the other cells. If the cell stays in the reverse polarity condition, which is normally the case, then the fully charged voltage may be one or more cell voltage below the correct value. The danger is that these flipped polarity cells are now being charged in the wrong polarity and will gas violently and probably expire.

When a battery pack is assembled the manufacturers normally use well-matched cells so the difference in the individuals cells' capacity is as small as possible. Cheap battery packs rarely meet these criteria. However, although when first assembled the cells may be within a few percent of each other the capacity throughout the life of the battery pack will vary and the originally well-matched cells will drift away and eventually one or more cells will be mismatched and lower in capacity.

The only guaranteed way to flip the cell back to the correct polarity is to isolate it from the others and then 'zap' it with a large electrolytic capacitor charged up to about 30V. This will often salvage an otherwise junk battery pack. After several charge and discharge cycles the pack should return to full capacity. The danger of constant current charging is that it doesn't know a cell or two may have flipped polarity and then severe damage may occur to the whole battery pack.

To set up the charger, connect a resistor across the output in place of the battery. The resistor needs to be a fairly high value to simulate the fully charged condition. In most cases a 4k7Ω will suffice. Adjust VR1 to obtain the correct cut off voltage.

The timer circuit uses a binary divider and logic gate square wave oscillator. The IC is the On Semi (previously Motorola Semiconductors) MC14536B CMOS logic circuit. The same device is made by a number of manufacturers;

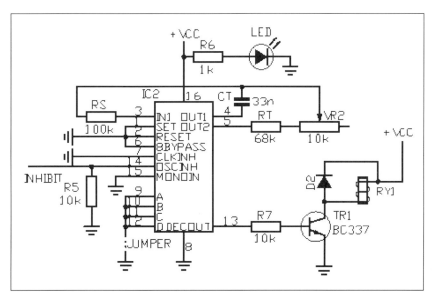

Fig 14.11: 14-hour timer circuit for battery charger

ST-Microelectronics part number is the HCC/HCF4536B. The IC is in a 16-pin DIL package and operates over the supply voltage range of 3 to 15V. This IC contains a 2^{24} binary counter and latch as well as the oscillator. The oscillator requires two resistors and a capacitor to set the frequency (RT, RS and CT). The fine setting of the frequency is by VR2, which allows RT to be varied. The capacitor used for CT needs to have good temperature stability and a polyester foil capacitor is the optimum type if the best accuracy is required. If the time isn't that critical within a half-hour or so then a ceramic capacitor may be used.

When the IC is powered up, the oscillator runs and the binary divider counts down to zero. When the count reaches zero the output latch is set and this can be used to control an external circuit. The total binary count is 16.7772 million clock pulses.

The required oscillator frequency is 16.7772 million divided by the number of seconds in 14 hours. 14 hours is 14 x 3600 seconds or 50,400 seconds. Hence, the clock period required is 3ms. The counter decrements on every rising edge of the clock waveform. As there are two pulses for each clock cycle in a binary divider, this is a frequency of 166.66 Hz. The last 16 stages of the counter can be configured to change the divider ratio with four control lines in a BCD format. This allows different divider counts to be selected. The four control pins are left floating to select the maximum count.

The binary counter is split into three sections each of 2^8 or 256 counts, so the total count is 256 x 256 x 256. In order to speed up the testing the sections can be bypassed so a simulated 14 hour timer can be tested in a few seconds with the correct oscillator frequency. This is performed by the jumper link between the BCD control pins. For normal operation the BCD pins are floating or ungrounded and the internal pull-up resistors set the inputs high. When BCD pins are grounded the binary counter has only eight stages enabled and hence the counter will clock over in 2^8 clock pulses. This is a total divider ratio of 256 clock pulses and hence with the required oscillator frequency will latch the relay after 1.53 seconds.

When the counter has reached zero the output at pin 13 goes high and turns on the transistor TR1 controlling RY1. A second contact on RY1 supplies a high logic level to pin 14 of the MC14536B that stops the counter advancing any further. Without this clock inhibit signal the counter would roll over after another 14 hours and start the charger again. The charger will remain in the trickle charge mode indefinitely until the charger is switched off. Hence, it can be switched on and left for extended periods with no danger to the battery pack being charged.

This charger may also be used for charging small lead-acid gel-cells with an appropriate regulator IC and current limiting resistor. A 12V/7AH gel-cell should be charged at a maximum current of 700mA and a cut off voltage of 14.0V.

Fast electronic fuse

In many items of equipment, fusing is a necessity to protect the item from damage due to a short circuit. When a fuse blows the possibility is that a replacement is not immediately available. This circuit uses four transistors to simulate a very fast fuse to interrupt the current if it exceeds a limit. The circuit is reset with a push button.

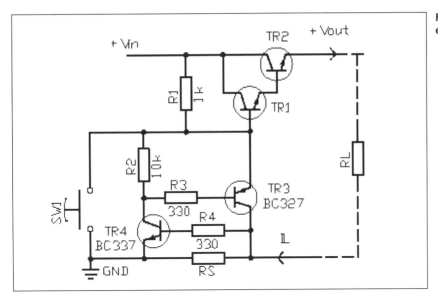

Fig 14.12: Resettable electronic fuse

TR2 is a power transistor capable of passing the required maximum current and is suitably heatsinked. TR1 is a medium power transistor to drive TR2. The current level required will determine suitable components for TR1 and TR2. (TR1 and TR2 could be combined into a common Darlington package). TR3 and TR4 are connected as a thyristor (SCR) and when the return current flowing in RS develops a voltage of about 0.6V TR4 will begin to turn on. When the collector voltage of TR4 starts to fall it turns on TR3 which supplies extra base current to TR4, hence it will turn on more. Because of the configuration this causes the combination of TR3 and TR4 to be regenerative and the pair will quickly latch hard on, so pulling the base of TR1 to ground. This switches off TR1 and TR2 so protecting the equipment. The circuit will remain latched until the reset button SW1 is pressed to resume normal operation. Should the fault condition still exist the circuit will latch off again. If the short has been removed the circuit operates normally.

There will be a small voltage drop across TR2 and this should be allowed for when the supply feeding the fuse is set up. This circuit can be added to an existing power supply and the voltage sensing feedback resistor for the power supply taken from the point Vout, hence including the fuse within the feedback loop.

Nickel cadmium cell zapper

Nickel Cadmium cells can develop a partial internal short due to long periods of inactivity. All Ni-Cd cells suffer from this, especially those that are not used very often, such as cordless screwdrivers and other domestic appliances. The cell may appear to take a normal charge and the terminal voltage immediately after charging is often correct but the cell quickly loses its charge over a few days or even hours.

This is caused by what is known as a 'Soft-Short' across the cell. This is the result of a crystalline growth between the two plates of the cell and is often a few hundred ohms to as much as a few kilohms. If not removed this will cause

A military base in this country is located in an area where ambient temperatures of +35°C or more are common in the summer. The warehouse is not air-conditioned. The roof is made of corrugated iron and the internal temperature on a summer day was often in excess of +60°C. The warehouse is used to store man-pack radios and battery packs. The annual loss of revenue due to battery packs deteriorating was high. The supplier of the battery packs was very happy with the situation because the annual sales of replacement battery packs amounted to millions of Rands. By purchasing a number of ex-supermarket freezers at a nominal cost to store the battery packs the annual costs dropped dramatically. So saving a large drain on the tax payers money!

the cell to gradually grow worse as the short becomes harder (lower resistance) because the chemical growth increases.

What most amateurs do not realise is that all Ni-Cd cells will self-discharge, due to the inherent internal leakage current, down to zero cell voltage in a period of about three months, irrespective of the charge-state when placed in storage. Elevated ambient temperatures will accelerate the discharge; storing Ni-Cd battery packs in the freezer will slow down the self-discharge rate. Hence, there is no real benefit to be gained by charging the cell before placing it in storage, it will simply take a little longer to discharge down to zero volts.

A common way of removing a soft short is to charge a large electrolytic capacitor up to about 30V and then discharge the capacitor into the cell. The very large current spike blows the soft short similar to a fuse. This is commonly known as 'zapping' the cell. A large constant charging current does not normally remove a soft short and so this technique is not as effective and can cause excessive gassing in the cell. Zapping a cell with a high voltage and high current pulse is a safe way to remove the internal shorts. The affected cell *must* be isolated from the rest of the battery pack for this to be successful. Most battery packs can be carefully split open and the individual cells terminals accessed. Measure each cell voltage in turn and determine which cell(s) are very low in terminal voltage and mark them in some way. (Some cells may reverse polarity under heavy discharge and these must be returned to the correct polarity before charging. Zapping is a quick and safe way to achieve this).

A quick and easy way to tell if the cells in the battery pack are working correctly, is to charge each cell via a low value resistor connected in series with a 12V, 1A supply for a short time - seconds rather than minutes! A resistor of about 330Ω / 5W normally works. Connect a voltmeter across the cell and watch the cell terminal voltage as the 12V supply is switched on. If the cell voltage rises quickly to around 1.2V the cell is probably OK. Time the charging current to be, say, 30s for each cell. Perform this test on each cell and then leave the battery pack for 24 hours. After 24 hours any cell with a problem will be much lower in voltage than good cells.

For those amateurs who do not have a bench power supply able to give 30V a good alternative is to use a boost converter from 12V to charge up a zapping capacitor. A circuit I made some time ago is shown in **Fig 14.13**. This uses a 10W audio amplifier IC as a square wave generator that doubles the input voltage and charges up a large electrolytic capacitor. The IC chosen behaves like a LM741 with a 3.5A output stage. (In fact this circuit was one I designed for a 10W hand-

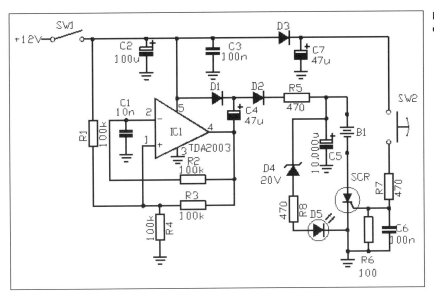

Fig 14.13: Ni-Cd cell zapper circuit

held VHF transceiver that had a Ni-Cd battery pack with 11 cells, which when fully charged was about 15.6V. This meant it couldn't be charged from a normal 12V vehicle because the 12V battery in the vehicle only rose to 14.4V when the alternator was charging, and with the engine off the battery voltage sank to around 13V. Hence, the need to generate a higher voltage to feed the charge regulator).

The cell to be zapped (B1) is connected between the charged capacitor C5 and a high current SCR. The voltage doubler uses IC1, a TDA2003 audio amplifier IC, to generate ≈12V square wave pulses. R2 and C1 set the frequency of oscillation of about 1kHz. The output of IC1 is coupled via C4 to the voltage doubler diodes D1 and D2. These diodes can be 1N4002 because the frequency is quite low and efficiency isn't an issue for this circuit. The peak voltage appearing at R5 is approximately 24V. This charges up C5 slowly because of the value of R5. When C5 has fully charged the LED will be lit as the zener turns on at 20V. The oscillator is now switched off by opening SW1. When push button SW2 is pressed the SCR gate is driven positive by the charge stored in C7 and the SCR turns on discharging the capacitor via the cell being zapped.

SCR needs to be a high current thyristor such as a BT-152 or larger. A relay contact or push button switch could be substituted for the SCR but the contacts will be eroded rapidly because of the high inrush current.

To use, connect the cell to be zapped by a pair of leads with crocodile clips, ensuring the polarity is correct. Connect a voltmeter across the cell to indicate the terminal voltage. Switch on SW1 and wait for the large capacitor to charge up, this will take a few seconds. Switch off SW1 and press SW2 to discharge the capacitor into the cell. After the pulse of current the cell terminal voltage should jump up to about 0.8 to 1V. Stubborn cells may require several repeated zaps before they return to normal voltage. If five or more zaps do not recover the cell it is probably past redemption. When the cell seems to be cleared of the soft short, place it on charge at C/10 for 14 hours and measure the terminal voltage. It should be above 1.4V if the cell is recovered. Several charge/discharge cycles are normally needed to bring the capacity back to nominal.

Nickel cadmium cell rejuvenator

This circuit is one I built to assess the different charging methods for Ni-Cd cells. I first came across this idea in an application note by Westinghouse Electronics in the 1980s. Westinghouse claims that this charging method can rejuvenate tired Ni-Cd cells and return them to near 100% capacity. I found that with the average cells we were using for hand-held two-way radios we could often attain 90% capacity from cells that would normally be scrapped due to low capacity. However, if the cell has been persistently over charged resulting in gassing then the loss of electrolyte means the cell is basically scrap and nothing short of replacing the lost electrolyte will cause the cell to recover. Hence, it isn't guaranteed to work with all cells.

The principle of the rejuvenator is charging the cell with a much larger current than normal, typically five times the normal rate, and the charger rapidly alternates between charging and discharging. If the majority of the energy pumped into the cell during charging is almost immediately extracted by placing a load across the cell, the net charge is quite low. The repetitive charging and discharging claims to "shake up the chemicals" and give a beneficial result. Westinghouse calls this "Pulse-Charging".

Typically we could charge at C/2 and discharge at C/4, so the net charge retained is only 50%. Westinghouse used a 100% charge and 75% discharge ratio for its tests, hence the energy retained was 25%. This requires an oscillator with a 3:1 pulse width. This technique may not suit all cell types; fast charge cells seem to give lower capacity improvements than normal charge cells from my experience. The indication from experiments is that fast charge cells appear to require charge rates of 5C to 10C to attain the best benefit. For large cells, such as the D-size cells, this is a charging current of about 10 to 20A and a discharge current of 5 to 10A per pulse.

The circuit shown in **Fig 14.14** is dimensioned to suit AA rechargeable cells of 500mAH nominal capacity. The circuit is powered by a 12V/1A supply. IC1 and IC2 are National Semiconductors LM317 adjustable voltage regulators. IC1

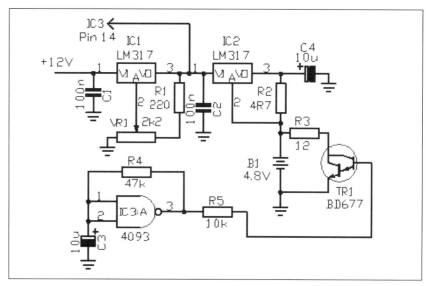

Fig 14.14: Ni-Cd rejuvenator circuit

is set up as a conventional voltage regulator to supply an output voltage approximately 2V more than the battery fully charged voltage. This is the 'drop-out' voltage of the LM317 at about 500mA to 1A current. For a four-cell pack this requires about (4 x 1.5V) +2V = 8V. IC2 is configured as a constant current source by the resistor in series with the output. The LM317 internal reference voltage between the Output and Adjust pin is 1.25V. With R2 as 4.7Ω the maximum current IC2 can source is 1.25V/4.7Ω = 265mA. This is ≈5 times the normal charge current of an AA cell.

TR1 is a BD677 medium power Darlington NPN transistor (TO-126 package) rated at 4A with a discharge resistor in series with the collector. The current drawn by TR1 when it is turned on is the battery voltage divided by the value of R3, neglecting the saturation voltage of TR1 which is about 0.6V. With the value shown this is approximately 4.8 / 12 = 400mA. When TR1 turns on the constant current supplied by IC2 is a portion of the total discharge current. Hence, the actual current being drawn from the battery pack is (400mA - 250mA) = 150mA. This is a value of 3C/10 in terms of battery capacity. Hence, the charging is at 5C/10 and the discharge is at 3C/10. The net charge into the battery is the difference, being 2C/10. Therefore the battery should reach a fully charged state in 14 / 2 hours = 7 hours.

A simple CMOS gate square wave oscillator built around IC3A, which is one quarter of a CD4093 NAND gate, provides the drive pulse for TR1. This supplies a pulse of about half an second on and half a second off with a 50% duty cycle. There may be some advantage is increasing the clock frequency, in which case you can vary the value of R4 or C3. In experiments on various capacity cells a frequency of up to 1kHz was used. Lowering the value of R4 or C3 will increase the frequency. IC3A is powered from the 8V output of IC1.

Resistors R2 and R3 need to be adequately rated, 5W wire-wound types would suit most applications. Similarly IC1, IC2 and TR1 need to be mounted on heatsinks with insulating washers to prevent shorting.

When using this pulse charging technique it is prudent to monitor the cell temperature periodically. If the cells are getting too hot to touch (+50°C or more) this is definitely too hot and the charger should be switched off to allow the cell temperature to fall to ambient. It is also essential to connect a voltmeter across the cells to measure the terminal voltage. If the fully charged voltage is too high the cells will start to gas. Adjust the fully charged voltage with VR1. Connect a voltmeter across R2 and monitor the voltage drop. Disable the discharge transistor TR1 by shorting the base to ground. When the cells are fully charged the voltage across R2 should be close to zero if VR1 has been correctly set.

15

Power Supply Test Equipment

> **Honesty:** *"It is better to tell the truth and run, than to lie and get caught in the act."* William C Hunter

The caption at the top of this page is unfortunately very true for some power supplies. I have seen a lot of cosmetically nice looking supplies, but the circuitry inside and the test results are a quite different story! Because the outside of the supply looks pretty and cosmetically pleasing does not mean that the same sort of care has been lavished on the internal parts.

In an earlier chapter, I briefly covered some of the test procedures for linear power supplies. Whether we are testing a simple linear regulated supply, a high voltage supply or a switch-mode supply, many of the test set-ups are similar. For many of the tests you will require standard items of test equipment. As some amateurs may not have all of the required items it may be necessary to enlist the assistance of a club member who is better equipped. To save repeating myself over and over here is a basic list of test equipment that the well-equipped amateur should have in his shack.

- Analog Multimeter; ideally an AVO 8
- Digital Multimeter; 1kV FSD AC/DC, 10A FSD AC/DC
- Oscilloscope; 10MHz B/W, 5mV/div to 5V/div + X1 & X10 'scope probes
- Load Resistors; suitable for current to be measured

The load resistors requires a little extra explanation. Many of the tests we will be performing will require a fixed value of load resistance, but the problem with this is that the current drawn is proportional to the applied voltage. Whereas this may be perfectly adequate for a great many power supplies, in the case of a power supply intended to power an HF transceiver the test method requires that the load be cycled between two preset levels. This can be done with fixed resistors but it becomes tedious to select and set up resistors when several different load currents are needed.

Fig 15.1: A set of high wattage resistors used by the author for PSU testing. Each resistor is 6.8 ohm, 100W. These were rescued from a defunct 1kW AM broadcast transmitter. When testing a 13.8V supply each resistor draws about 2A

A simple dual load resistor

I mentioned in an earlier chapter how a couple of low value resistors can be utilised to perform simple transient tests. The basis of the circuit is shown in **Fig 15.2**. The switching transistor can be either a NPN Darlington or a mosfet; Fig 15.2 shows a

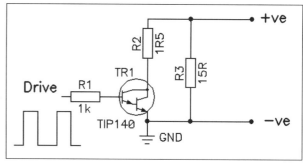

Fig 15.2: A simple dual load resistor circuit for transient testing

Darlington. The drive circuit is a simple variable frequency oscillator. The current drawn from a 13.8V supply will be approximately 1A and 10A. The 1.5Ω resistor needs to dissipate high power, ≈130W. The use of 15Ω 20W wire-wound resistors for all the resistors will be OK. The 1.5Ω resistor will consist of 10 x 15Ω, 20W wire-wound resistors wired in parallel.

A far better method is to use a simple piece of circuitry which not only allows the current drawn to be infinitely varied but also has the distinct advantage that once the current has been set to a value it remains constant, even if the supply output voltage changes for any reason. This is known as a 'Constant Current Load', or 'Current Sink', and can be made with a few power transistors and an op-amp. The power dissipation can be anything we desire by correctly sizing the heatsink the power transistors are mounted on. A slight modification to the basic circuit allows us to inject an audio signal to 'modulate' the load current. This audio signal can be anything from a few Hertz to many kilohertz and can be either sinusoidal, triangular or a square wave. With such an item of test equipment we can fully explore the transient response of low voltage / high current power supplies. In fact until I first used one of these I was blissfully unaware of how bad some of my early designs were!

Lamps as loads

Remember my earlier comments about using lamps as loads. Well, don't be coerced into using them in a moment of laziness. The cold filament resistance is often about four to ten times less than the running value; as a consequence the current drawn when first switched on (the in-rush-current) is very high and can cause a power supply current limiting circuit to latch-up. If you really must use a lamp as a load as a temporary measure, then you should insert a low value resistance in series of approximately 25% of the calculated running value to prevent this disastrous condition.

A home brewed current sink

Fig 13.3 shows the circuit of the current sink I built many years ago. I have updated some of the components for more modern types, mainly the shunt transistors and used TIP140 Darlingtons with a current rating of 10A maximum and a collector-emitter voltage of 60V which should cater for most

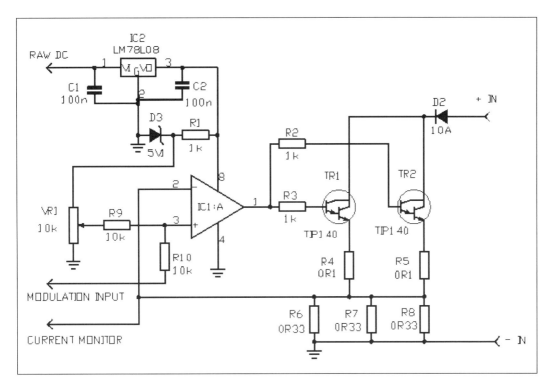

Fig 15.3: Variable current sink power stage

applications. I have only shown two parallel connected shunt transistors, as the intention is to rate the sink at 10A. If you require more current then simply increase the number connected in parallel. Do not forget the current sharing resistors (R4 and R5) in each emitter. If you prefer old fashioned 2N3055s then you will need to insert an extra transistor between the output of IC1 and the 3055s to increase the current gain, Darlingtons have this already built-in! Anyway, TIP140s are cheaper than 3055s and can safely dissipate 125W when correctly heatsinked. You could probably substitute N-channel mosfets for the NPN transistors but I haven't tried this yet.

The equipment requires a DC supply of around 12V and this is regulated with an 8V low power regulator to drive the dual op-amp, an LM358 and the oscillator circuit. This is supplied by a small mains transformer, bridge and electrolytic capacitor, I am sure that by now you can work out the necessary circuitry so I haven't included it here. The variable VR1 needs to be a type that can be reset accurately. I found a number of multi-turn panel mounting controls at a local swap meet (rally) and used one in my version.

The TIP140 transistors need mounting on a substantial heatsink as they are operating as 'variable resistors', (the same as a series pass regulator), and will generate a lot of heat. The current sharing and sensing resistors need to be adequately rated. The resistors R4, R5, R6, R7 and R8 are sized for 10A and need to be 5W wire wound types. About 20% of the power will be dissipated in these 'tail resistors'. The polarity protection diode D2 can be eliminated if you are confident you will always connect the power terminals correctly!

The rest of the circuit consists of a variable frequency square wave generator and the metering. This is shown in **Fig 15.4**.

Fig 15.4: Variable current sink pulse generator

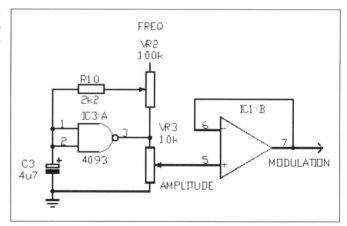

VR2 sets the frequency of the pulse generator and VR3 the amplitude of the maximum current. In operation, the minimum current is set by VR1, having first turned VR3 to minimum, and then the peak current is adjusted by VR3. For operation as a constant current sink, the 8V supply to the CD4093 oscillator is switched off. The connector SKT1 allows a 'scope to be connected to monitor the current waveform. The frequency of the square wave oscillator can be varied over a wide range by changing the capacitor value, and it delivers a 50% duty cycle. With the frequency control at minimum with the values shown the frequency is around 2Hz, and 100Hz at maximum. This range is adequate for SSB and CW. The preset VR4 sets the current meter to give an accurate indication, adjust it with your DVM in series with the supply to get the correct reading.

A more elaborate frequency source could be made using one of the multi function waveform generator ICs, such as a 8038, but I find that a simple square wave generator works just as well for the sort of power supplies we are likely to build. If you need a shorter pulse, a CD4528 monostable or a LM393 configured as a 'one-shot' monostable can be inserted between the output of the CD4093 and the amplitude pot. This would allow a variable length pulse to be generated at a fixed frequency. A circuit for the LM393 is shown in **Fig 15.5**:

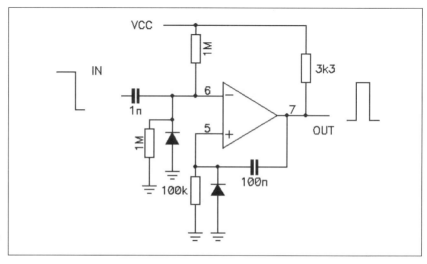

Fig 15.5: Optional 'one-shot' monostable circuit

The duration of the pulse is determined by the resistor connected to ground on the non-inverting input and the capacitor connected from here to the output. To make the pulse width variable substitute a variable resistor.

The formula to calculate the pulse period is: $T = R \times C$

where R is in ohms and C is in Farads. For a resistor of 100kΩ and a capacitor of 100nF the pulse width will be ≈10ms.

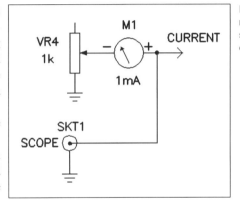

Fig 15.6: Current metering and transient response circuit

The monostable is triggered by a falling edge voltage applied to the inverting input via a low value capacitor, typically 1nF. The potential divider across the inverting input needs to be made from two equal high value resistors, 1MΩ is shown in the circuit above. The two 1N4148 diodes prevent the inputs being driven negative more than 0.7V.

The current and voltage transient is measured with a 1mA meter and an external oscilloscope (see **Fig 15.6**).

Typical test set up

In **Figs 15.7 to 15.10** are a few photographs of a typical test set up. The 'guinea-pig' is a 12A Japanese supply that I bought at a swap meet. Despite being assured it was in first class working order it was not! The symptoms were a lot of noise from the mains transformer and an output voltage which took a steep dive when anything approaching full load was applied. It didn't take long to diagnose the fault. The main smoothing capacitor ripple voltage was excessive with about 10V p-p ripple. The problem was traced to the bridge rectifier. It was 'running on 3 cylinders', ie one of the internal diodes had gone open circuit. Upon removing the bridge it was obvious what had happened. The bridge had a

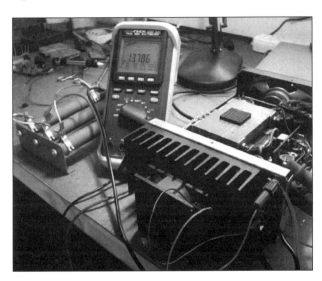

Fig 15.7: The repaired power supply under test. The load is three parallel 6.8Ω, 100W resistors drawing 6A. The voltage was set to exactly 13.8V off load. We can see that the output voltage has only dropped by 14mV when a 6A load is applied. A small computer fan helps to keep the heatsink temperature down during extended testing. The voltmeter is connected directly across the output terminals

Fig 15.8: The faulty bridge rectifier had a crack, which caused an internal fault

Fig 15.8: The faulty bridge rectifier had a crack, which caused an internal fault

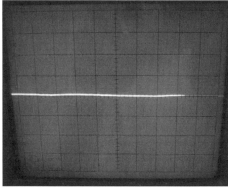

crack across the bottom due to excessive heat, from not being screwed down properly, the screw was loose! A 35A bridge was wired into the circuit and testing commenced.

I would have expected a better DC output voltage regulation than the 14mV measured. The reason was traced to the way the power supply wiring was done. The four pass transistors each had an individual wire from the emitter resistors back to the driver board, where the voltage sensing was done, and then a single heavy gauge wire from there to the output terminal. The regulator was correctly regulating the output voltage but the length of wire from the driver board, which carries the

Fig 15.9: The input ripple at 500mV per division with a 6A load. Notice that the waveform is almost triangular and not a sinewave. This is typical of a large value capacitor-input smoothing filter

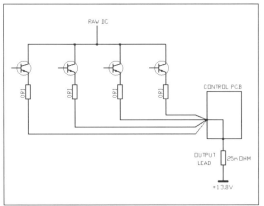

Fig 15.10: Output ripple voltage at 6A load. The 'scope vertical sensitivity is at maximum with 50mV per division, AC coupled. The ripple measures 5mV p-p, which is an excellent result

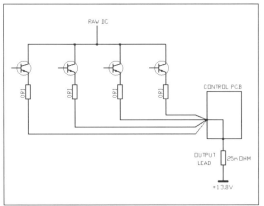

Fig 15.11: Original wiring of the output stage

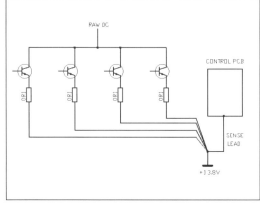

Figure 15.12: Rewired output

total current to the output positive terminal, was out of the feedback loop and acting as a resistor. Rewiring the supply to eliminate this improved the regulation to less than 3mV voltage variation with full load. The output terminals were mounted on the back panel close to the pass transistors. Why this strange wiring route was chosen is a mystery. The individual emitter wires were shortened and connected directly to the positive terminal. From there a small gauge wire was run to the control board for voltage sensing.

Although the results so far were good the transient tests were a dismal failure. The supply exhibited high frequency instability during shock loading with a two-resistor shunt load. The problem was traced to the use of an excessive value of output capacitance. Across the output terminals is a 1000µF electrolytic and a second one situated on the driver board close to the regulator IC. Why two capacitors were fitted is a mystery that only the original designer can answer. Removing the electrolytic from the driver board stopped the instability and had no effect on the output ripple voltage. It is a big mistake to fit too large an electrolytic across the output terminals. It often, as in this case, causes instability under transient loading. The output capacitor value should be as low as possible to allow the regulator IC to correctly control the output voltage variations.

Figs 15.13 and 15.14 show the situation after the wiring was modified and the regulator was changed to give a good critically damped response. The worst response was at approximately 170Hz with a 50% duty cycle and the pictures show the effect at this frequency. The control loop in this supply has a cut off frequency of about 120Hz, so the 170Hz transient waveform is outside of the control loop bandwidth.

Fig 15.13 shows the output voltage variation for a step change of 7A with an idle current of 2A. The top trace is the control voltage to the current sink, when the trace is high the additional current is switched on. This shows a dip in the output voltage of approximately 30mV. This is a percentage change of 0.2% (1/500) from the nominal 13.8V and should not be of any concern to the attached equipment. Note how the output voltage returns to the nominal in a very short period when the load is reduced, typically in 20µs. The spikes at the step change of current look quite bad on this display but if we increase the vertical resolution to 1V/div (Fig 15.14) you will see they are quite small.

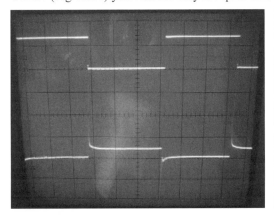

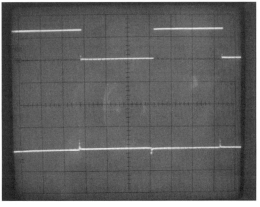

Fig 15.13: Transient test waveform. Lower trace 50mV/div

Fig 15.14: The output voltage waveform shown at 1V/div

The overshoots at the step changes are about 400mV worst case and last for less than 10µs.

To give you an idea how important the idle current is, see **Fig 15.15** where the idle current has been reduced to approximately 100mA. This idle load is a small 12V cooling fan to keep the heatsink cool. The step change is still 7A but the overshoot when the load is removed is much worse. This is caused by the output capacitor holding the

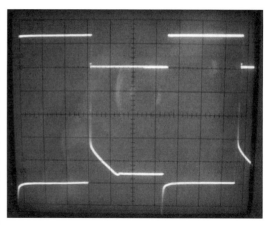

Fig 15.15: The lower trace shows the transient response when a 7A load is cycled on and off

voltage up; with a very small idle load it takes a long time for this to discharge. This is another reason why we should not place a large capacitor across the output terminals.

The vertical scale is still at 50mV/div and the horizontal scale is 1ms/div. The peak overshoot, ignoring the spikes, is about 80mV and it takes ≈1.2ms to return to a stable state. The dip in output voltage when the 7A load is applied is still of the order of 25mV. This effect is typical of a linear regulated supply with close to zero load. However, even 80mV of overshoot is very small and should not worry the attached equipment in any way. In percentage terms it is about 0.6%.

Measuring high currents

I mentioned in an earlier chapter that most digital voltmeters (DVMs) can only measure currents up to 10A, even the AVO-8 series meters are limited to the same sort of current. As we often need to measure currents considerably more than this we need to devise an alternative method.

In professional circles, the way this is done is to use an external 'Current-Shunt', indeed the company who manufacturers the AVO-8 series supply such a piece of equipment as do many other manufacturers of test equipment. It consists of a rectangular copper bar with hefty terminals to connect the main circuit to and an additional set of small terminals to connect the meter to. The exact value of the resistance is adjusted by 'necking-down' the bar to bring the resistance upwards. These are available up to several hundred amps, but are quite expen-

Fig 15.16: A typical current shunt for measuring high currents

sive. The output voltage from the shunt will depend on the manufacturer but typically it will be 50mV or 100mV at full current rating.

An alternative to a proper current shunt is to purchase one of the automotive ammeters often sold in shops. These are normally centre-zero types to show the charge and discharge currents. This type of meter is usually a moving-iron movement and not very sensitive for low currents.

The best method for a home constructor is to manufacture a current shunt using several low value wire wound resistors connected in parallel. Suppose we wish to measure currents up to 20A with some degree of accuracy. The shunt must not cause an excessive voltage drop to the current flowing in it, so the resistance value needs to be kept very low. Let us settle for a maximum voltage drop of, say, 50mV when 20A is flowing. Using Ohms Law we can calculate the required resistor value.

$$R = \frac{50\text{mV}}{20\text{A}} = 0.0025\Omega \quad \text{which is } 2.5\text{m}\Omega$$

If we start with 0.1Ω resistors we would need 40 resistors connected in parallel to get the correct value. Not a very practical solution. Let us look at another method of making a very low value resistor.

Normal enameled copper wire can be used if we know the resistance per unit length. Measuring very low values of resistance is tricky with a standard DVM, most lack the ability to measure values less than 0.5Ω with any certainty. Using the resistance per unit length in standard copper wire tables is an accurate way to make a shunt.

Looking at the tables in Appendix 1 gives some values of resistance per unit length and the current carrying capacity. The current flowing must not cause the copper wire to heat up, as this will change the resistance. Using a 16SWG copper wire with a resistance of $8.51\text{m}\Omega/\text{m}$, we will need a length of 294mm to obtain a resistance of $2.5\text{m}\Omega$. Although the current rating of this gauge is only 3.86A, this is for a long length, and so we can safely increase the current rating for a short piece.

Another possibility is to parallel two or more pieces of wire of a smaller diameter. Suppose we choose a wire gauge of 20SWG. This has a resistance of $25.8\text{m}\Omega/\text{m}$. Selecting two wires in parallel means that we need a resistance of twice the final value. Hence, we find that a piece with a resistance of $5\text{m}\Omega$ needs to be a length of 194mm.

Having selected a suitable shunt resistor we need to measure the voltage developed across this. For our example we chose a FSD voltage of 50mV. Using a standard meter movement means that we need a fairly sensitive movement. A standard 1mA meter will have a FSD voltage of 75mV. So with the shunt just designed it will indicate full scale when a current of 30A is flowing.

Having made a shunt it is important not to add any extra resistance in series that will upset the measured result. This means that the wiring to and from the shunt needs to be a substantial size and the meter measuring points need to be made directly across the ends of the shunt to avoid extra resistance.

Now let us calculate the power dissipated in the shunt. Power is the product of V x I, so for a current of 30A flowing with a voltage drop of 75mV we get the answer 1.5W. For a 20A current the result is 1W.

A home-made current probe

For switch mode and other supplies it is sometimes necessary to see what the current is actually doing. For DC we can use a DVM with a suitable shunt, for AC signals found in switching converters that cannot be referenced to ground this will not work. What we require is a means of tapping into a part of the cir-

cuit and then seeing the resultant waveform on an oscilloscope. Professional current probes are like 'clamp-on' ammeters
but have a lead to connect to a 'scope, like
a 'scope probe with a BNC connector.

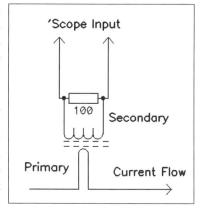

For this we require a current transformer. This can be made simply using a
ferrite toroidal core (a non-gapped core)
and some enameled copper wire. If we
wind a large number of turns on a toroid
and pass the wire carrying the current we
want to examine through the center then it
is a current transformer. The secondary is
the large number of turns and this needs to
be shunted with a low value non-inductive

Figure 15.17: Simple current probe

resistor. The voltage developed across the resistor is then the result of the primary to secondary turns-ratio and the resistor load. With a 100:1 turns ratio the
secondary voltage developed is quite small but it can measure quite large primary current excursions.

Often we require quite large ratios and so we will use maybe 50 or 100 turns
as the secondary and one turn for the primary. A schematic of a current transformer (CT) is shown in **Fig 15.17**. The secondary current flowing is quite small
and so we can use light gauge wire for this, typically 28 SWG would be suitable.

Although the probe is not calibrated to an exact voltage versus primary current it is simple to do this with a little ingenuity. If the toroidal core is slipped
over the positive output lead of our 10A supply for 13.8V and the supply is then
transient tested with a 1A and 10A load we can measure the secondary voltage
knowing that we have a 9A peak current variation.

Suppose we measure a varying voltage which displays a peak voltage variation of 90mV when connected to our 'scope. This means the calibration factor
is 10mV per Ampere flowing. The secondary voltage developed can be 'potted-
down' with resistors to arrive at a suitable calibration factor. Assume the voltage displayed is a positive going voltage when the current increases to 10A. If
it goes the opposite way (that is negative) it means we have to reverse either the
primary wire so it passes the opposite direction through the core or reverse the
secondary wires where they connect to the 'scope input. Once you have established the direction that causes the voltage to go positive, mark the core in some
way to show the correct orientation for when next you need to use it.

Using a ferrite core with a wide band response means the current probe can
be useful to many megahertz and can even be used for antenna measurements.
The secondary wires to the 'scope should be shielded; using a coaxial cable like
RG-58/U would be a good method.

Testing high voltage transformers

Often when building a linear amplifier using a valve the mains transformer
required is a quite a specialised item. For those lucky to be in the position to
have a custom transformer wound, as long as the transformer is correctly specified there should be very little trouble. However, for people who find a second

> Before discussing the methods we can use, first of all we need to appreciate the extreme hazards involved. In many cases the transformer will have a secondary voltage of anywhere from 1kV to as much as 3kV. These sorts of voltage are very hazardous and great care needs to be taken when testing. Failure to observe the correct safety precautions could result in a severe electric shock or death if you come in contact with the high voltage. Hence, any testing needs to be with these factors in mind and very well insulated wires and instruments need to be used to reduce the possibility of electric shock.

hand transformer at a swap meet or a mobile rally it is necessary to perform some testing to confirm the transformer is suitable for the task. This was briefly covered in Chapter 13 and the precautions contained there need to be observed before testing an unknown transformer.

Basically this entails loading up the secondary with some high power load resistors and measuring the secondary voltage and current. As well as this we need to also measure the primary current and voltage at full load. Knowing these parameters means we can then ascertain if the transformer is suitable for the envisaged application.

Finding suitable load resistors for the envisaged power dissipation is not easy. In some cases the transformer may be rated at 1kVA or more. Because it is difficult to find very high voltage rated resistors of the required power dissipation I often use an alternative method. This utilises electric lamps. Normal incandescent lamps are obtainable for voltages to suit the public mains supply. In the UK this is 230V AC. If several incandescent lamps are connected in series the required voltage can be obtained as well as the power dissipation. For example, if the secondary voltage is 2200V AC then ten lamps connected in series will suffice. If each lamp is rated at 100W, the total load is 1kW, or 1kVA.

Fig 15.18 shows the basic circuit for testing a high voltage transformer intended for a bridge rectifier with a center-tapped secondary.

For the test we require several meters. Two of these are AC ammeters with current ratings to suit the envisaged currents. For the meter monitoring the primary current this may need to be as much as 20A for a high power transformer. The secondary current will need a lower full-scale meter of about 2A RMS in most cases. The secondary voltage also needs a suitable meter. Most multimeters are often only rated up to 1kV but some types such as the Avo 8 have an additional voltage range of 3kV AC or DC.

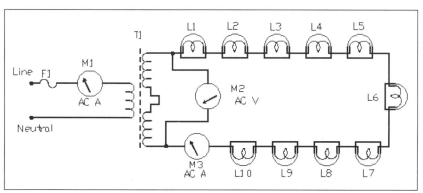

Fig 15.18: Test circuit for a high voltage transformer

Each lamp is fitted in a batten-lamp holder and screwed to a piece of wood. The wiring used needs to have adequate insulation, the center from RG-58/U coax is a suitable type. The primary circuit requires an adequately rated fuse in case one of the lamps flashes over.

The testing follows the steps listed below:

Firstly all lamps are removed and the mains applied to the primary. The secondary voltage is measured and noted. The primary voltage and current are also recorded; these are needed to establish the magnetising current.

Next the lamps are inserted and the transformer powered up. The lamps will then be lit at near full brilliance. In this condition the secondary voltage and current are recorded as well as the primary current and voltage.

To calculate the power delivered by the secondary we multiply the voltage and current to get the total VA rating delivered to the load. Let us assume the readings are:

Step 1   Secondary voltage = 2200V
              Primary current = 150mA at 230V AC (magnetising current)

Step 2   Secondary voltage = 2100V
              Secondary current = 500mA
              Primary current = 5A at 225V AC

We need to measure the primary voltage because the primary voltage will normally show a slight dip between off load and full load because of voltage drops in the house wiring. Here a normal DVM will normally suffice.

From these measurements we can establish the transformer efficiency, power output and magnetising current percentage.

For a secondary voltage of 2100V at a current of 500mA the power delivered to the load is 1050VA, which is the same as 1050W because the load is resistive.

At the primary input current of 5A at 225V the input power is 1125VA or watts. The transformer efficiency is therefore 1050/1125 = 93.3%. This is a bit lower than a good transformer would be expected to give, figures typically would be around 95 to 97% for a good transformer. It may be that the transformer is not able to give the required secondary current because of a high primary or secondary winding resistance.

The off load primary current of 150mA is equivalent to a magnetising current of 3% of the full load current and as this is well below 10% the transformer is acceptable.

By substituting lower wattage lamps in the test circuit we can see how the load effects the efficiency and secondary voltage drop. If ten 40W lamps are used, the maximum load power is 400VA or watts. For higher power, 150W or 200W lamps can be used, these will dissipate either 1500W or 2000W when ten lamps are used. Other secondary voltages can be accommodated by series and parallel combination of suitable lamps. For example, twenty 100W lamps connected as two lamps in parallel and ten pairs in series would be suitable for a 2000VA rating transformer with a secondary voltage of about 2200V.

Appendix 1: Useful Data

The relationship between the transformer primary voltage and current, secondary voltage and current, and the turns ratio is illustrated below The left-hand diagram covers the conventional mains transformer and forward converter and the right hand side covers the Flyback converter.

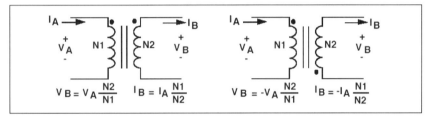

$$V_B = V_A \frac{N2}{N1} \qquad I_B = I_A \frac{N1}{N2} \qquad V_B = -V_A \frac{N2}{N1} \qquad I_B = -I_A \frac{N1}{N2}$$

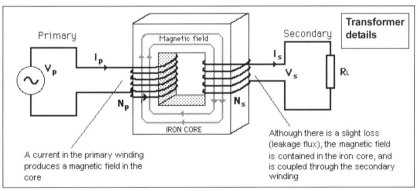

Transformer details

Primary

Magnetic field

Secondary

I_p V_p N_p IRON CORE I_s V_s R_L N_s

A current in the primary winding produces a magnetic field in the core

Although there is a slight loss (leakage flux), the magnetic field is contained in the iron core, and is coupled through the secondary winding

Rectifier parameters

The various rectifier schemes are detailed below.

Full wave bridge - Resistive load

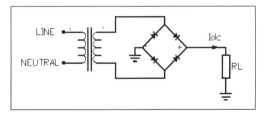

LINE NEUTRAL Idc RL

$$V_{DC} = 0.9 \times V_{AC} \qquad I_{DC} = 0.9 \times I_{AC}$$

Full wave bridge rectifier - Capacitor input filter

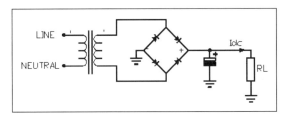

$$V_{DC} = 1.414 \times V_{AC} \qquad I_{DC} = 0.62 \times I_{AC}$$

Full wave bridge rectifier - Choke input filter

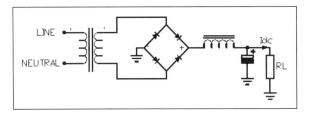

$$V_{DC} = 0.9 \times V_{AC} \qquad I_{DC} = 0.94 \times I_{AC}$$

Full wave bi-phase - Resistive load

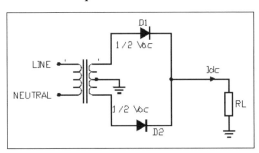

$$V_{DC} = 0.45 \times V_{AC} \qquad I_{DC} = 1.27 \times I_{AC}$$

Full wave bi-phase - Capacitor input filter

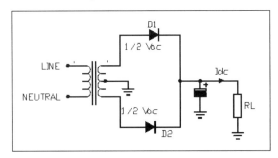

$$V_{DC} = 0.707 \times V_{AC} \qquad I_{DC} = 1.0 \times I_{AC}$$

Full wave bi-phase - Choke input filter

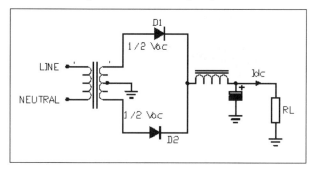

$$V_{DC} = 0.45 \times V_{AC} \qquad I_{DC} = 1.54 \times I_{AC}$$

Half wave - Resistive load

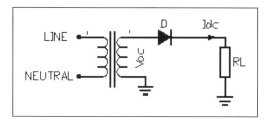

$$V_{DC} = 0.45 \times V_{AC} \qquad I_{DC} = 0.64 \times I_{AC}$$

Half wave-Capacitive input filter

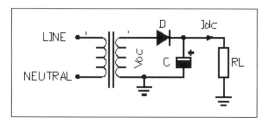

$$V_{DC} = 1.414 \times V_{AC} \qquad I_{DC} = 0.28 \times I_{AC}$$

Where V_{AC} is the total voltage across the secondary (for a centre-tapped secondary used for the bi-phase rectifier this is the two windings connected in series).

Rectifier rating

For full-wave rectifiers the average current flowing in the rectifier diodes is $0.5 \times I_{OC}$. The PIV rating of the diodes is $1.414 \times V_{AC}$ except for the half-wave rectifier where it is $2.828 \times V_{AC}$.

Wire tables

Note: The diameter quoted is for a bare wire

Wire Size - AWG	Diameter in mm	Nearest SWG equivalent	British SWG No.	Diameter in mm
1	7.348	1		
2	6.544	3		
3	5.827	4		
5	4.621	5		
6	4.115	8		
7	3.665	9		
8	3.264	10		
9	2.906	11		
10	2.588	12	12	2.642
11	2.305	13		
12	2.053	14	14	2.00
13	1.828	15		
14	1.628	16	16	1.62
15	1.450	17		
16	1.291	18	18	1.22
17	1.150	18		
18	1.024	19	19	
19	0.912	20	20	0.914
20	0.812	21	21	0.800
21	0.723	22	22	0.711
22	0.644	23	23	0.600
23	0.573	24	24	0.558
24	0.511	25	25	0.500
25	0.455	26	26	0.457
26	0.405	27	27	0.400
27	0.361	29	29	0.355
28	0.321	30	30	0.315
29	0.286	31	31	0.310
30	0.255	33	33	0.280
31	0.227	33	33	0.250
32	0.202	36	36	0.190
33	0.180	37	37	0.176
34	0.160	38	38	0.150
35	0.143	38	38	0.150
36	0.127	40	40	0.122
37	0.113	41	41	
38	0.101	42	42	0.101
39	0.090	43	43	
40	0.080	44	44	0.081

IEC R40

The following table lists the overall diameter for the three different grades of Magnet Wire. The highest voltage type being Grade 3. The current capability is based on a current density of $11A/mm^2$.

In practice for the smaller diameter wire sizes the current density can be safely increased to approximately two to three times the table value. In a switch-mode converter the peak current is $\approx\sqrt{3}$ times the average current due to the triangular waveform.

Diameter mm	Area mm²	Grade 1 (mm)	Grade 2 (mm)	Grade 3 (mm)	Current (A) average
2.650	5.515	2.730	2.772	2.811	60.665
2.360	4.374	2.438	2.478	2.516	48.114
2.120	3.529	2.196	2.235	2.272	38.819
1.900	2.835	1.974	2.012	2.048	31.185
1.700	2.269	1.772	1.809	1.844	24.959
1.500	1.767	1.570	1.606	1.640	19.437
1.320	1.368	1.388	1.422	1.455	15.268
1.180	1.093	1.246	1.279	1.311	12.023
1.060	0.882	1.124	1.157	1.188	9.702
0.950	0.708	1.012	1.044	1.074	7.788
0.850	0.567	0.909	0.939	0.968	6.237
0.750	0.441	0.805	0.834	0.861	4.851
0.670	0.352	0.722	0.749	0.774	3.872
0.600	0.282	0.649	0.674	0.698	3.102
0.530	0.220	0.576	0.600	0.623	2.420
0.475	0.177	0.519	0.541	0.562	1.947
0.425	0.141	0.466	0.488	0.508	1.551
0.375	0.110	0.414	0.434	0.453	1.210
0.335	0.088	0.372	0.391	0.408	0.968
0.300	0.070	0.334	0.352	0.369	0.770
0.265	0.055	0.297	0.314	0.330	0.605
0.236	0.043	0.267	0.283	0.298	0.473
0.212	0.035	0.240	0.254	0.268	0.385
0.190	0.028	0.216	0.228	0.240	0.308
0.170	0.022	0.194	0.205	0.217	0.242
0.150	0.017	0.171	0.182	0.193	0.187
0.132	0.013	0.152	0.162	0.171	0.143
0.118	0.011	0.136	0.145	0.154	0.121
0.106	0.008	0.123	0.132	0.140	0.088
0.095	0.007	0.111	0.119	0.126	0.077
0.085	0.005	0.100	0.107	0.114	0.055
0.075	0.004	0.089	0.095	0.102	0.044

Resistance of standard copper wire

Wire Gauge SWG	Diameter (inches)	Diameter (mm)	Ohms per metre	Current Rating (A)
10	0.128	3.25	2.041×10^{-3}	15.44
12	0.104	2.64	3.09×10^{-3}	10.2
14	0.080	2.03	8.16×10^{-3}	6.03
16	0.064	1.62	8.51×10^{-3}	3.86
18	0.048	1.22	14.5×10^{-3}	2.17
20	0.036	0.91	25.8×10^{-3}	1.22
22	0.028	0.71	42.6×10^{-3}	0.73
24	0.022	0.55	69.1×10^{-3}	0.45
26	0.018	0.45	103.2×10^{-3}	0.30
28	0.0148	0.37	152.7×10^{-3}	0.20
30	0.0124	0.315	217.6×10^{-3}	0.15

Effective resistance of winding wires

The apparent resistance of a bare copper wire increases with frequency due to the skin effect. The real resistance of a wire used in a switching supply is given by:

$$R_{total} = R_{dc} + R_{ac} \quad \text{and} \quad R_{ac} \approx 0.47\pi d\sqrt{f} \times 100 \times R_{dc}$$

where d is the diameter in centimetres, f is the switching frequency in Hertz

Ratings of rubber or PVC insulated mains cables

Area (mm^2)	No of wires & dia in mm	Current Rating
0.5	16/.020	3
0.75	24/.020	6
1.0	32/.020	10
1.5	30/.025	15
2.5	50/.025	20
4.0	56/.030	25

Fuse wire ratings

In an emergency, ordinary copper wire can be pressed into service to replace fuse links if the correct replacement is not available. However, the fusing current does depend to some extent on the type of holder, and the temporary replacement should be refitted with the correct fuse wire or cartridge fuse at the earliest opportunity.

Fuse rating (Amps)	Copper wire dia (mm)	Nearest SWG
1	0.05	47
2	0.08	43
3	0.125	41
5	0.15	38
10	0.25	33
15	0.315	30
30	0.50	25

Appendix 2: Software Listings

Software for designing switchmode supplies

The software listed below is designed to run on Microsoft Basica or GWBasic. All the software is the copyright of JH Fielding, ZS5JF. Permission is granted to use and copy this provided the originator is acknowledged and the software remains unchanged.

Standard buck converter

```
10  CLS:COLOR 11,1:CLS
20  PRINT
30  PRINT"     Buck Converter Design"
40  PRINT"     Written by J.H.Fielding"
50  PRINT:COLOR 15,1
60  INPUT"   Minimum supply voltage      ";VMIN
70  INPUT"   Maximum supply voltage      ";VMAX
80  INPUT"   Output voltage          ";VO
90  INPUT"   Maximum output current     ";IMAX
100 INPUT"   Maximum ripple current %   ";IL
110 INPUT"   Frequency of operation (kHz) ";F
120 F=F*1000
130 IL=IL/100
140 IL=IL*IMAX
150 T=1/F
160 CLS:PRINT:COLOR 14,1
170 DMAX=VO/VMIN
180 DMIN=VO/VMAX
190 DM=DMAX*100
200 TON=T*DMAX
210 PRINT" Maximum duty cycle at Vmin   = ";DM;"%"
220 L=(VO*(VMAX-VO))/(IL*F*VMAX)
230 PRINT" Pk-Pk Inductor ripple current = ";IL;"Amps"
240 IRMS=(IL/2)+IMAX
250 PRINT" Average Current in inductor  = ";IRMS;"Amps"
260 TD=TON*1000000!
270 LM=L*1000000!
280 PRINT" Minimum Inductance required  = ";LM;" uH"
290 PRINT:COLOR 15,1
300 PRINT"   Use this value of inductor ? [Y/N]"
```

These listings are available for download from the RSGB web site: www.rsgb.org/books/extra/powersupplies.htm

259

```
310 X$=INKEY$
320 IF X$ ="" THEN GOTO 310
330 IF X$ = "y" OR X$= "Y" THEN GOTO 360
340 IF X$="N" OR X$="n" THEN GOSUB 790
350 L=LM
360 PRINT:COLOR 15,1
370 INPUT"   Forward voltage of catch diode    ";VD
380 INPUT"   On resistance of switch          ";RDS
390 INPUT"   Estimated resistance of inductor  ";LR
400 INPUT"   Estimated ESR of Capacitor        ";CR
410 PRINT
420 CLS:COLOR 14,1:PRINT:PRINT
430 DH=VO/VMAX
440 DL=VO/VMIN
450 PRINT" Inductance                =";LM;  "uH"
460 PRINT" Duty cycle at max input voltage = ";DH*100;"%"
470 PRINT" Duty cycle at min input voltage  = ";DL*100;"%"
480 PC=(IL/2)*CR
490 PL=(IMAX+IL/2)*LR
500 PD=(IMAX*VD)
510 PRINT" Worst case loss in diode    = ";PD;"watts"
520 PRINT" Worst case loss in inductor    = ";PL;"watts"
530 PRINT" Worst case loss in capacitor   = ";PC;"watts"
540 PRINT" RMS current in output capacitor = ";IL/2 ;"Amps"
550 PRINT" Peak current in diode     = ";IMAX+IL/2 ;"Amps"
560 VC=((IL)*CR)*1000
570 PRINT" Output ripple voltage    = ";VC   ;"mV pk-pk   "
580 PO=IMAX*VO
590 COLOR 10,1
600 PRINT:COLOR 15,1
610 PRINT
620 PSW=(IMAX+IL/2)*RDS
630 PT=PC+PL+PD+PSW
640 E1=PO/(PT+PO)
650 LL=(PT+PO)/VMIN
660 HL=(PT+PO)/VMAX
670 E=E1*100
680 PRINT" Worst case loss in switch    = ";PSW;"watts"
690 PRINT" Total power losses (except core)= ";PT   ;"Watts"
700 PRINT" Approx. Low line input current  = ";LL;"Amps"
710 PRINT" Approx. High line input current  = ";HL;"Amps"
720 PRINT" Estimated efficiency (approx.)  = ";E;" %"
730 PRINT:COLOR 10,1
740 PRINT" RUN AGAIN [Y/N] "
750 X$=INKEY$
760 IF X$="y" OR X$="Y" THEN GOTO 10
770 IF X$="n" OR X$="N" THEN SYSTEM
780 IF X$="" THEN 750
790 INPUT"   Enter value of inductor in uH    ";LM
800 RETURN
```

Standard boost converter

```
10 CLS:COLOR 11,1:CLS
20 PRINT
30 PRINT" Boost Converter Design"
40 PRINT"    Written by J.H.Fielding"
50 PRINT:COLOR 15,1
60 INPUT"    Minimum supply voltage      ";VMIN
70 INPUT"    Maximum supply voltage      ";VMAX
80 INPUT"    Output voltage          ";VO
90 INPUT"    Maximum output current      ";IO
100 INPUT"    Minimum output current     ";IMIN
110 INPUT"    Diode forward voltage      ";VD
120 INPUT"    Frequency of operation (kHz) ";F
130 INPUT"    Maximum inductor ripple %    ";R
140 F=F*1000
150 T=1/F
160 DL=IO*R/100
170 CLS:PRINT:COLOR 14,1
180 D=1-(VMIN/(VO+VD))
190 D2=1-(VMAX/(VO+VD))
200 DM=D*100
210 PRINT"    maximum duty cycle    =";DM;"%"
220 PRINT"    minimum duty cycle    =";D2*100;"%"
230 IMAX=IO
240 TON=T*D
250 LMIN=(VMIN *(VO-VMIN))/(DL*F*VO)
260 IL=(VMIN/LMIN)*T*D:COLOR 14,1
270 PRINT"    Pk-Pk inductor ripple I = ";IL;"Amps"
280 IRMS=(IL/2)+IO
290 PRINT"    RMS Current in inductor =";IRMS;"Amps"
300 TON=TON*1000000!
310 PRINT"    Maximum Switch on time = ";TON; "uS"
320 L=LMIN*1000000!
330 PRINT"    Inductance (min)     = ";L;" uH"
340 PRINT:COLOR 15,1
350 PRINT"    Use this value of inductor ? [Y/N]"
360 X$=INKEY$
370 IF X$ ="" THEN GOTO 360
380 IF X$ = "y" OR X$= "Y" THEN GOTO 400
390 IF X$="N" OR X$="n" THEN GOSUB 830
400 PRINT:COLOR 15,1
410 INPUT"    On resistance of switch       ";RDS
420 INPUT"    Estimated resistance of inductor  ";LR
430 INPUT"    Estimated ESR of Capacitor      ";CR
440 PRINT
450 CLS:COLOR 14,1:PRINT:PRINT
460 PRINT" Inductance               = ";L; "uH"
470 PRINT" Duty cycle at max input voltage  = ";D2*100;"%"
480 PRINT" Duty cycle at min input voltage  = ";D*100;"%"
490 PC=(IL/2)*(IL/2)*CR
500 PL=(IO+IL/2)*(IO+IL/2)*LR
510 PD=(IO*VD)
520 PRINT" Worst case loss in diode    = ";PD;"watts"
```

```
530 PRINT" Worst case loss in inductor  = ";PL;"watts"
540 PRINT" Worst case loss in capacitor  = ";PC;"watts"
550 PRINT" RMS current in output capacitor = ";IL/2 ;"Amps"
560 PRINT" Peak current in diode    = ";IO+IL/2 ;"Amps"
570 VC=(IL)*CR*1000
580 PRINT" Output ripple voltage    = ";VC  ;"mV pk-pk"
590 PO=IO*VO
600 COLOR 10,1
610 PRINT:COLOR 15,1
620 PRINT" Recalculated input currents     "
630 PRINT
640 LL=(PO/.85)/VMIN
650 HL=(PO/.9)/VMAX:COLOR 14,1
660 PRINT" Approx. Low line input current  = ";LL;"Amps"
670 PRINT" Approx. High line input current = ";HL;"Amps"
680 PSW=(LL*LL)*RDS
690 PT1=PC+PL+PD
700 PT=PC+PL+PD+PSW
710 E1=PO/(PT1+PO)
720 E=E1*100
730 PRINT" Worst case loss in switch    = ";PSW;"watts"
740 PRINT" Total power losses (except core) = ";PT  ;"Watts"
750 E2=PO/(PT+PO)
760 PRINT" Estimated efficiency (approx.)  = ";E2*100;" %"
770 PRINT:COLOR 10,1
780 PRINT" RUN AGAIN [Y/N] "
790 X$=INKEY$
800 IF X$="y" OR X$="Y" THEN GOTO 10
810 IF X$="n" OR X$="N" THEN SYSTEM
820 IF X$="" THEN 790
830 INPUT"   Enter value of inductor in uH   ";L
840 RETURN
```

Synchronous buck converter

```
10 CLS:COLOR 11,1:CLS
20 PRINT
30 PRINT" Synchronous Converter"
40 PRINT"   Written by J.H.Fielding"
50 PRINT:COLOR 15,1
60 INPUT"   Minimum supply voltage    ";VMIN
70 INPUT"   Maximum supply voltage    ";VMAX
80 INPUT"   Output voltage       ";VO
90 INPUT"   Maximum output current    ";IMAX
100 INPUT"   Maximum ripple current (%)  ";IL
110 INPUT"   Frequency of operation (kHz) ";F
120 F=F*1000
130 T=1/F
140 CLS:PRINT:COLOR 14,1
150 IL=IL/100
160 IL=IMAX*IL
170 DMAX=VO/VMIN
180 DMIN=VO/VMAX
190 DM=DMAX*100
200 TON=T*DMAX
```

```
210 PRINT" Maximum duty cycle at Vmin   = ";DM;"%"
220 LMIN=(VO*(VMAX-VO))/(IL*VMAX*F)
230 PRINT" Pk-Pk Inductor ripple current = ";IL;"Amps"
240 IPK =(IL/2)+IMAX
250 PRINT" Peak Current in inductor    = ";IPK ;"Amps"
260 TD=TON*1000000!
270 LM=LMIN*1000000!
280 PRINT" Minimum Inductance required  = ";LM;" uH"
290 PRINT:COLOR 15,1
295 PRINT" Use this value ? [Y/N]"
300 X$=INKEY$
310 IF X$ ="" THEN GOTO 300
320 IF X$ = "y" OR X$= "Y" THEN GOTO 340
330 IF X$="N" OR X$="n" THEN GOSUB 770
340 L=LM
350 PRINT:COLOR 15,1
360 INPUT" On resistance of top switch ";RDS
370 INPUT" On resistance of bottom switch ";BSW
380 INPUT" Estimated resistance of inductor ";LR
390 INPUT" Estimated resistance of capacitor";CR
400 CLS:PRINT:COLOR 14,1
410 DH=VO/VMAX
420 DL=VO/VMIN
430 PRINT" Inductor value selected        = ";L;"uH"
440 PRINT" Duty cycle at max input voltage = ";DH*100;"%"
450 PRINT" Duty cycle at min input voltage = ";DL*100;"%"
460 PC=(IL/2)*(IL/2)*CR
470 PL=(IMAX+IL/2)*(IMAX+IL/2)*LR
480 PD=(IMAX*IMAX)*(BSW)
490 PRINT" Worst case loss in inductor = ";PL;"watts"
500 PRINT" Worst case loss in capacitor = ";PC;"watts"
510 PRINT" RMS current in output capacitor = ";IL/2 ;"Amps"
520 PRINT" Peak current in bottom switch = ";IMAX+IL/2 ;"Amps"
530 VC=((IL)*CR)*1000
540 PRINT" Output ripple voltage    = ";VC  ;"mV pk-pk"
550 PO=IMAX*VO
560 COLOR 10,1
570 PRINT:COLOR 15,1
580 PRINT
590 PSW=((IMAX+IL/2)*(IMAX+IL/2))*(RDS)
600 PT=PC+PL+PD+PSW
610 E1=PO/(PT+PO)
620 E=E1*100
630 HL=(PT+PO)/VMAX
640 LL=(PT+PO)/VMIN
650 PRINT" Worst case loss in top switch = ";PSW;"watts"
660 PRINT" Worst case loss in bottom switch = ";PD;"watts"
670 PRINT" Total power losses (except core) = ";PT ;"Watts"
680 PRINT" Approx. Low line input current = ";LL;"Amps"
690 PRINT" Approx. High line input current = ";HL;"Amps"
```

```
700 PRINT" Estimated efficiency (approx.) = ";E;" %"
710 PRINT:COLOR 10,1
720 PRINT" RUN AGAIN [Y/N] "
730 X$=INKEY$
740 IF X$="y" OR X$="Y" THEN GOTO 10
750 IF X$="n" OR X$="N" THEN SYSTEM
760 IF X$="" THEN 730
770 INPUT"    Enter value of inductor in uH    ";LM
780 RETURN
```

Standard forward converter

```
10 CLS:COLOR 11,1:CLS
20 PRINT
30 PRINT"    Forward Converter Design"
40 PRINT"    Written by J.H.Fielding"
50 PRINT:COLOR 15,1
60 INPUT"    Minimum supply voltage      ";VMIN
70 INPUT"    Maximum supply voltage      ";VMAX
80 INPUT"    Output voltage          ";VO
90 INPUT"    Maximum output current      ";IO
100 INPUT"    Frequency of operation (kHz) ";F
110 INPUT"    Forward voltage of diode    ";VD
120 F=F*1000
130 T=1/F
140 INPUT"    Efficiency assumed ( % )    ";E
150 PO=IO*(VO+VD)
160 E=E/100
170 IIN=PO/(E*VMIN)
180 PIN=IIN*VMIN
190 CLS:PRINT:COLOR 14,1
200 PRINT"    Power input = ";PIN; "watts"
210 PRINT"    Average input current = ";IIN ; "amps"
220 PRINT:COLOR 15,1
230 INPUT"    maximum duty cycle allowed =  % ",D
240 INPUT"    Select Ae of core   (mm2)";AE
250 INPUT"    Select Bmax of core (mT) ";BM
260 INPUT"    Select Vcesat of switch (volts) ";VCESAT
270 PRINT:D=D/100
280 AE=AE/100
290 BM=BM*10
300 NP=((VMIN-VCESAT)*1E+09)/(4*F*AE*BM)
310 TON=T*D
320 COLOR 14,1
330 PRINT"    Primary turns (minimum) = ";NP
340 INPUT"    Select primary turns    ";NP
350 TON=TON*1000000!
360 PRINT"    Maximum Switch on time  = ";TON; "uS"
370 PRINT:COLOR 15,1
380 INPUT"    AL value of chosen core = ";AL
390 L=(NP*NP)*AL/1000
400 COLOR 14,1:CLS:PRINT:PRINT
410 N=(VO+VD)/(VMIN*D)
420 NS=N*NP
```

```
430 PRINT" Number of turns on primary        = ";NP
440 PRINT" Number of turns on secondary      = ";NS
450 PRINT" Inductance of primary       = ";L;"uH"
460 DM=D*(VMIN/VMAX)
470 COLOR 14,1
480 PRINT" Duty cycle at max input voltage = ";DM*100;"%"
490 PSW=(IIN*VCESAT)
500 PRINT" Worst case loss in switch at low line = ";PSW;"watts"
510 PD=(IO*VD)
520 PRINT" Worst case loss in diode        = ";PD;"watts"
530 IAVGH=(PO/VMAX)/E
540 IAVGL=(PO/VMIN)/E
550 PT=PSW+PD
560 PRINT" Average input current at high line  = ";IAVGH;"Amps"
570 PRINT" Average input current at low line = ";IAVGL;"Amps"
580 PRINT" Total power losses (except core) = ";PT  ;"Watts"
590 PO=IO*VO
600 E=PO/(PT+PO)
610 E=E*100
620 PRINT" Estimated efficiency          = ";E;" %"
630 PRINT:COLOR 10,1
640 PRINT
650 PRINT
660 PRINT"   CALCULATE OUTPUT INDUCTOR [Y/N] ?"
670 X$=INKEY$
680 IF X$="y" OR X$="Y" THEN GOTO 770
690 IF X$="n" OR X$="N" THEN GOTO 710
700 IF X$="" THEN 670
710 PRINT
720 PRINT" RUN AGAIN [Y/N] "
730 X$=INKEY$
740 IF X$="y" OR X$="Y" THEN GOTO 10
750 IF X$="n" OR X$="N" THEN SYSTEM
760 IF X$="" THEN 730
770 PRINT:COLOR 15,1
780 INPUT"   SELECT RIPPLE CURRENT % ";IR
790 IL = IO*(IR/100)
800 VS=(VMAX)*(NS/NP)
810 L=(VO*(VS-VO))/(IL*F*VS)
820 L=L*1000000!
830 PRINT:COLOR 14,1
840 PRINT" Minimum inductor value =";L;"uH"
850 ILPK=IO+IL/2
860 PRINT" Peak inductor current   =";ILPK;"Amps"
870 COLOR 10,1:GOTO 710
```

Standard flyback converter

```
10 CLS:COLOR 11,1:CLS
20 PRINT
30 PRINT"   Flyback Converter Design"
40 PRINT"   Using Current Mode Control"
50 PRINT"   Written by J.H.Fielding"
60 PRINT:COLOR 15,1
```

```
70 INPUT"    Minimum supply voltage      ";VMIN
80 INPUT"    Maximum supply voltage      ";VMAX
90 INPUT"    Main output voltage        ";VO
100 INPUT"    Maximum output current (A)   ";IO
110 INPUT"    Diode forward voltage        ";VD
120 INPUT"    Frequency of operation (kHz) ";F
130 F=F*1000
140 INPUT"    On resistance of switch (ohms) ";RDS
150 COLOR 15,1
160 INPUT"    Efficiency assumed ( % )    ";E
170 E=E/100
180 PO=IO*VO
190 IAVG=PO/(E*VMIN)
200 PIN=IAVG*VMIN
210 CLS:PRINT:COLOR 14,1
220 PRINT"    Power input       = ";PIN; "watts"
230 PRINT"    Average input current = ";IAVG; "amps"
240 PRINT:COLOR 15,1
250 PRINT"    maximum duty cycle allowed =  % "
260 INPUT" (recommended Dmax = 45%)";D
270 PRINT:D=D/100:COLOR 14,1
280 TONMAX=(1/F)*D
290 PRINT"    Maximum Switch on time = ";TONMAX*1000000!; "uS"
300 VI=VMIN-(RDS*IAVG)
310 LP=E*((VI)*(VI))/(2*PO*F)
320 PRINT"    Primary inductance (min) = ";LP*1000000!;" uH"
330 PRINT:COLOR 15,1
340 INPUT"    AL value of core (nH/t) = ";AL
350 AL=AL/1E+09
360 N=LP/AL:COLOR 14,1:CLS:PRINT
370 NP=SQR(N)
380 PRINT" Minimum number of turns on primary = ";NP
390 PRINT:COLOR 15,1
400 INPUT" Choose number of turns for primary ";NP
410 PRINT:COLOR 14,1
420 LP=(NP*NP)*AL
430 PRINT" Primary inductance = ";LP*1000000!;" uH"
440 COLOR 15,1
450 NS=NP*((VO+VD)*(1-D))/(VMIN*D)
460 PRINT
470 COLOR 14,1
480 PRINT" Minimum number of turns for secondary = ";NS
490 PRINT
500 COLOR 15,1
510 INPUT" Choose number of turns for secondary ";NS1
520 LS=(NS1*NS1)*AL
530 PRINT:COLOR 14,1
540 PRINT" With ";NS1;"turns sec inductance = ";LS*1000000!;" uH"
550 VT=VO/NS1:N=NS1/NP
560 PRINT" Secondary constant       = ";VT;" volts/turn"
570 VSPK=(VO+VD)+(N*VMIN)
580 IPK=(5.5*PO)/VMIN
590 PRINT" Primary peak curent   - low line  = ";IPK;"Amps"
```

```
600 PRINT" Secondary peak voltage - low line = ";VSPK;"volts"
610 VPK1=(VO+VD)+(N*VMAX)
620 DMAX=(VO)/((VO+(N)*VMAX))
630 COLOR 14,1
640 PRINT" Secondary peak voltage - high line  = ";VPK1
650 PRINT" Duty cycle at maximum input voltage = ";DMAX*100;"%"
660 PSW=(IAVG*IAVG)*RDS
670 PRINT" Worst case loss in switch - low line = ";PSW;"watts"
680 PD=(PO/VO)*VD
690 PRINT" Worst case loss in diode        = ";PD;"watts"
700 IAVGH=(PO/VMAX)/E
710 IAVGL=(PO/VMIN)/E
720 PIV=VPK1*1.5
730 PRINT" Average input current at high line = ";IAVGH;"Amps"
740 PRINT" Average input current at low line = ";IAVGL;"Amps"
750 PRINT" Minimum diode PIV required     = ";PIV ;"Volts"
760 PRINT:COLOR 10,1
770 PRINT" Do you want to calculate turns for other outputs [Y/N] "
780 X$=INKEY$
790 IF X$="y" OR X$="Y" THEN CLS:COLOR 15,1:PRINT:GOTO 880
800 IF X$="n" OR X$="N" THEN GOTO 820
810 IF X$="" THEN 780
820 PRINT
830 PRINT" RUN AGAIN [Y/N] "
840 X$=INKEY$
850 IF X$="y" OR X$="Y" THEN GOTO 10
860 IF X$="n" OR X$="N" THEN SYSTEM
870 IF X$="" THEN 840
880 INPUT" Secondary output voltage required ";VS2
890 INPUT" Diode forward voltage         ";VF2
900 NS2=(VS2+VF2)/VT
910 VPK2=VPK1*(NS2/NS1)
920 PIV2=VPK2*1.5
930 PRINT" Secondary turns required is ";NS2
940 PRINT" Minimum Diode PIV required ";PIV2;"volts"
950 PRINT:COLOR 14,1
960 PRINT " Another secondary ? [Y/N] "
970 X$=INKEY$
980 IF X$="y" OR X$="Y" THEN GOTO 880
990 IF X$="n" OR X$="N" THEN GOTO 820
1000 IF X$="" THEN 970
```

Standard SEPIC converter

```
10 CLS:COLOR 11,1:CLS
20 PRINT
30 PRINT" SEPIC Converter Design"
40 PRINT"    Written by J.H.Fielding"
50 PRINT:COLOR 15,1
60 INPUT"    Minimum supply voltage     ";VMIN
70 INPUT"    Maximum supply voltage     ";VMAX
80 INPUT"    Output voltage          ";VO
90 INPUT"    Maximum output current    ";IO
100 INPUT"    Minimum output current    ";IMIN
```

```
110 INPUT"    Output Diode forward voltage ";VD
120 INPUT"    Frequency of operation (kHz) ";FD
130 F=FD*1000
140 T=1/F
150 CLS:PRINT:COLOR 14,1
160 D1=((VO+VD)/(VMIN+VO+VD))
170 D2=((VO+VD)/(VMAX+VO+VD))
180 PRINT"   maximum duty cycle    =";D1*100;"%"
190 PRINT"   minimum duty cycle    =";D2*100;"%"
200 TON=T*D1
210 L=((VO)*(VMAX*VMAX)*(VO+VD-VMIN)*T)/((2*VO*IMIN)*(VO+VD)*(VO+VD))
220 COLOR 14,1
230 TON=TON*1000000!
240 LM=L*1000000!
250 PRINT"   Maximum Switch on time = ";TON; "uS"
260 PRINT"   Inductance (min)    = ";LM;" uH"
270 PRINT:COLOR 15,1
280 PRINT"   Use this value of inductor ? [Y/N]"
290 X$=INKEY$
300 IF X$ ="" THEN GOTO 290
310 IF X$ = "y" OR X$= "Y" THEN GOSUB 840
320 IF X$="N" OR X$="n" THEN GOSUB 830
330 PRINT:COLOR 15,1
340 INPUT"    On resistance of switch        ";RDS
350 INPUT"    Estimated resistance of inductor  ";LR
360 INPUT"    Estimated ESR of Capacitor      ";CR
370 PRINT:CMN=(L*(IO*IO)*(VO*VO))/(VMIN*VMIN*VMIN*VMIN)
380 CMIN=CMN*1000000!
390 RC=IO*(SQR(VO/VMIN))
400 CLS:COLOR 14,1:PRINT:PRINT
410 PRINT" Inductance                = ";LM; "uH"
420 PRINT" Coupling Capacitor - minimum    = ";CMIN; "uF"
430 PRINT" Coupling Capacitor - ripple current = ";RC; "Amps"
440 PRINT" Duty cycle at maximum input voltage = ";D2*100;"%"
450 PRINT" Duty cycle at minimum input voltage = ";D1*100;"%"
460 IC=IL/3.4641
470 PC=(IC*IC)*CR
480 PL=(IO+IL/2)*(IO+IL/2)*LR
490 PD=IO*VD
500 DP=(IO)*((VO+VD)+1)/(VMIN)
510 PIV=(VO+VMAX)
520 PRINT" Diode Peak Inverse Voltage    = ";PIV;"Volts"
530 PRINT" Worst case loss in inductor    = ";PL;"watts"
540 PRINT" RMS current in output capacitor  = ";IC ;"Amps"
550 PRINT" Worst case loss in output capacitor  = ";PC;"watts"
560 PRINT" Peak current in diode         = ";DP ;"Amps"
570 VR=2*(IC*CR)*1000
580 PRINT" Output ripple voltage        = ";VR ;"mV pk-pk"
590 PO=IO*VO
600 COLOR 10,1
610 PRINT
620 PSW=((IO+IL/2)*(IO+IL/2))*RDS
630 PT1=PC+PL+PD
```

```
640  PT=PC+PL+PD+PSW
650  E1=PO/(PT+PO)
660  E=E1*100
670  LL=(PT+PO)/VMIN
680  HL=(PT+PO)/VMAX
690  PRINT" Total throughput power        = ";PO;"watts"
700  PRINT:COLOR 15,1
710  PRINT" Worst case loss in switch     = ";PSW;"watts"
720  PRINT" Worst case loss in diode      = ";PD;"watts"
730  PRINT" Total power losses (except core) = ";PT ;"Watts"
740  PRINT" Approx. Low line input current  = ";LL;"Amps"
750  PRINT" Approx. High line input current = ";HL;"Amps"
760  PRINT" Estimated efficiency (approx.)   = ";E;" %"
770  PRINT:COLOR 10,1
780  PRINT" RUN AGAIN [Y/N] "
790  X$=INKEY$
800  IF X$="y" OR X$="Y" THEN GOTO 10
810  IF X$="n" OR X$="N" THEN SYSTEM
820  IF X$="" THEN 790
830  INPUT"    Enter value of inductor in uH    ";LM
840  L=LM/1000000!
850  IL=(VMIN*(VO+VD))/((F*2*L)*(VMIN+VO+VD))
860  IL1=IO*(VO/VMIN)+IL/2
870  IL2=IO*((VMIN+VD)/(VMIN))+IL/2
880  CLS:COLOR 14,1:PRINT
890  PRINT"    Using inductance of ";LM;" uH"
900  PRINT"    Peak-Peak current in L1 = ";IL1;"Amps"
910  PRINT"    Peak-Peak current in L2 = ";IL2;"Amps"
920  RETURN
```

Synchronous SEPIC (using two mosfet switches)

```
10   CLS:COLOR 11,1:CLS
20   PRINT
30   PRINT" Synchronous SEPIC Converter Design"
40   PRINT"    Written by J.H.Fielding"
50   PRINT:COLOR 15,1
60   INPUT"    Minimum supply voltage      ";VMIN
70   INPUT"    Maximum supply voltage      ";VMAX
80   INPUT"    Output voltage           ";VO
90   INPUT"    Maximum output current      ";IO
100  INPUT"    Minimum output current      ";IMIN
110  INPUT"    Sync diode on resistance    ";RD
120  INPUT"    Frequency of operation (kHz) ";FD
130  F=FD*1000
140  VD=(IO)*RD
150  T=1/F
160  CLS:PRINT:COLOR 14,1
170  D1=((VO+VD)/(VMIN+VO+VD))
180  D2=((VO+VD)/(VMAX+VO+VD))
190  PRINT"    maximum duty cycle   =";D1*100;"%"
200  PRINT"    minimum duty cycle   =";D2*100;"%"
210  TON=T*D1
220  L=((VO)*(VMAX*VMAX)*(VO+VD-VMIN)*T)/((2*VO*IMIN)*(VO+VD)*(VO+VD))
```

```
230 COLOR 14,1
240 TON=TON*1000000!
250 LM=L*1000000!
260 PRINT"    Maximum Switch on time = ";TON; "uS"
270 PRINT"    Inductance (min)     = ";LM;" uH"
280 PRINT:COLOR 15,1
290 PRINT"    Use this value of inductor ? [Y/N]"
300 X$=INKEY$
310 IF X$ ="" THEN GOTO 300
320 IF X$ = "y" OR X$= "Y" THEN GOSUB 840
330 IF X$="N" OR X$="n" THEN GOSUB 830
340 PRINT:COLOR 15,1
350 INPUT"    On resistance of switch        ";RDS
360 INPUT"    Estimated resistance of inductor  ";LR
370 INPUT"    Estimated ESR of Capacitor       ";CR
380 PRINT:CMN=(L*(IO*IO)*(VO*VO))/(VMIN*VMIN*VMIN*VMIN)
390 CMIN=CMN*1000000!
400 RC=IO*(SQR(VO/VMIN))
410 CLS:COLOR 14,1:PRINT:PRINT
420 PRINT" Inductance                = ";LM; "uH"
430 PRINT" Coupling Capacitor - minimum     = ";CMIN; "uF"
440 PRINT" Coupling Capacitor - ripple current = ";RC; "Amps"
450 PRINT" Duty cycle at maximum input voltage = ";D2*100;"%"
460 PRINT" Duty cycle at min input voltage  = ";D1*100;"%"
470 IC=IL/3.4641
480 PC=(IC*IC)*CR
490 PL=(IO+IL/2)*(IO+IL/2)*LR
500 PD=IO*VD
510 DP=(IO)*((VO+VD)+1)/(VMIN)
520 PIV=(VO+VMAX)
530 PRINT" Switch Diode Peak Inverse Voltage = ";PIV;"Volts"
540 PRINT" Worst case loss in inductor    = ";PL;"watts"
550 PRINT" RMS current in output capacitor  = ";IC ;"Amps"
560 PRINT" Worst case loss in output capacitor = ";PC;"watts"
570 PRINT" Peak current in diode         = ";DP ;"Amps"
580 VR=2*(IC*CR)*1000
590 PRINT" Output ripple voltage        = ";VR ;"mV pk-pk"
600 PO=IO*VO
610 COLOR 10,1
620 PRINT:COLOR 15,1
630 PRINT
640 PSW=((IO+IL/2)*(IO+IL/2))*RDS
650 PT1=PC+PL+PD
660 PT=PC+PL+PD+PSW
670 E1=PO/(PT+PO)
680 E=E1*100
690 LL=(PT+PO)/VMIN
700 HL=(PT+PO)/VMAX
710 PRINT" Worst case loss in switch     = ";PSW;"watts"
720 PRINT" Worst case loss in diode     = ";PD;"watts"
730 PRINT" Total power losses (except core) = ";PT  ;"Watts"
740 PRINT" Approx. Low line input current  = ";LL;"Amps"
750 PRINT" Approx. High line input current = ";HL;"Amps"
760 PRINT" Estimated efficiency (approx.)   = ";E;" %"
```

```
770  PRINT:COLOR 10,1
780  PRINT" CALCULATE THE NUMBER OF TURNS REQUIRED [Y/N] ?"
790  X$=INKEY$
800  IF X$="y" OR X$="Y" THEN GOTO 930
810  IF X$="n" OR X$="N" THEN GOTO 1000
820  IF X$="" THEN 790
830  INPUT"    Enter value of inductor in uH    ";LM
840  L=LM/1000000!
850  IL=(VMIN*(VO+VD))/((F*2*L)*(VMIN+VO+VD))
860  IL1=IO*(VO/VMIN)+IL/2
870  IL2=IO*((VMIN+VD)/(VMIN))+IL/2
880  CLS:COLOR 14,1:PRINT
890  PRINT"    Using inductance of ";LM;" uH"
900  PRINT"    Peak-Peak current in L1 = ";IL1;"Amps"
910  PRINT"    Peak-Peak current in L2 = ";IL2;"Amps"
920  RETURN
930  CLS:PRINT:COLOR 15,1
940  INPUT"   AL VALUE OF CORE SELECTED ";AL
950  LP=LM/1000
960  L=LP/AL
970  N=1000*SQR(L)
980  PRINT
990  PRINT"    NUMBER OF TURNS = ";N
1000 PRINT:COLOR 14,1
1010 PRINT" RUN AGAIN [Y/N] ?"
1020 X$=INKEY$
1030 IF X$="y" OR X$="Y" THEN GOTO 10
1040 IF X$="n" OR X$="N" THEN SYSTEM
1050 IF X$="" THEN 1020
```

Off-line flyback converter

```
10   CLS:COLOR 11,1:CLS:PRINT
20   PRINT"    Off-Line Flyback Converter"
30   PRINT"    Using Current Mode Control"
40   PRINT"    Written by J.H.Fielding"
50   PRINT:COLOR 15,1
60   INPUT"    Minimum supply voltage (AC)    ";VMIN
70   INPUT"    Maximum supply voltage (AC)    ";VMAX
80   INPUT"    Main output voltage        ";VO
90   INPUT"    Maximum output current (A)   ";IO
100  INPUT"    Short circuit current (A)    ";ISC
110  INPUT"    Diode forward voltage        ";VD
120  INPUT"    Frequency of operation (kHz) ";F
130  F=F*1000
140  INPUT"    On resistance of switch (ohms) ";RDS
150  COLOR 15,1
160  VMIN = VMIN*1.414
170  VMAX = VMAX*1.414
180  INPUT"    Efficiency assumed ( % )    ";E
190  E=E/100
200  PO=ISC*VO
210  IAVG=PO/(E*VMIN)
220  PIN=IAVG*VMIN
```

```
230 CLS:PRINT:COLOR 14,1
240 PRINT"    Power input        = ";PIN; "watts"
250 PRINT"    Average input current = ";IAVG; "amps"
260 PRINT:COLOR 15,1
270 PRINT"    maximum duty cycle allowed =   % "
280 INPUT" (recommended Dmax = 45%)";D
290 PRINT:D=D/100:COLOR 14,1
300 TONMAX=(1/F)*D
310 PRINT"    Maximum Switch on time = ";TONMAX*1000000!; "uS"
320 IPK=(2*PO)/(E*(VMIN*D))
330 IRMS=IPK*(SQR(D/3))
340 VI=VMIN-(RDS*IRMS)
350 LP=E*((VI*D)*(VI*D))/(2*PO*F)
360 PRINT"    Primary inductance (min) = ";LP*1000000!;" uH"
370 PRINT:COLOR 15,1
380 INPUT"    AL value of core (nH/t) = ";AL
390 AL=AL/1E+09
400 N=LP/AL:COLOR 14,1:CLS:PRINT
410 NP=SQR(N)
420 PRINT" Minimum number of turns on primary = ";NP
430 PRINT:COLOR 15,1
440 INPUT" Choose number of turns for primary ";NP
450 PRINT:COLOR 14,1
460 LP=(NP*NP)*AL
470 PRINT" Primary inductance = ";LP*1000000!;" uH"
480 COLOR 15,1
490 NS=NP*((VO+VD)*(1-D))/(VMIN*D)
500 PRINT
510 COLOR 14,1
520 PRINT" Minimum number of turns for secondary = ";NS
530 PRINT
540 COLOR 15,1
550 INPUT" Choose number of turns for secondary ";NS1
560 LS=(NS1*NS1)*AL
570 PRINT:COLOR 14,1
580 PRINT" With ";NS1;"turns secondary inductance = ";LS*1000000!;" uH"
590 VT=VO/NS1:N=NS1/NP
600 PRINT" Secondary constant        = ";VT;" volts/turn"
610 VSPK=(VO+VD)+((NS1/NP)*VMIN)
620 PRINT" Primary switch peak curent      = ";IPK;"Amps"
630 PRINT" Secondary peak voltage - low line  = ";VSPK;"volts"
640 VPK=(VO+VD)+((N)*VMAX)
650 DMAX=(VO)/((VO+(N)*VMAX))
660 COLOR 14,1
670 PRINT" Secondary peak voltage - high line  = ";VPK
680 PRINT" Duty cycle at maximum input voltage = ";DMAX*100;"%"
690 PSW=(IAVG*IAVG)*RDS
700 PRINT" Worst case loss in switch - low line = ";PSW;"watts"
710 PD=ISC*VD
720 PRINT" Worst case loss in diode        = ";PD;"watts"
730 IAVGH=(PO/VMAX)/E
740 IAVGL=(PO/VMIN)/E
750 PRINT" Average input current at high line  = ";IAVGH;"Amps"
```

```
760 PRINT" Average input current at low line  = ";IAVGL;"Amps"
770 PRINT:COLOR 10,1
780 PRINT" Do you want to calculate turns for other outputs [Y/N] "
790 X$=INKEY$
800 IF X$="y" OR X$="Y" THEN CLS:COLOR 15,1:PRINT:GOTO 890
810 IF X$="n" OR X$="N" THEN GOTO 830
820 IF X$="" THEN 790
830 PRINT
840 PRINT" RUN AGAIN [Y/N] "
850 X$=INKEY$
860 IF X$="y" OR X$="Y" THEN GOTO 10
870 IF X$="n" OR X$="N" THEN SYSTEM
880 IF X$="" THEN 850
890 INPUT" Secondary output voltage required ";VS2
900 INPUT" Diode forward voltage        ";VF2
910 NS2=(VS2+VF2)/VT
920 PRINT" Secondary turns required is ";NS2
930 PRINT:COLOR 14,1
940 PRINT " Another secondary ? [Y/N] "
950 X$=INKEY$
960 IF X$="y" OR X$="Y" THEN GOTO 890
970 IF X$="n" OR X$="N" THEN GOTO 830
980 IF X$="" THEN 950
```

Choke calculator
(for buck converter or extra filtering pole)

```
10 CLS:COLOR 11,1:CLS:PRINT
20 PRINT"    AL to Turns Calculator    "
30 PRINT" J.H.Fielding    "
40 PRINT:COLOR 15,1
50 INPUT"   INDUCTANCE REQUIRED (uH)";LM
60 L=LM/1000000!
70 PRINT
80 INPUT" AL VALUE OF CORE (nH/t) ";AL
90 LP=LM/1000
100 L=LP/AL
110 N=1000*SQR(L)
120 PRINT:COLOR 14,1
130 PRINT" NUMBER OF TURNS = ";N
140 PRINT:COLOR 10,1
150 PRINT" RUN AGAIN [Y/N] ?"
160 X$=INKEY$
170 IF X$="y" OR X$="Y" THEN CLS:GOTO 10
180 IF X$="n" OR X$="N" THEN SYSTEM
190 IF X$="" THEN 160
```

Index

Note: **Subjects in bold are chapter headings.**